GiNA'S
THERAPY

FREE PROOF COPY
– NOT FOR RESALE

For further information contact:
Deirdre Roberts
deirdre.roberts@mercierpress.ie
+353 (0) 21 461 4456
+353 (0) 87 263 3011
www.mercierpress.ie

Connect with us Online

Facebook.com/MercierPress

Instagram @MercierPressBooks

Twitter @MercierBooks

YouTube @MercierPress

Silvia Sbaraini

Instagram @silviasbaraini1

#GinasTherapy

GINA'S
THERAPY

SILVIA
SBARAINI

MERCIER PRESS

MERCIER PRESS
Cork
www.mercierpress.ie

© Silvia Sbaraini, 2020

ISBN: 978 1 78117 764 8

A CIP record for this title is available from the British Library.

Printed and bound in the EU.

for Michael, my love

'Apart from getting hit, it was great.'
– Lee Meager, former boxing champion

CONTENTS

PROLOGUE

Some events shift the world on its axis and things are never the same again. A birth. A death. A diagnosis.

Looking back, life inevitably divides into 'Before' and 'After', like some clichéd diet advert. As I pinpoint the day my world began to shift, I wonder if I knew, subconsciously, that something significant was afoot. Like an animal sensing a storm brewing. But it's easy to reinterpret with hindsight, and just as easy to get it wrong. So, to tell my story, I shall resuscitate the past, breathe it back into the present, live it as if for the first time.

It's the end of April 2004. A normal Thursday, during a normal week, full of the normal people, tasks and routines of life before. Well, normal for me.

KNOCK, KNOCK, KNOCKIN' ON MY FRONT DOOR

'This one's going well,' says Moya.

'Do I have eyes this time?'

'No. And only one leg.'

Great. When Moya introduced herself at a party, saying she was an artist and would like to paint me, I'd envisaged portraits of vibrant beauty. She told me I looked like 'a post-iconic Debbie Harry'. Despite realising that 'post-iconic' meant 'gone to seed', I was flattered. In your forties, compliments are not as forthcoming as they used to be. I reasoned that, if I agreed to pose, I'd be entitled to refer to myself as 'a model'. And even if Moya had a Lucian Freud style – brutal in its fleshy honesty – at least I'd be immortalised. But it turns out Moya's work is unflatteringly abstract, which explains why I never appear with a full set of limbs or facial features. And why she rarely sells anything. You have to give the well-to-do, buying public what they want, and what they want are pleasant-looking young women, not middle-aged catastrophes.

I used to be married to an artist. It was wonderful, if you happened to like having an installation of gas masks and Victorian nighties swinging from wire coat hangers in a corner of your living room. But if you needed a bill paid or food on the table, it was rubbish. As if thinking of the devil has summoned him, I hear Olly's distinctive tap-tap-tapping on my front door. Olly's arrival is, as always, accompanied by a creeping, soporific brain mist, which causes all rationality to desert me. This effect must have something to do with his dazzling good looks, which, infuriatingly, have not diminished with time. Olly has devoted himself to remaining permanently stoned for the twenty-six years I have known him.

He taps again. I sigh, then get up from the table in the dining room, where I have been typing on the laptop while Moya paints me. Quite often during these combined working sessions I'll forget she's here. Although I don't have to sit still for Moya, I am mindful of what objects are about me, for she will include them in the composition. The memory of seeing myself with a two-litre bottle of cola incorporated into my torso still disturbs me.

I open the door to Olly, and am consumed by his smiley emerald eyes, black dancing lashes, and lips, lips, lips that make me quake. Every time I see Olly I fall in love. Every time I fight this off. I have trained myself to remember what a useless git he is. So I now recall: the bailiffs arriving, even though he'd *promised* he'd paid the bills; leaving him to babysit Skylark and coming home from work to find her playing in the gutter and him stoned, asleep in the back garden; Olly claiming he slept with one of my friends because he 'mistook' her for me. If I allow myself to remember any more, I fear tipping myself over the edge, so I usually restrict it to three, but there is a range of hundreds, probably thousands, from which to choose.

I sigh again. Sighing replaces pouting when you get to my age.

'It's me,' says Olly dumbly, but with a magnificent, sunbeam smile.

He makes for the front room. He has come to watch my Freeview TV as he only has an analogue, and because his girlfriend presents a bargain programme on the Happy Holidays Channel and he likes to roll spliffs and talk to her from the sofa.

'Tea?' he enquires hopefully.

I wonder when the 'Olly effect' will wear off. He is forty-four now, but it still shows little sign of waning. Perhaps it's our shared history. We met when I was twenty-two and he was eighteen. We have spent our adult lives loving and hating each other, often simultaneously. Well, I have. Olly just smiles glibly, whether you're telling him you'd die for him or want to bash his skull in. He's always taken the path of least resistance, but it seems to have paid off. And he does have artistic talent, sort of. He was ahead of his time in the late seventies, as was pointed out in a review only last weekend.

There was an unsurprising lack of appreciation for his early artistic endeavours: installations consisting of disorientating, joining rooms constructed from plasterboard, onto which random cartoon images were projected along with strobe lighting. Fortunately, Olly went on to discover the more peaceful, and successful, craft of sculpting. Now he spends his days carving smooth egg shapes out of stone. His sculptures are beautiful: fine grained, but with the tiniest flaws which 'make' them, their sheer surfaces offering themselves up to be touched. Critics have called them sublime and transcendental, the perfection of their form sacred and moving. And those qualities are discernible, to the spiritually inclined. But I have come to see them as a reflection of Olly: a lovely surface with nothing underneath.

I'm being unfair, probably. Trying to reduce my painkiller consumption, having got rather attached to them after a recent operation, is no doubt making me extra crotchety. It was only day surgery, keyhole, but the healing has been slow. Moya took a message for me earlier, from the hospital. They asked me to ring back as soon as possible. I did, but it went straight to their answering machine. Now I'm waiting for them to call me back. The surgery was to remove a large cyst, but the doctor had to take the ovary as well, because it had become so twisted. That was weeks ago, but the follow-up appointment still hasn't come through, which must be why they're phoning.

Olly, yes, he earns a good living, or has done in the last ten years or so, the decade in which we finally divorced, so I haven't felt the benefit of it. He has an undeserved lucky streak, too. Like the time his sculpture sank the ship that was transporting it to Italy. It had been commissioned for a small fortune by a luxury car manufacturer, but insured for five times as much, so Olly's now waiting for the huge payout.

But I'm worried about what he'll do with the money. When he was seventeen, a doting, childless great-aunt left her small estate to him. Olly decided to go travelling, India being the final destination. But he only got as far as Dover, where he spent six months gobbling up drugs, returning penniless, just in time to meet me.

I think all this as I make his tea and, despite myself, I do it carefully. I use a pot, as he prefers, and sweeten it with a spoonful of golden sugar that clusters together as if slightly moist.

'Just going to add a nip of whiskey,' says Moya, as I hand her a large black coffee and she goes to retrieve her hip flask from her jacket pocket.

Moya's not much of a one for conversation. She speaks in sharp barks – the truth, as she sees it. Needless to say, most people find her difficult company. She's a lesbian of the old school: rides a Norton motorcycle, wears men's suits, smokes cigars, all that. She has a noble face, always tanned. She lives on the coast, a ten-minute drive away from my house, with her partner, and spends a lot of time, when not dismembering her fellow humans on canvas, bobbing about in boats. Her idea of nirvana is to live in Cornwall, for the light and the fishing, but her partner doesn't want to leave Kent. Moya was a member of the local lifeboat team for twenty-five years. As I pass her on my way to the front room, I think: there is a woman who has saved lives. But it doesn't stop me wanting to wax off her moustache.

Olly is smoking a spliff when I bring in his tea. His girl-friend, Simone, is in full flow for *Spain on a Shoestring*. Simone wants to be a serious, specifically Shakespearian, actress and has been auditioning unsuccessfully for the RSC for years. She en-acts her holiday-selling persona with subtle irony.

'Simone. Nice top. Nice colour,' says Olly, talking to the TV. 'Used to have a jacket that colour. Or was it a car? Can you remember, Gina?'

Olly now goes off into a 'thinking' stupor while dropping ash on my sofa. He's a bit like a grown-up child who should have left home years ago. What's he still doing here – on my furnishings, in my life, drinking my tea?

The sound of Donna, my cleaner, clattering down the stairs with the hoover interrupts my thoughts. Even a shapeless, gingham housecoat with *Domestic Darlings* emblazoned across the chest can't detract from Donna's long fair hair and curvaceous charms, although the look she goes for is more girl gang leader than beauty queen.

'I see shithead's here again,' Donna observes, as she glances into the front room on her way to the kitchen. Olly nods back happily.

'And the lesbo,' Donna mutters, eyeing Moya, who is sneakily glugging another little snifter straight from hip flask to mouth, bypassing dilution in coffee. 'Artists? Piss artists more like. How am I supposed to do me job with them cluttering up the place?'

'Can I get you a cup of anything, Donna?' I ask.

'Nah, not when I'm in the middle of work. And I've got to unblock this poxy hoover again. I'm charging for the extra time, mind.'

As Donna begins to dismantle the hoover on the kitchen floor I return to my laptop on the dining-room table.

For the last few years I have been writing for *Eurotica*, a bi-monthly magazine. Stories have to be both European and erotic in nature, and I need to submit an outline to the editor today. So far, I have opened a new document and typed 'story outline' at the top. This one is to be about love and sex in middle age and out of doors, 'al-fresco adventures' being the theme of the next issue. I am middle-aged; I go outside; I have an imagination: it must be possible.

Half an hour later, I am still circling the empty, whitewashed room that is my mind, when the phone rings. I rush to answer, thinking it's the hospital, but it turns out to be Richard, my editor.

'Gina, darling, how's it progressing?'

'Um. Slowly. Could you give me a better hook?'

'Older protagonists,' Richard enthuses, 'wise, experienced,

second chance at love, passions reawakened, better than it's ever been. Think holiday romance, sultry heat, out in the full force of bursting nature, that type of thing. And Golden Years Health Products are running a full-page advertisement for their vitamins, so try to get in something about dietary supplements being sexy.'

'Hmm.'

'Oh, don't be so precious! The bulk of our readers are in the forty-plus age range. Just imagine the characters are in their twenties, then give the men streaks of steely grey in their still impressively full heads of hair and the women saggy tits. No! Not saggy. *Never* saggy. Give them … let me think … breasts weighted by the depth and breadth of experience.'

'I'll try.'

'And don't forget the cod liver oil or vitamin E,' Richard concludes, before his customary, 'Bye-ee.'

I hang up and stare into space.

'What about a lesbian story?' suggests Moya.

I gingerly ask Moya if she has any ideas for plotlines, preferably with an outdoorsy, nature theme.

'Fell in love with a fish porter from Billingsgate once,' she replies, not quite so helpfully.

I type up a story outline involving a female painter (Moya minus a couple of decades, donkey jacket and smell of motorcycle oil, and with the addition of untameable corkscrew curls, brooding eyes and beautiful hands) who has an erotic encounter with a mermaid (Donna with tail and capacity to speak without swearing) while out on the water (exchange Whitstable for Lake Como) metaphorically fishing for inspiration. With the deadline fast approaching and feeling totally uninspired, I am reduced to borrowing and mangling a song title from Tim Buckley and call the story *Siren Song*. I email the outline to Richard, stating that it is 'an experimental work exploring the fantasy and fairy-tale genres but with a modern twist'.

'Front door again,' says Moya, though I haven't heard a thing. 'It's like Bedlam today.'

I listen hard, and can just make out a nervy, unfamiliar tap-tapping. I leave my laptop once more, to open the door to a skinny, shivering woman with her head bowed. She is wearing sunglasses, though the sky is uniformly grey.

'Is this the right house?' she mumbles.

She must want Leon, my ex-psychotherapist and, more recently, neighbour.

'Are you looking for Dr Comiskey?' I ask.

She nods and, as she raises her head, removes the sunglasses. Immense suffering is contained within the very flesh and sinew of her features, as if a knitting needle has been thrust into her heart and is now being withdrawn very, very slowly. Potential collapse twitches around the edge of her grimace; one small move and the whole lot is going to give way.

'Next door,' I say, gently, and she moves away; I make a mental note to remind Leon to put up a brass plaque.

'Hello,' calls a voice, 'is this number nineteen?'

I look over to see a man standing on the pavement.

'Yes?' I call back. I then notice that he's squinting at my roof. 'Oh, you must be the building surveyor.'

'That's right,' he says, as he begins to walk up the front path, before stopping short, apparently shocked by me. 'You look like –'

'I know, passing resemblance to Debbie Harry – past her

best, older sister maybe, the fat years, like Elvis.'

'No, no. My mother.'

'Oh.'

Why do people keep disrupting my day? Surely this amount of distraction isn't normal, even for me? Or maybe it is, but I'm more uptight than usual – anxious about the hospital. When I was being discharged after the op and they couldn't make a follow-up appointment because the computers were down, they said they'd be in touch. When I didn't hear from them, I assumed everything was fine. Now this phone call has got me worried. But all I can do is wait for them to get back to me. I try not to get annoyed with Mr Building Surveyor. He's just making conversation and is here to do the job I asked him to, which is give the place a once-over before I employ a builder to do a total refurbishment.

'Really, I look like your mother?' I say, feigning interest, after clocking that he looks rather energetic and fit for a man in his middle years, forty-five I'd guess, and that his hair is still more black than grey.

'Yes. She was a wonderful woman. Very striking. She posed for many artists.'

Artists. Again. I am hexed. Some are cursed by boils, migraines, insanity. I am a woman cursed by artists.

'I pose too,' I say. 'It's not all it's cracked up to be. Anyway, you'd better come in. It doesn't look like I'm going to get much work done today.'

Once inside, I explain the history of the house to him: how it used to be divided into three flats, and how, over the years, I rented, then bought, the ground and first floor ones, converting them back into a single dwelling. Then, last year, when the small attic flat – reached via a metal fire escape in the back garden – came up for sale, I was determined to buy it. So, I made the big decision to sell a house I'd inherited years ago and had been renting out, and bought it, along with the freehold of the building. Now I'm planning the final reunion of the whole place. I should have enough to pay for the renovations with, hopefully, a little to spare.

19 River Street has the layout of a typical Victorian house: a lounge at the front, a dining room with French doors to the garden, which opens into a long, galley kitchen, and two bedrooms and a big bathroom (that used to be a bedroom) upstairs. I think I'm going to turn the attic flat into one large room with an en suite. I recently finished a short-term admin contract at the college and haven't applied for anything else so that I can supervise the refurb. I have earned *some* money over the years from my writing efforts, but have always had to work – mainly office jobs – at least part-time, as well. This will be the first time I haven't had a 'sensible job', as my mum used to say, for donkey's years. Still, if I run low on cash, I can always do some temping.

I show the building surveyor where the staircase needs to be reinstated from the first to the second floor. Then we go outside, so that he can hold mysterious devices against bricks and poke holes in the window frames.

'What's your professional verdict then?' I ask, as we stand in the back garden. 'Any major problems?'

'No structural ones. Just the usual maintenance and refurbishment I'd expect for a large Victorian semi. You say you used to rent that attic flat?'

'Yes. I moved in with my daughter when she was little. I

always dreamed of buying the whole place and converting it back into one big house. Silly really.'

'Not at all. I'm sure it'll be worth it when it's finished. Should be very straightforward to put the staircase back in. And get rid of this,' he says, tapping the old fire escape. 'You sure you don't want to keep it?'

'No. It's a death-trap.'

'It could do with some minor repairs and a coat of paint, but I'd hardly call it that.'

'No, it is. There was a terrible accident and … well, someone died, falling from the top.'

'Really? When was that?'

'Fifteen years ago.'

'But how? It's structurally sound.'

I shrug and look at the grass.

'I don't know,' I answer softly.

'How ghastly. Get rid of it then. I'll drop my report in next week.'

After I've said cheerio to the surveyor and made my way back to the laptop – through the fog of Moya's cigar smoke, and after checking there haven't been any phone calls while I've been outside – I find an email from Richard. He requests that I submit a story outline more in keeping with *Eurotica*'s readership, stating that the fantasy and fairy-tale genres are not. He advises something a little more 'real and gripping', and ends 'not up to your usual standard', although he approves of the lesbian theme.

I don't know why he's being so uppity. I email back another outline about a camp, gardening magazine editor called Raymond, whose only pleasure in life is to visit Soho to be wrapped in cling film and flagellated by a stranger (that'll teach him to get drunk at the Christmas party and reveal his secrets to me). Richard emails ten minutes later to say he's had a change of heart about the painter and the mermaid, his single request being that I re-title the story *Sea Spray*. The only decent thing about it was the nicked title, but never mind because – ha – I win.

I glance up to see Moya smiling blearily at me.

'Smoking break,' she states, as she ignites another cheroot. I decide to join her.

As I draw the flame of the lighter to the tip of the forbidden cigarette and inhale the first satisfying lungful (I know, I know, I should give up) there is a pounding on the front door. My heart leaps shockingly. Such an unignorable knock can mean only one thing. A thirty-year reign of resentment is behind that banging, a force that provokes a futile desire to scramble for cover. What began as a hopeful fluttering, an unfurling promise of joy, somehow transformed into this. She's pounding again, harder, with more hatred. I must answer, as delay will only make her angrier. I have no choice but to face my personal persecutor once again.

'Mother,' she accuses, as I open the door.

'Yes,' I admit, while hopelessly scanning my mind for a good enough excuse not to let her in.

She barges past, eyeing my cigarette – which I fail to hide adequately behind my back – with pleasurable disapproval. I follow her down the hallway. This is what she sees: Olly glazed, staring at the television and talking to himself while smoking a vast (even I'm surprised by the size) spliff; Moya singing a (alcohol-induced) sea shanty while attacking the canvas with a painting knife; Donna swearing profusely at a particularly offensive bit of dirt while scrubbing the kitchen floor. My daughter then stands for a moment and reads my *Eurotica* story, glaring from the computer screen, before fake-gasping 'Pure pornography!' The final straw appears to be when a voice (no doubt Knitting Needle Woman from earlier) screams from next door, 'No, no, no, I can't take any more!'

In less than five minutes Skylark has gone. Sorry, my daughter's name is now Susan. I named her Skylark in 1971 and she renamed herself as soon as she was eighteen. Susan makes it clear with every look, every comment, every roll of an eye, that I always was, am and will be, an unfit, despicable excuse for a mother and that she will never, ever forgive me. Sometimes I wish that I, too, had the option of inflicting such demanding reproachfulness on my own mother, but she is dead, though not exactly gone.

True, I did have Susan when I was sixteen. But at least I kept her and struggled on alone. True, I did then meet and marry Olly who, though not badly intentioned, was an utterly useless stepfather. True, I may have earned us a living precariously, but earn it I always did. Unlike me, Susan studied hard, did well at school, took a sensible job, saved herself for the right man – an organised and efficient accountant called Graham – and had one child, meticulously planned, at the age of twenty-six. Note: one child only, because motherhood is not turning out to be as perfect as Susan expected it to be. I have heard it said that grandchildren are the grandparents' revenge and this has proved to be the case most wonderfully for me. For no child ever presented herself with such an old-fashioned and pleasing flurry of fair, flouncy curls, angelic features and skip-along gait, as my granddaughter Christine – Chrissy for short. And no child's personality was ever so at odds with her appearance. She is a difficult, stubborn and obsessive girl, and she gets on marvellously with me.

Before Susan marched back out of the front door with a 'Mother, will you and this godforsaken house never change?', she requested that I pick Chrissy up from school tomorrow and bring her back here for tea. Although Susan works flexitime and knocks off early on Friday, she prefers not to collect Chrissy. For she needs a break from her daughter as much as I did from her when she was a child. When I consider the female line of my family, I feel the generations have become muddled somehow, the mothers and daughters the wrong way round. Chrissy should have been my daughter and Susan my mother's.

I'd rather leave my mother out of this, but know she will come back to haunt, literally, as mothers have a tendency to do. Sometimes I feel trapped between them – my mother and my daughter – the unhappy filling in a prissy, resentful sandwich, from which I wish I could quietly escape.

I retreat into a plan to get everyone out of my house as quickly as possible, so that I can then enjoy a double dose of brain-addling, sleep-inducing, opium-based painkillers. Some habits from the seventies die hard, though it's all on prescription these days.

2

POO 'N' ART

As I close my front door at five to three the following afternoon, having spent the day writing up *Sea Spray*, Leon opens his.

'Good afternoon, Gina. Where are you off to?'

'The school, picking up Chrissy.'

'I was just going over to the shop. We can walk together.'

'Um, okay.'

Although it finished a long time ago, I spent four years in psychotherapy with Leon. I try to behave normally in his company, but it's hard. Leon bought the other semi attached to mine a couple of months ago, having checked and double-checked that I was okay, both with my ex-therapist moving in next door and with him setting up his psychoanalytic psychotherapy practice there. 'The past is the past,' I said. And, 'Live and let live.'

Now, I'm not so sure. I hear shouting and howling through the walls and, since he's rented out a room to a woman who does biodynamic body therapy, there is some crashing and banging about, too. There is one patient I've christened The Wailing Man, as this is what he does for fifty minutes, off and on, three times a week. I caught a glimpse of him the other day. He is tall, early fifties, with a dark-grey suit and light-grey hair. He arrived as competent and business-like as an on-call GP and left looking like a mugging victim, red-faced and weeping.

Leon and I walk along together, the sunshine accentuating his dark-orange hair. It's the last day of April and there's a promise of heat in the air. Leon's a head taller than me, and moves quickly, purposefully. I find myself almost skipping to keep up with him. Patients are supposed to fall in love with their therapists – it's all part of transference – but I can't say I did with mine. It wasn't Leon's ginger hair, which I rather like, or that he isn't a decent person, because he is, but the fact that he came to know so many embarrassingly intimate things about me. How could any woman fall in love with the psychological equivalent of her gynaecologist? But I do respect Leon – for his earnestness, intelligence and honesty, and for his patience with me in therapy. He was a lifeline through my marriage break-up, but then he should have been for those fees.

'Are you okay?' he asks.

I seem to have developed a habit, similar to pregnant women, of absentmindedly rubbing my belly where I had the surgery.

'I'm fine.'

The hospital phoned back this morning to make a follow-up appointment. The secretary said one should have been arranged weeks ago. I asked if everything was alright. She kept repeating the word 'routine' and saying not to worry, although she seemed to avoid saying there was nothing to worry about. She was keen for me to come in this afternoon, but I didn't want to let Chrissy, and Susan, down. She made an appointment for Tuesday, what with Monday being a bank holiday. Maybe I should have rushed up there today, but I can't imagine a couple more days will make any difference.

'I see Olly's in the local paper this week,' says Leon, 'something about him doing a sculpture for the city. Do you know what it's going to be?'

'No idea. I haven't asked. Same as usual, I suppose – another egg.'

I suspect Leon dislikes Olly, sees him as ridiculous and irresponsible – I certainly criticised him enough in therapy. But I remain oddly loyal to Olly. I suppose he constitutes family and, no matter how much one may despise one's own relations, few can bear to hear somebody else criticise them with equal enthusiasm. For although Olly and I are divorced, we are still somehow, sometimes, 'together'. After each failed relationship, few of which could be called love affairs, as that would be to credit them with more romance than they deserve, we retreat into each other's houses and beds (well, my house, my bed). This is not dissimilar to the pattern of our marriage, for Olly at least.

As Leon and I are about to part company at the shop next to the school, I come over – as my mother would have said – all giddy. I hold on to Leon until the world rights itself again.

'What's wrong, Gina? Shall I take you home? Shall I get Chrissy for you?'

What can I say? I've had an ovary removed, so am all over the place hormonally. I'm forty-eight and menopausal. That was probably a tsunami of hot flush knocking me off my feet.

'I'm okay, honestly. Better already. I've just been feeling a bit wobbly recently, since the ... oh, it doesn't matter. I'm fine now, really.'

Leon insists on accompanying me into the school grounds to make sure I'm alright, even though I really do feel okay. As we stand outside the classroom, I notice one of Donna's younger brothers waiting for an even younger sibling. Donna is the eldest of seven children. The brother – named Keanu, although just about everybody calls him Canoe – is fourteen and has recently been expelled from his third secondary school for threatening another pupil with a knife. He is skinny, pale and spotty, and is wearing two baseball caps, one on top of the other.

The classroom door opens and children file out, but not my Chrissy. Finally, Mrs Hatcher, her strident, no-nonsense teacher, pops her head round the door and scans the straggling parents.

'Has anyone seen Christine Parker's mother or father? Who's collecting her today? Oh, the grandmother.'

Mrs Hatcher eyes me ominously, then says, 'Can I have a word,' in a way that intones no hint of a question.

I go into the classroom. Leon follows.

Mrs Hatcher, who's obviously assumed that Leon is Chrissy's grandfather, ushers us into child-sized chairs in front of her desk. Rather than make a fuss and tell Leon to wait outside or explain that he's not her grandad, I decide to go with it – I'm sure Mrs Hatcher doesn't need to discuss anything serious. I spot Chrissy at the fish tank, doing something that involves getting a forearm wet and weedy. We wave to each other, then she makes to come over.

'Not until you have finished your task, Christine,' warns Mrs Hatcher, before taking the seat behind her desk and turning her attention on us. 'I'm afraid I have some rather serious news, which I'd be grateful if you could pass on to Christine's parents. The school has been left with no option other than to refer Christine to a psychologist.'

I wait to hear what Chrissy has done. Mrs Hatcher lowers her eyes and voice.

'It's the toilet problem,' she whispers. 'The issue with the … the number twos.'

Oh no. I've been having a long-running argument with Susan about the damage I may or may not have caused by giving a certain book to Chrissy a couple of years ago.

'Do you mean faeces?' asks Leon.

Mrs Hatcher nods.

'Interesting,' he comments.

Mrs Hatcher frowns.

'What exactly has been happening?' I ask.

Mrs Hatcher clearly appreciates the chance to get things off her chest. Apparently, Christine has, for approximately two years now, had a rather obsessive interest in poo, first flagged by Mrs Marshall in Reception, and which has recently accelerated in intensity with the emergence of a cartoon character called Trudy the Turd. And today, under the guise of doing an experiment for her Healthy Living science project, Christine was caught distributing bags of prunes to fellow pupils, on the condition that their next poo be done in a container of some kind and given to her for investigation.

'Dakota Bradshaw vomited after consuming nearly three packets and Jordan Jacobs became so hyperactive on fruit sugars he had to be restrained until his mother arrived to take him home. She was none too pleased,' states Mrs Hatcher.

'Oh.'

I look at Chrissy. She smiles angelically, the sunlight turning her mass of fluffy curls into a halo of hazy gold.

'Well,' I venture, 'Chrissy has shown initiative in conducting her own science experiment. Although I do appreciate it was not an appropriate one.'

Mrs Hatcher raises an unsympathetic eyebrow.

'And I feel I may be partly to blame,' I find myself admitting, 'in that I did give Chrissy *Everything You Ever Wanted to Know About Poo* one Christmas, as a stocking filler, you might say.'

Leon stifles a cough.

'Yes, Christine's mother has told me all about *that*. She is fully on board with regards to the seriousness of this situation and in complete agreement about trying to bring this disturbed and disgusting behaviour to a halt.'

'Maybe drawing attention to it will make it worse,' I suggest. 'Perhaps if we ignore it, it'll go away.'

Mrs Hatcher places her hands carefully on the desk.

'In my vast and varied experience as a teacher, ignoring a persistent problem has never made it go away. This requires pro-active management.'

I don't know what else to say as Chrissy comes over and hugs me, scrunched as I am in the under-sized chair.

'Anal fixation is quite common in young children,' chips in Leon.

Mrs Hatcher's eyes widen.

'In fact,' he continues, 'their own faeces are the most precious thing an infant has, being the first object which can truly be said to be their own. Children do not share the adult's revulsion at their excrement. On the contrary, they find it fascinating and the act of defecation deeply pleasurable.'

I glare at Leon.

'Although,' he carries on, oblivious, 'I do admit that such an interest is more typical of a two-year-old, whereas Chrissy is seven. Can you remember what her potty training was like, Gina?'

'Very strict,' I hiss, 'and rather early.'

'I would suggest,' says Leon, 'that Chrissy is fixated at the anal stage, having been potty trained by her over-anxious mother too early, and that her "disturbed and disgusting behaviour", as you ill-informedly refer to it, is a kind of working through and should, therefore, be encouraged by those around her.'

Mrs Hatcher says nothing, although her face is growing redder by the second.

'Embrace the poo,' Leon concludes, after a short, thoughtful pause. He looks to me, as if for agreement, and then, although I can't be completely sure, appears to wink.

Mrs Hatcher stands abruptly.

'I will not tolerate excrement in my classroom!' she bellows. 'This morning, Christine gave me a present. It was gift-wrapped with ribbon and bow. Inside the box was a turd. *That* is not acceptable, normal or to be encouraged.'

'It was from a pregnant llama, Mrs Hatcher,' says Chrissy, 'one of my best specimens. I collected it on our field study trip to the wildlife centre. Don't you remember?'

One point to Chrissy, I'd say, but I can't take any more. I manage to struggle to my feet without leaving the child's chair wedged to my bottom. I tell Mrs Hatcher I'll pass on the message, gather up Chrissy and her belongings, and get out of the classroom and through the school gates as quickly as possible, leaving Leon behind.

As Chrissy and I near the house, he catches up with us.

'Why did you run off like that? Were you feeling dizzy again?'

'Why do you think, Leon? It was awful, and you were hardly helping the situation.'

'That woman knows nothing about the inner psychic life of the developing child. Calls herself a teacher! She could do with analysis herself.'

Like many who believe in psychotherapy, Leon is evangelical about its benefits, seeing it as the answer to everything.

'It's not her job to understand the child's inner psychic life. She's there to teach times tables, number bonds, hist–'

'Mrs J!' calls someone from behind. 'Oi, Mrs J!'

We turn to see Donna, minus her *Domestic Darlings* house-coat, advancing towards us. She really is a perfectly balanced, natural beauty: narrow of shoulder and hip, with a heavy bosom and nipped-in waist, which glides seamlessly into a neat, rounded bottom and slim shapely legs. Her long fair hair falls in soft waves to the small of her back, romantically framing her baby face of large, pale blue eyes, button nose and full, slack mouth. Donna entrances men of all ages, nationalities and social standing. Although her coarse language and raucous cackles do tend to break the spell somewhat.

I gasp as Donna reaches us. She is drenched in a synthetic perfume so strong it could sear the top layer from an eyeball at twenty yards. Leon blinks furiously.

'Just wanted to let you know,' she says, 'it's supposed to be a right scorcher tomorrow and we're having a barby. Mum and Dad have got me doing the rounds, inviting everyone.'

'Well, I, I'm …' I grope about for an excuse.

'You better come,' Donna says, 'cos it's a celebration, too. I've been trying to break into a new career, see, and it looks like it might be happening. Course, I won't be able to clean for you no more if it does.'

Donna has spoken about enrolling in a college course – Nail Technology or Hair Art or something.

'And what might this new career be?' asks Leon.

'Glamour modelling!' Donna declares, her eyes narrowing with the thrill and, well, glamour of the possibility. 'If you got it, flaunt it, that's what I say. I'll show you me pics at the barby tomorrow. One o'clock sharp. Bring a mate.' And she saunters off.

Leon appears momentarily speechless. I sense that he, unlike Donna, was not raised on an estate where barefoot children play in their nightclothes on communal waste ground before being put to bed at 4.30 in the afternoon, where couples explore their differences by smashing each other through windows, where the residents' idea of turning their gardens into 'outside living spaces' is to throw the old three-piece suite onto the front lawn and leave it for a couple of years to grow fungi and animal droppings (Chrissy would appreciate that).

'Maybe you'd like to come with me to the barbecue tomorrow?' I suggest to Leon. 'It'll give you a chance to meet some of the other, um, local characters, and for us to get to know each other as friends, rather than psychotherapist and … well, you know.'

'Yes, of course. Why not?'

I don't tell him I can think of a dozen reasons. Number one being that Dougie Spokes, Donna's dad, is a notorious hard man, with an even more notorious short fuse. Still, too late now.

'What's for tea, Grandma?' asks Chrissy.

We are in the back bedroom, which she has slowly taken

over with her poo collection: various specimens in clear-lidded and labelled plastic containers.

'What would you like?' I reply.

Chrissy thinks long and hard.

'Hmm … lentils, chickpeas and mungy beans.'

'Okay. And it's *mung* beans.' Although mungy does seem a more accurate name for them.

I go downstairs and look through the cupboards, amazed to find I still possess such foodstuffs – although they do tend to keep for decades – left over from my New Age flirtation with wholefood vegetarianism. However, after a particularly trying December, with only a nut roast and soft drinks to look forward to on Christmas Day (which is also my birthday), I decided to ditch all that rubbish and go for a meat-eating, full-fat, tobacco-and-alcohol-friendly lifestyle. What harm can it have done me? Apart from the skin allergies, high blood pressure and cholesterol, persistent cough and frequent bouts of sinusitis, not to mention the ovarian cyst and recent surgery, I'm as fit as a flea.

As I'm searching for the 'best before' date on a packet of adzuki beans, the phone rings.

'Hi Gina. Just a quick call – are you okay to go to the sports centre again now?'

Despite the toxic lifestyle, I do regularly go to keep-fit classes and swim. But I was told to take it easy after the operation and haven't exercised since – doctor's orders.

'Hi Joy. I've got my post-op check next week, so I should probably wait till after that.'

'That's taken a hell of a long time to come through. Are you alright? You sound a bit funny.'

'I'm fine, it'll be fine. Nothing to worry about.'

'What day's the check-up?'

'Tuesday.'

'Not long then, that's good. Because I've been piling it on since you've been out of action. I don't know how. I've hardly been eating a thing.'

'You can go without me, you know.'

'Yes, but ...'

Joy begins to reel off an exhaustive list of excuses. I wait for her to finish, then arrange to meet her in the pool for aqua-aerobics on Tuesday evening, before saying goodbye.

Joy is my best – well, certainly my oldest – friend. We met in the dinner queue on the first day of infant school. Joy's parents were Jamaican and I was fascinated by her appearance, so different to mine; perhaps I still am. Our part of Kent wasn't exactly renowned for its ethnic diversity, so Joy stood out. I marvelled at the contrast between the dark skin on the backs of her hands and her pale palms, the lines etched in muddy brown, her short, exceptionally curly eyelashes, her Afro hair. We were regularly told off for pulling it into fantastic shapes while sitting at the back of the classroom. Joy's pet hamster used to run up her arm to the top of her head and snuggle down into it. Joy learned to carry out the many tasks of a small girl – making perfume mixtures out of petals, organising dolls and teddies into strictly regimented classes, flouncing – with a sleeping hamster on her head. I was impressed.

Joy, like me, was an only child and fatherless. When she was fourteen, her mother died very rapidly from cancer and she was left alone. A maiden aunt, one of her mother's many sisters, came to look after her until she was eighteen. After her mother's death, Joy ballooned. She went from slim, but sturdy and athletic, to enormous in six months, and stayed there. But Joy isn't shapelessly fat, she is all bottom, breasts and cleavage. She is a seamstress and can run up anything designed to fit, or should I say disguise, a body perfectly. Apart from running a funky market stall, she offers a bespoke tailoring service, which is often used by local dignitaries. The only gossip I can pass on is that the mayor requests that all his suits be lined with lilac chiffon. We have no idea why, either.

I briefly consider whether the foods Chrissy has requested, which I'm sure are something to do with another 'science experiment', can be made into an edible meal in less than three hours, but conclude that it's unlikely. I go back upstairs to find Chrissy in the front bedroom, poking about in my jewellery boxes. I warn her that dinner may take a very long time. She wrinkles her nose.

'Boiled eggs instead then, Grandma,' she decides, sensibly.

'Right you are.'

'Look,' she cries, as she glances out of the window, 'it's Grandpa. Grandpa's coming!'

I watch Olly amble down the street. I resist the urge to yank open the sash and yell 'Get 'em off!' because he still has that effect on me. Instead, I attempt to put in place, like an invisible armour protection, my duty to myself to resist all things Ollyan. Whatever he wants – and Olly always wants something, be it money, advice, sex, food, company – I shall refuse. Lately, I've been slipping back into the old habit of letting him turn up and interrupt my life anytime he fancies, and it's got to stop.

Chrissy clatters down the stairs ahead of me and opens the front door. Olly goes to walk in, but I block him. This is made slightly more difficult physically, as well as emotionally, by

Chrissy having attached herself lovingly around his waist.

'Erm,' is all Olly can manage.

'Yes?' I ask, brusquely.

'I was wondering. Gina. If I could borrow. Something.'

I suggest to Chrissy that she go and play in the back garden. She's reluctant, but when I tell her we might have badgers, she immediately scoots off in search of new specimens.

'Just till next week,' Olly continues, fidgeting, 'just till Stella sorts out all this legal stuff with the sunken sculpture and everything.'

'And what exactly is it you want to borrow?' I ask, though I know already.

'Just a bit of money – I'll pay you back next week. Promise.' Olly smiles.

'How much?'

'About four hundred pounds?'

'No! Why?'

'Simone kept saying how she wasn't going to stay round mine any more because it was in too much of a state. So I thought I'd get Donna in to do a bit of spring cleaning. A couple of them turned up and were at it for days. Ended up with a bill for over three hundred quid. And I need a bit for food and …'

I know the rest is for hash.

'I didn't know you'd employed Donna,' I stall, while trying to get my armour protection up and working again.

'Yeah. Thought she'd help keep the old place spick and span, like she does yours.'

'You're not, I mean … don't try and sleep with her, will you?'

Olly's eyes take on a particularly blank, glazed look which, given his usual expression, is quite some achievement.

'You've already tried, haven't you?'

Olly sighs.

'What did she say?'

'That she'd rather lick Sonny's arse.'

Sonny is Olly's next-door neighbour's smelly, yappy Jack Russell, which keeps escaping into his garden and pissing against his half-finished egg sculptures. My estimation of Donna increases, while I am reminded once again that, although Olly may have an intoxicating effect on me, many other women find him to be a moronic waste of space and not in the least bit attractive.

'No, I won't give you money,' I say, and close the door.

After dinner, Chrissy invites me to one of her 'shows' in the back bedroom. Where other small girls might prance about pretending to be princesses or ballerinas, Chrissy's show involves a detailed talk about, then examination and discussion of, her poo collection.

'Why didn't Mrs Hatcher like the llama poo?' she asks sadly. 'It was one of my best specimens.'

'I think you know why,' I reply, because I'm sure Chrissy's not quite as innocent as she makes out. 'Most people don't like poo, they just want to flush it away. It smells and they find it yucky.'

'Keyologists look at old poos to see what animals and humans used to live off.'

'That's true. And they're called *ar*chaeologists.'

'Doctors look at poo to find out what's wrong with you.'

'Sometimes, for certain things.'

'People use camel poo to build houses.'

'Hmm,' I murmur, while silently cursing the extensive

research behind, and factually correct basis of, *Everything You Ever Wanted to Know About Poo.* 'I see what you mean, but most people don't look at it that way. And you have to live with other people, don't you? So try not to go on about it all the time. And certainly don't use other children for your science experiments. You made them quite ill.'

'Alright,' Chrissy nods, a little guiltily, I think. 'Grandpa said there was an artist once who put his poo in tin cans, like baked beans, and sold it. But I think Grandpa was making it up, like the bears he says live at the bottom of his garden, and the baby dinosaurs waiting to be born from his eggs. I said, "Why don't they hatch then?", but he said it takes years before they're ready to come out because ... because they're very shy.'

Chrissy surprises me with a wide-eyed, wonder-filled look that only a child can give. At seven years old, she is such an odd mix of rational thought and magical belief. She can, for example, give a well-informed, logical account of how a digger would be used to excavate the foundations of a house – a bricklayer would build the basic structure and a carpenter would put in the windows and doors – but will conclude with a 'and pixies would put the roof on'.

'Actually, the poo-in-cans thing is true,' I admit. 'A famous London gallery bought some a few years ago.'

'How much for?'

'About twenty thousand pounds. It cost more than gold.'

'Really? Can I sell my poo in tin cans?'

'No, Chrissy, you're not a famous artist.'

She frowns.

'I'm good at drawing. Maybe I'll become a famous artist.'

Oh *no*!

'To the gallery it wasn't just poo, it was ...' I stumble. How can I explain the nature of the ironic statement, the role of avant-garde in modernism, briefly summarise the controversial subject of what constitutes art? As I mumble noncommittally, Chrissy helps me out.

'Maybe the artist's poo was like Trudy the Turd,' she says, 'poo with character.'

'Yes, perhaps that's it.'

Susan arrives to pick up Chrissy at seven o'clock sharp. Opening the front door, I see that she has already retreated down the path and is standing by her car. Olly is also still here, sitting on my front step, smoking a roll-up.

'Grandpa, it's true,' says Chrissy, 'that artist put his poo in tin cans and people bought it!'

'Told you,' smiles Olly. 'Though a few have exploded over the years. Warhol used wee in some of his pictures, but I don't know if they were any good. Never caught on like the tins of soup. And Ofili uses elephant poo. He won the Turner Prize. A friend of mine at college squashed rabbit droppings into his clay forms, but they blew up in the kilns. Never could work out if it was the dung that did it or if he hadn't wedged the clay properly. Now, when Grandma was at college,' Olly grins up at me, 'she used to paint light-bulbs, and they used to explode. But that was definitely the paint, not the bulbs, wasn't it, Gin?'

Yes, it's true, the psychedelic light-bulbs were one of my least successful, not to mention highly dangerous, ideas. I met Olly on the Foundation Course at the local Art College, but only stayed for one term after discovering, having searched high and low, from front to back, even down the gritty, repellent sides of the metaphorical sofa, and to my eternal disappointment – for I had enthusiasm by the bucketful – that I had absolutely no discernible talent.

'And then,' Olly continues, 'there's Chadwick. She made sculptures by weeing in the snow, with her husband, and then they –'

'Olly!' I nearly scream, as I register Susan's expression: that of someone having their face torn in half (although I must admit to deliberately letting Olly go on, being secretly amazed that his brain is still capable of retaining so much information).

Olly follows my gaze to Susan, then mimes zipping his lips.

'When you're an artist,' he whispers to Chrissy as he hugs her goodbye, 'you can get away with anything.'

'I'm going to be an artist, Mummy,' declares Chrissy, as she clambers into the back of the car. '*That* is what I am going to be!'

I decide this is not a good time to tell hands-on-hips Susan about Chrissy's referral to a psychologist. Instead, I wave happy bye-byes and say over-brightly and over-loudly that everything's fine and Chrissy's been an angel.

Olly continues to sit on my front step.

'Go away.'

'I've got no food.'

'You earn loads. What's happened to it all?' But I know Olly isn't lying, I've just never met anyone worse with money.

'Stella organises all that. She's my agent. That's what I pay her for. I've had this month's allowance, but it's kind of gone quicker than I thought.'

It's ridiculous that Stella has to manage Olly's finances for him but, really, I'm grateful to her on his behalf. Olly can't be trusted to pop out to buy a pint of milk, let alone organise his earnings as an artist. If it wasn't for her, it's unlikely he'd make any sort of a living from his work. It's Stella who negotiates commissions and contracts, organises publicity and exhibitions, and banks and invests the profits. She also advised him, soundly, to buy a property and build his own studio. And she's cleverly cultivated Olly's reputation as an 'artistic recluse', thus preventing him from being exposed as the drug-addled pinhead he really is.

I go back into the house and return with the lentils, chickpeas, mung beans and a tenner, then hand them to Olly.

'Thanks, Gina,' he says, looking at me like a deprived orphan who has just been given his only and unexpected birthday present. 'I couldn't come in for a –'

'No,' I yell, and slam the door, before waiting to find out what 'a –' could be.

Maybe it's my hormones – I mean, how well can a woman function with one ovary? Maybe I am hitting the menopause. Maybe it's Olly, maybe it's the check-up on Tuesday, maybe it's Chrissy having to see a psychologist, maybe it's just life, but I start crying. I go into the front room, pull the curtains and try to get a grip. I consider, then discard, in turn: phoning Joy, comfort eating, reading, knocking myself out with painkillers, watching TV, drinking to oblivion, working, smashing something to pieces.

After spending two hours hunched on the sofa, chain-smoking, I decide the safest bet is to go to bed. Climbing the stairs, I realise that I am soon to be visited by the ghost of my mother. She is gathering on the landing in an anxious, foot-shuffling sort of way, in the form of a – not unattractive – blue mist which, despite its haziness, gives the impression that matching hat and gloves are being worn. Maybe if I dash past before she has time to firm up, throw myself into bed and feign sleep, she'll leave me alone. Occasionally, my clairvoyant friend, Lara, will try to persuade me to let her hold a séance to allow my mother to 'come through'. But what would be the point? She turns up whenever she wants anyway, uninvited and unchannelled. I remain transfixed halfway up the stairs, unsure whether to go back down again or make a run for the bedroom, while my mother hovers on the landing. We are unable to approach or retreat. Such was our relationship when she was still alive.

The telephone rings in the dining room and I rush downstairs to answer it, relieved it has made the decision for me.

'Georgina, I must speak with Georgina,' says the aged, but commanding, voice.

'This is Gina,' I say, loudly and clearly, for it is Milady Manors, my grandmother on my mother's side. She's about a hundred years old (seriously, she *is* about a hundred years old), hard of hearing, and lives on the south coast of England in a grand house, which is part theatrical school (lower floors) and part old folks' home (upper floors) for retired 'artistes'. Milady Manors was her stage and then radio name, but it has stuck, and not without her encouragement.

'Georgina, dear, have you seen your mother lately?'

'Yes,' I reply. 'I think she's here now.'

'She's been visiting me an awful lot, too. Most inconvenient. Something seems to have got her into a tizzy, something about your house.'

My heart sinks.

The attic flat. The fire escape. It was my mother who fell to her death from the top. Why? I don't know. Nobody does. Not the police, Olly, nor any of Olly's space-cake friends. Susan and

I were away the weekend it happened. Suicide? So very, very unlikely. An accident? But she was such a cautious person and always wore sensible shoes. A freak gust of wind? A malicious buckling of the metal steps? There are no answers. To me, the fire escape is a death-trap, but there was, and is, nothing wrong with it. I'm so glad it can be removed, now I've bought the top flat. I'm sure that Mum would have been glad, too.

'You've got to sort this out,' Milady continues, while I am lost in thought, not speaking.

'Yes, yes, but … I don't know how.'

'I think you do. Don't deny your psychic gift. We've all got it, as I am certain you are aware. Your mother did, and look what happened to her. Help to find a way to put her to rest. Fifteen years in limbo is time enough for anyone.'

'Okay, okay. I'll try.'

'Good. And tell her that hat and gloves ensemble doesn't work. Poor girl never did have any dress sense. And the hovering. Such a nuisance. Reminds me of when she was a child. Always grizzling, whining, hanging about. Never doing anything useful or entertaining. Tell her to come through properly or not at all. Some people!' And Milady clicks off.

'Some people!' was Milady's catchphrase on her popular radio show of the 1930s – *Milady Says* – which was based on one of her variety acts. She played a financially embarrassed aristocrat of dubious morality. 'Some people!' she would conclude each episode haughtily, to peals of laughter. It was harmless entertainment, usually based on Milady surreptitiously trying to raise cash ('that most vulgar of beasts') and turning on comic misunderstandings with the vicar, the Ponsomby-Smythes or the head gardener. Milady produced twins – my mother,

Shirley, and her brother, Edward – in 1933. I don't think she ever forgave them, or my mother at least, for interrupting her career. Uncle Edward has been quite a successful stage actor and he and Milady adore each other, but the awful truth is that Milady never appeared to get on with, or even like, Mum; chalk and cheese. Poor Mum. I've always liked and admired Milady; I would stay with her during school holidays, while Mum was working in the cake shop. As for the family's psychic gift, I'm not entirely convinced. When I was younger, Milady regularly organised séances and spiritual events, but I'm sure they were largely an excuse to touch up men under the tasselled velvet tablecloth and put on funny voices.

The telephone rings again, making me jump. I half-expect it to be my mother, forsaking the usual routes of communication from the other side – apparition, dream, clairvoyance – and opting to use the landline instead. But it's Olly. I sigh with relief on hearing the banality of his talk. Olly tells me he's tried boiling all the food I gave him earlier, but it still appears inedible; what should he do? Note: this is typical of Olly – of just about everyone I know, come to think of it. No 'How are *you*, Gina?' or 'Is this a good time to call?' No. But what would I reply? 'I have spent the evening feeling depressed and being haunted by my mother'? Hold on a minute, this *is* Olly and you can say anything to him: shockproof.

'Olly, I'm feeling depressed and being haunted by Mum.'

'Oh, babes. Shall I come over?'

'Yes.'

'Do you have any bacon and eggs?'

'Yes.'

'Five minutes.'

When Olly arrives an hour later, he presents me with a stew pot full of the food I gave him earlier, as proof that he has attempted cooking. It is a revolting mess. At one point it must have caught fire. I tell him to chuck the whole thing in the wheelie bin, which is sitting on the front path.

Mum has gone. She always seems to disappear when Olly's around. I begin to cook Olly a fry-up (his favourite meal of all time), after handing him my little enamelled hash pot, which he accepts enthusiastically. We now re-enact a scene we have played out for over twenty-five years: me cooking, while Olly rolls spliffs as we chat.

Olly asks about the spring cleaning he's had done: is three hundred pounds too much? He thought it would be around fifty quid. Should he get someone in regularly? And what about his garden? The trees need pruning. And the bindweed, what's the best thing for getting rid of that? For a creative type, Olly can produce some pretty mundane conversations.

I don't understand the sudden concern with his place; it's always been untidy and overgrown. Olly lives a ten-minute walk away in a 1960s bungalow, on a small estate of identical dwellings. Most of his neighbours are retired, infirm or just severely lacking in imagination. It is a land of neatly clipped privet hedges, block paved drives and 'tasteful' garden ornaments. Olly's bungalow is on a corner plot and has an unusually large garden, in which he has built his studio, with the help of his brother, Marty. In such a conservative neighbourhood, Olly has fitted in with amazing ease. I think it's because he's an artist. People like to have an artist in their midst, it makes them feel more important and interesting, less ordinary. Although some find it vaguely threatening, artistry implies the unnecessary, whimsical, laughable, or else the challenging, problematic, incomprehensible. Olly, however, has learnt to avoid any suspicion of absurdity or anarchy by, when needs must, referring to himself as a stonemason, which is not untrue. Thus, the neighbourhood men respect Olly because he is large, good-humoured and can generally be found wielding manly masonry tools and covered in stone dust. And the women like Olly because he is large, good-humoured and can generally be found wielding manly masonry tools and covered in stone dust. I was present when Olly finally persuaded two warring neighbours, who had feuded for twenty years about parking, hedges, overhanging trees and so on, to make peace. Olly held their hands together, like Bob Marley at the One Love Concert, over a boundary fence – the site of much previous hostility – and closed his eyes in triumph. The rival sides looked intensely uncomfortable, but had no choice other than to make up.

It's because of this sort of thing that I can't help but retain some remnants of love for Olly. He may be irresponsible and erratic, but he is also warm-hearted, extremely generous and can get on with anyone. He treats everyone the same and is oblivious to money, status or fame. He is, to use an old-fashioned word, guileless. But when he asked me to marry him, I should have realised what his assertion that he'd always be a 'free spirit' really meant: that he'd always be unfaithful. To be honest, I probably did realise, but thought I could handle it or that marriage would change him. Olly wasn't even particularly secretive about his girlfriends, seeing brief sexual encounters and relationships as one of the excitements and pleasures of life. Perhaps I also believed that for one stoned week during the seventies, but I grew less able to cope with it as time went on and was no good at being a 'free spirit' myself. I didn't want to be; I just wanted Olly.

When I hand Olly his fry-up, he hands me a spliff. I haven't indulged for a while, but what the hell. A couple of hours later we have had gentle, companionable sex and munched our way through a packet of chocolate chip cookies, and I am recovering from another crying fit about not wanting to grow old, fall to pieces or have bits of me removed, in which Olly has joined me in tearful sympathy. I lay my head on Olly's broad, heavy chest while he strokes my hair, twisting little strands between his fingers. It is bliss. For about four minutes. Then he begins snoring and I go into the back bedroom and continue to cry about loving Olly and hating him, wishing I knew my father, missing my mother, but sometimes being glad she's gone, and loving and hating Susan. I also shed joyful tears at the recognition that I can simply love Chrissy and she simply loves me back. When I hold this feeling close to me, the fact that the only witness to my deep, tortured angst is a row of containerised turds makes me feel marginally less desperate. I finally manage sleep.

I'm woken by a hammering on the front door. It's dark and I have no idea what time it is. I feel for my bedside lamp, forgetting I'm in the back bedroom, where I finally fell asleep to escape Olly's snoring. I try to stand and make my way to the light switch, but am totally disorientated. I still feel stoned and, yes, cross-eyed. I stumble over Chrissy's poo collection, scattering the tubs across the floor. There's more banging, but it can't be Susan – middle of the night melodramatics are not her style. Unless there's something wrong with Chrissy! I find my way out of the room and rush down the stairs, pulling a towel from the banister to wrap around my naked body. I fling open the front door.

Simone, Olly's girlfriend, pushes past me.

'Where is he?' she demands.

I restrain the urge to kick her hard in the guts, then pull her back into the night by her long, dark hair while shrieking, 'Get out of my house, you stupid bitch.'

'He's upstairs,' I say instead.

Simone manages to wake Olly (which is no mean feat in my experience, but I think the hail of body blows may have done it), and flush him out of the bedroom and down the stairs into the hallway. I return to bed in the back room while listening to Olly's dumb droning and Simone's hysterics. I go back to sleep with amazing ease, and in the hope that my life will be substantially improved when I next rejoin reality.

3

MAY DAY MAYDAY

It is. Bright sunlight beams its transfiguring glory beneath the hem of the curtains, warming my face, teasing me awake. Feeling unexpectedly refreshed and clear-headed, I get up early, put the washing on, sort through the week's post, then inspect the garden. It's May Day and I can't wait for summer to arrive. I've always loved it: the heat, light, colour; everything growing, budding, blossoming, until it's one glorious, over-ripe, Technicolor blur. Lying stunned and saturated in its splendour year after year may have given me the skin of a well-worn saddlebag, but never mind.

I eat breakfast at the little wrought-iron table on the patio, while looking through extraordinarily over-priced kitchen brochures. Even though essential maintenance work needs to be done to the house, I prefer to focus on the superficial. Forget the boring roof tiles, wall ties and repointing, I want over-stuffed chesterfields in rich velvet, heavy made-to-measure curtains stiff with expense, fancy lights, beautiful things. It was a wrench to sell the house I inherited from Mum to pay for all this, so I really hope it'll prove to be a wise decision – at least psychologically, if not financially.

I must have truly embraced middle age because I find

myself really enjoying brochure flicking, a muffled contentment warming me from within. The air is balmy, I can wear summery clothes again, and an incredibly angry twenty-something is no longer shouting in my face. Things are looking up.

I decide to objectively assess my body in preparation for summer. A season some women (slim, attractive, young ones) welcome with sensuous, open-armed abandon, while wearing strappy tops and shorts, but others recoil from in dismay, pulling the roll-necks of their black, shapeless jumpers over their heads and praying for three solid months of freak thunderstorms. Yes, I have to do it. Today. I must stand naked in front of the wardrobe mirror and assess the impact of pregnancy (even though it was over thirty years ago), a less-than-healthy lifestyle, prolonged sunbathing, time, gravity and, most recently, surgery.

I have a long bath, wax my legs and apply full make-up first. I then distract myself further by painting nails, plucking already plucked eyebrows and blow-drying hair. Then I straighten it. I wonder if I'm allowed to wear bra and knickers, light clothing perhaps? No. I draw the curtains and slip off my bathrobe. I look. I take a few steps away from the mirror. I look again. I squint. Not too bad. When viewed from a distance of eight feet, in semi-darkness, through half-closed eyes, my overall appearance is acceptable. Bugger. I get up close. I damn to hell Coco Chanel and Brigitte Bardot for making suntans popular, while I try to smooth out forehead lines and pull a haughty grimace. I then let go and the inevitable falls back into place. I curse as I inspect my roots, which need doing *again*, but thank the Good Lord for Sure 'n' Simple hair colouring. I also thank my father for the cheekbones and heart-shaped face. From my mother I only seem to have inherited brittle nails and a lack of height. I appear to be moving in a dangerous and unwanted direction from curvy to chunky, but reassure myself that I'll return to fitness once I'm able to go to the sports centre again. I did, in my late thirties, possibly as a reaction to the divorce, exercise and low-fat diet myself down to taut, micro proportions. Leon helped me get over this 'neurotically controlling behaviour induced by severe emotional stress'. Happy memories.

I allow my gaze to rest on my tummy. The keyhole surgery incisions – three small scars – are still red, but don't look awful. Gingerly, I touch them. The skin is smooth, but numb. I run my hands over my hips and belly, wobbling the flab; sorry, appreciating my curves. I make small circular movements over my abdomen. Closing my eyes, I press more firmly, then slump down on the bed. I realise I'm not assessing what I look like or mourning lost youth, but searching for another lump. Not that I found the first one. I'd made an appointment with my GP because I'd nearly fainted that morning, and thought I must have a virus or infection. While I was there, I mentioned other symptoms – bloating, feeling like I needed to wee all the time, odd pains – so she did a pelvic examination and found that one side was swollen. I was sent for a scan, which revealed the large ovarian cyst. Due to its size, the symptoms it was causing, and the fact it didn't look like one that would go away by itself, the decision was made to remove it.

Perhaps the follow-up at the hospital next week will turn out to be a good thing. It's reminded me that I need to take responsibility for my health, that I must stop – or at least try to stop – smoking, once and for all. I've a typical addict's mentality. When I'm smoking, I tell myself I'll give up at some unspecified point in the future, that I don't smoke *that* much, that it's relaxing, sociable, that there are so many worse things I could be doing. On those occasions when I've briefly managed to quit, however, I'll admit it's an expensive, offensive, life-shortening habit, with no pluses whatsoever. But then something happens and I start again – with just one – and soon I'm back to telling myself I'll stop at some unspecified point in the future, that I don't smoke *that* much … But I've no excuse not to give it another go, not to give it one hundred per cent this time. Starting right now.

As I get up from the bed – while fighting off a sudden, incredibly strong desire for a cigarette – I allow myself a momentary flood of regret for all those insecurities I fretted over as a teenager and young woman, about being fat or short or the shape of my nose. What a waste of time, what a waste of energy, what a waste of life. I then cast aside all such maudlin thoughts and resolve to restart exercise, once I've been given the all-clear, and ask Joy to sort me out some new outfits, after I've assessed my summer clothes.

As I go to open the wardrobe, I'm distracted by a grunting sound coming from the front of the house. I look out to see Olly on the path with his head in the wheelie bin. Then I remember that we are divorced, he shouldn't be here and he has a girlfriend. I go downstairs to find that Olly is trying to extract his stew pot from the bottom of the bin. He finally manages it and returns to an upright position.

'Wow, that's given me a massive headrush,' he comments, with a slightly startled, but not unhappy, expression.

'Did you, um, patch things up with Simone last night?' I ask.

'Yeah. Sorry about the noise and everything,' Olly replies. 'She's a hot-tempered woman.'

'How did you explain being round my place?' I enquire,

casually, confronted by a vision of a pathologically jealous Simone plunging a dagger into my heart.

'Well … I said I'd come round on, on a mission of mercy. I said you needed me and I couldn't say no.'

I frown.

'And what exactly was this mission of mercy?'

'I said you were having a breakdown, that you'd taken an overdose.'

'Olly! Did she believe you?'

'Not at first. She asked why you weren't in hospital and I said because … well, at that point I noticed the Holland & Barrett bag on the side.'

'And?'

'Erm. I said you'd swallowed a whole load of ginseng and slippery elm and whatnot.'

'You said I'd tried to kill myself by taking an overdose of herbal remedies?'

'Yeah. Then Simone went upstairs and saw that I'd been sleeping in the front bedroom and you were in the back. And the way you were lying there, Gin – all curled up in a ball, talking in your sleep and surrounded by tubs of shit – it kind of looked believable at three o'clock in the morning.'

I suddenly feel a lot less cheery, and in desperate need of a calming cigarette. I look at my watch; it's not even been ten minutes since I gave up.

'Chrissy,' says Olly, distractedly, 'is going to be an artist. Chip off the old block.'

Olly keeps forgetting that Susan and, therefore, Chrissy, are not related to him genetically. The fact that Susan's biological father was never involved in her upbringing may have contributed to this. When Olly used to point out resemblances to his side of the family – as Susan was growing up and much to her horror – I thought he was being kind or over-compensating. Really, I think he just forgot. I hope Chrissy hasn't 'inherited' anything else from Olly's imagined bloodline, like being an imbecile and a bastard.

He looks at me, 'Sorry for saying those things.'

'We really shouldn't end up in bed together, not when you're in a relationship with someone else.'

'I know. But we've been doing it for so long, I keep forgetting it's supposed to be wrong.'

'I think you'd better get going. I don't want Simone round here again.'

'Okay. It was good though, wasn't it?' Olly grins, before pecking me on the cheek goodbye.

In truth, however, Olly has never been a fantastic lover, although I was impassioned enough for the both of us, in the beginning at least. For it was love at first sight when I met him, on the very first day of term at Art College.

It was exceptionally cold for early autumn and the class was waiting outside a studio – a dilapidated mobile classroom – for someone to open it. I had just dropped Susan off at school and cycled over, excited and nervous, hoping Joy wouldn't forget to pick her up for me, and that I wasn't going to be the only mature student; I was twenty-two and it seemed a great deal older than eighteen at the time. I chained up the bike and walked over to join the others. And there was Olly, facing away from me. He was wearing a heavy, military-style overcoat with the collar up, and a long striped scarf wound around his neck and chin and over his nose, so that only the top half of his head was visible.

He stamped his feet and patted his arms up and down his sides to keep warm. I liked the look of Olly from the back, and the glimpses of his profile weren't bad either; I hoped the front of him wouldn't disappoint. As our tutor approached, Olly turned round. Wow. Of course, I couldn't tell what the other half of his face was like, as it was hidden by the scarf, but his green eyes were enough. They were so outrageously beautiful that I suffered a near-physical collapse and had to hold on to a wall for support. For though I'd had a baby, I had never been in love, never fallen, and what a terrible tumble it was. I kept on going, bouncing head over heels over head over heels, never touching the ground long enough to come to a halt. I didn't land until nearly sixteen years later, when Olly made a casual girlfriend pregnant and I decided enough was enough (she later suffered a miscarriage). Joy warned me from the start that it was not sensible to fall in love with a man purely on the basis of his eye colour and ability to carry off a Russian Army greatcoat. I should have listened.

I don't know how long it took me to realise that Olly's physical perfection didn't match what I'd assumed was inside; perhaps I never have. But no matter how bad things were, I could come home to the most astounding green eyes in the world. Superficial, perhaps, but colour has always affected me profoundly. A bright yellow can make me retch, a pale blue weep, a violent red induce a headache. The perfect green made me fall in love. My favourite colour has a lot to answer for. I chose my first car because it was olive green, the attic flat to rent due to the grass-green front door, the emerald engagement ring. Even my wedding dress was moss-green velvet – floor length with long, fluted sleeves; Susan commented that I looked like a lizard. And Olly's eyes were the most sublime green of all, gazing right at me. I block out the question clawing at the back of my mind, scrabbling to be let in, of why I've remained so long and so derangedly in love with a man who, apart from everything else, is pretty crap in bed.

I'm about to go back indoors when I catch the sound of a distant, familiar rumble. I sit on the front step and wait. Sure enough, five minutes later, Moya pulls up on her motorcycle. I wonder if she's forgotten something because we never work together on a Saturday, but she begins unpacking equipment from the sidecar.

'We didn't arrange for me to sit today, did we?' I ask, as she comes up the path.

'No.'

'Are you dropping something off?'

'No.'

'Um, why are you here then?'

'To work on your portrait.'

'But I'm going out.'

'No matter.'

I feel slightly affronted that I don't even need to be in the same building as Moya for her to paint me. Not having to sit still was strange enough, though I was relieved I didn't have to strip off. As I begin to wonder if everything's alright for Moya at home, Leon comes out of his house and reminds me that it's time we were getting to Donna's barbecue. He's even made food specially. Oh dear, why did I invite him? I still can't relax in his company and the Spokes are such a rough-and-ready bunch, I hope it's not a disaster.

'My goodness!' says Leon, as we arrive at the Spokes' house.

It is a boxy, 1960s end of terrace on the notorious Byron

Estate. Cemented to the top of brick pillars, signalling the entrance to the front garden, are huge bulldog heads, their expressions frozen in frenzied bloodlust. If you could see their bodies they would be rampant, like heraldic lions. As we walk up the front path, Dougie, Donna's dad, comes out to greet us. He is wearing tight black jeans slung low under his belly and a white, short-sleeved shirt, which strains to a parting over his barrel chest, where a heavy gold pendant nestles amongst wiry hairs. If I hadn't known Dougie since school, I can't imagine I'd have anything to do with him now. He's one of those people who, if you've done something, he'll have done it too, ten times over, ten times better. He asked me out when we were thirteen; I turned him down. He's carried a chip on his shoulder ever since, due to wounded male pride rather than any great affection for me.

'Hi, Dougie, this is Leon, my next-door neighbour. He's not moved in long, so I thought it would be nice for him to meet a few locals.'

'Good to meet you, mate,' says Dougie, administering a bone-crushing handshake. 'Did you cop a look at Gina when you went to view the house then – is that what made you wanna live next door?' Dougie winks.

'Er, no. It was because it was an excellent size and location for the setting up of my practice.'

'Your what?'

'My psychoanalytic psychotherapy practice.'

'Oh,' says Dougie. 'A head doctor, eh? Well, I hope you ain't gonna be analysing me all afternoon.'

'No, no, of course not,' Leon reassures. 'And it's really not like –'

'Coo-ee,' calls Dougie's wife – known to one and all as Tar, short for Tanya – as she comes round the side of the house. She is a deep, sunbed orange, and is wearing hipster jeans and a crop top. Everything is so tight, just looking at her makes me hold my breath. Tar is topped and tailed by a bleach-blonde mullet and red, high-heeled sandals.

Dougie slips an arm around his wife's waist.

'You're still one hot-looking woman, Tar. And if any man disagrees with me, I wanna know why,' says Dougie. He then smiles smugly at Leon. 'You married, Doc?'

'No.'

'Well, you might have all the fancy bits of paper in the world, but she's worth more than all that, don't you agree?' says Dougie, slapping Tar's backside.

Surprisingly, Leon does not lecture Dougie on the patriarchal vice of treating women as chattels, how psychotherapy can help balance marital power relations, or the political incorrectness of public arse slapping. He merely nods.

'What are you doing here?' I ask, as Olly wanders into the garden.

'I was invited. Dougie's been doing all my … taxying for me,' replies Olly, which, accurately translated, means: Dougie's been getting all my drugs for me.

'Yeah,' says Dougie. 'Very good tipper.'

'I see you're going to be making a sculpture for the city,' says Leon to Olly. 'Are you allowed to say what it's going to be?'

'Not sure yet,' replies Olly. 'The stone's being delivered to the studio in a couple of weeks. I'll have to wait and see how it inspires me.'

'We collect art,' says Dougie. 'Our house is chock-a-block with it.'

'Really?' says Leon. 'Any particular period?'

'Modern. No old rubbish. You collect, too?'

Leon shakes his head, 'I have one or two pieces, but you could hardly call them a collection.'

'Well, come in and admire mine then. They've cost me a bloody fortune over the years. I should start charging,' smiles Dougie, his eyes narrowing to the point of non-existence.

I thought Dougie might have waited five minutes before becoming moronically competitive with Leon. Still, as long as Leon keeps nodding and lets Dougie go on about how great he is, I'm sure all will go smoothly. After all, Leon is an experienced psychotherapist, so he should know how to handle a borderline psycho.

Dougie leads us into the house and through to the dining room where we are confronted by a triptych of framed, airbrushed Athena posters, popular in the eighties, particularly with teenage girls. They consist of a pair of legs in glossy high heels, a glossy pouting mouth sipping a cocktail, and a hand with glossy painted nails seductively tracing the edge of a bowl of glossy cherries.

'Glossy,' I murmur, as everyone nods appreciatively.

Dougie then outlines his various art collections, which are showcased on floor-to-ceiling shelves. These can be roughly divided into three categories: Native American, mythological beasts and famous people; even minor celebrities made of wax with wicks protruding from their heads are awarded a place.

'What do you think then?' asks Dougie.

'Modern art,' says Leon faintly.

'Great,' says Olly, without a hint of irony, his interest clearly lying outside, through the open patio doors to where the drink, food and females-in-light-summer-clothing are.

'I knew you'd be impressed,' beams Dougie.

'Come up and see the rest of them,' says Tar. 'The kids have gone collecting mad, too.'

As Dougie, Leon and I troop upstairs, Olly escapes into the garden and thus avoids squeezing into bedrooms lined with bunk-beds, which all house vast, regimented collections of one sort or another, be they dinosaurs, creepy 'Victoriana' dolls, grisly action figures or, in Keanu's case, pictures of Pamela Anderson (his apparent older-woman crush) and reproduction (I'm assuming) small arms. Every inch of wall is utilised and every bedroom could be mistaken for a poky shop crammed with ten times more merchandise than it needs to stock. I look out through a lace-curtained window onto the back garden and survey a world of slouching, Burberry-clad youths, small children fighting, and adults drinking and smoking. I experience an overwhelming desire to join them, and join in, especially with the smoking, although I have managed to resist so far. Over two hours. Not that I'm counting.

As we follow the Spokes back downstairs, Leon grips my hand.

'I've never seen anything like it,' he whispers in my ear.

'What, the awful taste? Haven't you got an Argos catalogue?'

'No, the collecting. It's a sign of the obsessive-compulsive personality. To find such an extent of hoarding behaviours in one family is extraordinary. It's a classic indicator of underlying psychopathology.'

If that's the case, I don't understand why I, too, don't possess an extensive collection of crinoline ladies or Swarovski crystal or, let's not get too highbrow about this, old toothbrushes and cardboard boxes.

'The object fixation synonymous with collecting represents a failure to successfully move through the anal-retentive phase. Like Chrissy with her specimens, the Spokes –'

'Oh, give it a rest, Leon. Don't you ever lighten up? You sound like a textbook.'

I must be relaxing with Leon because I've started to insult him. I know he's deep, but he can be exhausting. Sometimes, you just want to drink cheap wine, sit in the sun and not think.

As we step out through the patio doors, I resolve not to allow anything to interfere with my enjoyment of this blissfully summery day.

'Keanu,' I say to Donna's teenage brother, 'can you get me a drink?'

'Over there,' he mumbles, pointing to a laden table.

'Good. White wine please.'

After ten minutes of fumbling with corkscrews and knocking over bottles, he hands me a glass.

'Thanks,' I say.

'Thanks,' he repeats.

I'm unsure whether he's mocking me or is just not used to social gatherings. He must sense my confusion.

'I mean,' he explains, 'thanks for calling me Keanu. Every other bastard calls me Canoe. Sometimes I think it's my real name.'

I settle into a plastic chair with my pint glass of white wine and glance about me. There must be fifty people crammed into the back garden. They certainly are a patriotic bunch. I have never seen so much clothing or so many bodies adorned with the St George's flag. When I fall asleep tonight, I shall dream in red and white. Leon, of course, sticks out like a sore thumb, with his formal shirt, brogues and intelligent face. Olly blends in by being a large, intellectually untroubled bloke in non-descript clothing. I turn my attention to the women. They are either very petite – stalking about on spindly heels and showing off bare, brown midriffs – or vastly overweight, their bodies a series of landslides. Tar is engrossed in talk with a small gathering of females from teens to sixties who, despite the age range, all share a love of tight denim, peroxide and fags. Unfortunately, I'm equally enthusiastic, particularly about the fags. Why oh why did I decide to give up smoking today? After all, I don't smoke *that* much, and it's relaxing and sociable and …

Leon brings a chair over and sits next to me. He looks a little pale.

'You alright?' I ask.

'I think so. I just offered Dougie some veggie burgers I made earlier. He said he wouldn't allow such rabbit food to share a grill with his steaks, with his "proper men's food". Said he'd rather barbecue my hands. I couldn't tell if he was joking. I think he has some issues with aggression.'

'I don't doubt it, but I'm sure that was just his attempt at humour. He's an okay bloke, really, as long as you stay on the right side of him.'

As we sit chatting and drinking, Leon and I observe various small, feral children scattering each other about the grass. They are playing American wrestling, which is basically an excuse for the older, stronger ones to duff up the younger, weaker ones.

'Get us another, will you?' I ask Leon. 'Please?'

He frowns at my near-empty pint glass, but stands up and goes over to the drinks table. I'm drinking too much due to not smoking. This always happens. Whenever I give my lungs a break, I end up punishing my liver (drinking), stomach (over-eating) or teeth (sweet-sucking) instead. Why can't I develop a useful, non-destructive compulsion, like tidying the house or doing work or practising the trombone? Oh no, here comes Olly. And Simone.

'Apologies for last night,' she says, her intense, dark eyes threatening to pierce my soul. 'I had no idea what ... what was going on.'

'Don't mention it,' I say, with curt indifference, though this is hard to carry off when faced with your ex-husband's girlfriend who's a generation younger than you and thinks you're a desperate, mentally unbalanced, slippery-elm-overdosing freak. Simone patronises me with an insincere smile.

'Come on, Oliver,' she says, 'let's get a drink.'

As Simone glides away, with Olly trailing after her, I experience a ridiculous pang of jealousy. Leon returns with a small glass of wine and lemonade for me, and a dark, heavy bottle of unspecified spirits, apparently for himself. Just as he's pouring a large one, Dougie bangs on a baking tray, then calls for quiet.

'Now, not only have I got us all together cos it's the first decent barby weather of the year, but we are also here to celebrate our Donna becoming the first proper celebrity in the family. And here she is!'

Donna steps out through the patio doors to a round of applause. She twirls round on white stilettos to reveal 'Best of British' stitched in gothic lettering across the backside of her micro-sized, figure-hugging dress.

'Mum bought the dress, but the words was my idea,' she says proudly.

'I reckon my Donna puts the great in Great Britain,' declares

Dougie, to murmurs of admiration and approval, as Tar wipes away a tear.

'I ain't won yet, Mum,' Donna warns, 'but I reckon I should. My pics are well good. Don't you think?'

Donna hands round copies of a lads' mag called *Bloke*, which is running a Best of British Babes competition, i.e. get your girlfriend to pose topless, take a snap and send it in. The top twelve are featured in this month's issue, and the winner – as voted by readers – will receive a £5,000 prize and feature on a forthcoming front cover. Donna is suggestively holding a can of furniture polish in her photo, under the caption 'Busty Babe Donna, from Kent, Gets Satisfaction on the Job'. She's a disorientating mix of impossibly beautiful and incredibly tacky, evidently a winning combination for *Bloke* readers.

Donna tells us that the magazine has received an unprecedented amount of fan mail for her and requests for more photos, and that she is streets ahead in the competition. And *Domestic Darlings* has also received an unprecedented increase in enquiries since the magazine came out. Despite this, they are considering sacking Donna for generating 'inappropriate publicity for their local, reputable, family-run business'.

I eye Olly. He is comparing the artistic merits – in rather too much detail and rather too enthusiastically – of the various contenders, and declaring that Donna is definitely the best. Spring cleaning indeed! Leon, to his credit, is studiously avoiding the magazine.

As I go to the drinks table for a refill I 'accidentally' stamp on Olly's foot, causing him to drop his magazine. Simone avoids any such subtlety and simply elbows him hard in the chest.

I return to my seat next to Leon.

'I'm sorry,' I say.

'What for?'

'For inviting you. There's no one here you can talk to, there's nothing vegetarian for you to eat, since Dougie refused to cook your burgers, and the Spokes are hardly your kind of people.'

'I can talk to you,' Leon smiles.

We sip our drinks.

'You still in love with him then?'

'What?' I choke. 'Who?'

'Olly. Sorry, I shouldn't ask. None of my business.'

'No, it's okay. I suppose, you know, I've just not met anyone else. Is it that obvious?'

Leon looks me in the eye.

'What?' I ask.

'Don't you remember, Gina, why you finished therapy?'

'Um, because the divorce had come through and I was coping better. Wasn't that why?'

'Yes, but we were challenging your continued love for Olly, *despite* the divorce, trying to cure your fixation on him, the fact you were still seeing him regularly, still sleeping …'

I blush with embarrassment; I haven't done such a thing since I was a teenager.

'Anyway,' he continues, 'I suggested you cut off from him completely and the next week you finished therapy. Nothing I said could persuade you to stay in treatment or wind down slowly.'

'Really? I can't remember clearly. But, yes, I probably was that pathetic.'

'It's not pathetic. It's called resistance. I should have seen it coming. I should have handled it better. I always felt bad about it, that it finished too early, that –'

'Hello you two,' grins Dougie, as he suddenly looms over us, wearing an apron smeared with blood and barbecue sauce, and holding a can of lager in one hand and a fistful of metal skewers in the other. 'The sun is shining, the meat is sizzling, and my Donna looks set to become a proper celebrity. Life is sweet.'

'Hmm,' murmurs Leon, who clearly doesn't appreciate being interrupted mid-flow, and who has found the whole ogling-of-semi-naked-girls-in-magazine situation, not to mention the fact that Dougie is the father of one of them, less than comfortable.

'Sweet,' I echo, inoffensively, while staring at the cigarette drooping nonchalantly from Dougie's lip.

'What's it like then, Doc, chatting to a bunch of psychos all day?' asks Dougie. 'Can't say I'd fancy it.'

'My patients are not psychos, Mr Spokes, but perfectly normal people.'

'Why are they seeing you then?'

'For a variety of reasons. Because, for example, they are experiencing difficulties and need help dealing with them. Because they are trying to come to terms with issues from their past. Because they need support after a loss – of a loved one, of love itself, of a loved object. You have to be brave to go into therapy, and ready to change. Sometimes the challenges are too big, and you need to wait until you're ready.'

Leon looks at me. I look at my watch; four hours smoke free.

'I bet it's because they're all serial killers or poofs,' says Dougie.

'I used to be in therapy with Leon,' I say, as if this will somehow convince Dougie of the normalcy of Leon's patients.

'Did you? I didn't have you down as a loony, Gina. What was

she seeing you for then, Doc? Nymphomania? Ha, ha. She got pregnant when she was fifteen, you know. It was a right scandal at school. Wouldn't tell anyone who the father was. And she turned me down when we were thirteen.'

'Oh, do be quiet, Dougie,' I snap.

'Yes, I hardly think these personal topics of conversation are appropriate for an afternoon barbecue,' says Leon, glancing round the garden. A hush has descended and everyone seems to be listening, while pretending not to be. Four hours, ninety seconds, exactly.

'Ooh, get you, with your "personal topics of conversation appropriate for an afternoon barbecue",' Dougie mocks. 'And after the sort of stuff you must listen to all day. I bet you get a right cheap thrill out of hearing other people's fantasies and whatnot. It's warped. Some things are best kept in your own head.'

'Yes, like the detritus that's coming out of your mouth,' says Leon.

I stare at Leon. The drink must be loosening his tongue, must be causing his professional veneer to crack. Luckily, Dougie doesn't seem to know what 'detritus' means; he merely frowns for a second, then carries on.

'No need to get so shirty, just cos Gina's secret's out.'

'What's Gina's secret?' asks Olly, as he ambles over, closely followed by Donna.

'She used to see the Doc, here, for therapy,' says Dougie, twirling a finger around his ear, then tapping the side of his head. He then adds, in a whisper, 'Secret nut job.'

'Oh, for goodness' sake Mr Spokes,' says Leon. 'Gina is not mentally ill, and I find your attitude offensive and demeaning.'

'Alright, alright, keep your hair on,' says Dougie. 'Still, I reckon you must get your fair share of perverts.'

'Perverts!' exclaims Leon. 'When you're celebrating your own daughter's career move into pornography!'

Oh my God, this is turning into a slow-motion car crash, and I've no idea how to stop it.

'How dare you!' says Donna. 'This is *glamour* modelling. I wouldn't take me knickers off for all the money in the world. That's disgusting. And there ain't nothing wrong with showing off a beautiful body. It's artistic, innit?'

There are whistles of agreement from the assembled crowd.

'Right you,' shouts Dougie, jabbing Leon in the chest with a skewer. 'Outside. Now. No one insults my Donna like that and gets away with it.'

'We are already outside,' says Leon. 'I thought the blue skies overhead and green grass underfoot might have given it away. Eejit.'

I look at Dougie; his eyes have liquefied with violence. He picks up a beer bottle and smashes it against a nearby table, inspiring a collective jolt.

Leon stands abruptly, pushing his chair over.

I attempt to leap from my chair and put myself between them, but only succeed in landing face-down on the grass, no doubt due to the pint of wine earlier. By the time I manage to get myself upright, it's all over.

It was Donna who inflicted most of the damage on Leon, marking one side of his face with stiletto-heel puncture wounds. Leon, being a gentleman, didn't fight back. Dougie, mindful of his string of convictions and suspended sentences, didn't touch him. It's now Tuesday and I've just about recovered from the post-barbecue hangover, which wiped out the whole of Sunday and didn't do much for bank holiday Monday either, although it's totally killed off my desire to smoke. It's mid-morning and Leon has called in to apologise for what happened. Goodness knows what his patients must think of his bruised, swollen face. I tell him it's me who should be apologising, for taking him to the Spokes' in the first place.

'But why?' I ask, gesturing to his injured face, as we sit at the dining table with a pot of tea.

'Why what?' says Leon.

'Why say those things, why be so provocative?'

'I was defending you, in case you hadn't noticed. All that personal stuff he was shouting round the garden, it was plain wrong.'

'I know, but with someone like Dougie it's best to ignore what he says. It's all hot air and nonsense anyway. I was just surprised at you rising to it. Though I don't blame you. But you were so patient with me in therapy and –'

'We're not in therapy now, remember, as you never cease telling me,' says Leon.

'Point taken.'

We both study our fingernails.

'It's my fault, too,' says Leon, 'that we can't seem to move on from the past. I shouldn't have started talking about why therapy finished. If I keep bringing it up, you're not going to be able to forget about it, are you?'

'I suppose not,' I sigh. 'Okay then, let's try to begin afresh. Tell me about yourself. Give us a potted history. I know practically nothing about you, not even how old you are, where you grew up.'

'Foirty-tree. Dublin,' Leon replies, in a preposterously strong Irish accent. I don't know which is most surprising, as I'd have guessed he was the same age or a bit older than me and English born and bred.

He continues to talk with the Irish accent. It's strangely attractive, but I hardly understand a word. I shake my head and Leon returns to his English one.

'We moved here when I was fifteen. I lost the accent pretty quick. It was either that or have the mickey taken out of me every second of every day everywhere I went. Dada hated me for it. He was an Irishman of the old school. "Son, you're not a man till you've had your front teeth knocked out by a hurley stick." Mama was an angel, warm and caring. But Dada was a bully, a tyrant. Still is.'

'You sound like an Edna O'Brien novel,' I say.

Leon laughs.

'I probably do. Dada wanted me to do something manly, like him. He's a builder. Thought reading books was for sissies. When Mama passed away he moved back to Ireland. That's when I became interested in psychoanalysis, in trying to understand people, understand life.'

Leon gives me a wan smile. He goes to rub his face, but flinches when he touches the bruised skin.

'This is so weird, Leon. It's like you've transformed into a different person before my eyes.'

'Well, you never know what you're going to find until you crack someone open.'

I look at my watch.

'I have an appointment soon,' I say, 'I really should get going or I'll be late.'

'Of course, I didn't mean to interrupt your day,' says Leon, standing up.

He regards me, quizzically.

'Do you need a lift or anything? Where are you off to?' he asks.

I hesitate. I don't know why Leon's offering me a lift because he knows I drive. Or why he's asking where I'm going. Oh, I get it, perhaps he's testing to see if the appointment's real; he has just revealed lots of personal stuff about himself and now it might look as if I'm desperate to get away.

'I might as well tell you,' I say. 'I had surgery recently. I'm going for my check-up, my results, at the hospital. That's where I'm off to.'

'I'm sorry, Gina, I had no idea. Is someone going with you?'

'No. It's all going to be fine, nothing to worry about.'

'Alright. But let me know how it goes, won't you?'

'Will do.'

When I arrive at Gynaecology and Obstetrics I'm not listed as having an appointment. I explain that it was made a few days ago, over the phone, and that it's a follow-up for after surgery. I wait in the 'reception area' – a line of chairs in a corridor – while someone tries to find out where I should be, and who called me. As I rummage through my handbag for a tissue, I find two small, screw-lidded plastic pots, left by Chrissy, to be utilised in the event of new poo discoveries. She has written 'date', 'time' and 'where fond' on the labels; apart from the last one, she really is an accomplished speller. Eventually, a nurse comes to collect and escort me to another part of the building.

I'm shown into a room, only it's not Mr Winger, Consultant

Gynaecologist – grey-haired, must be retirement age, passion for golf and inability to call female genitalia anything other than 'downstairs' – who greets me, but a Dr Kimura, with 'Gynaecological Oncologist' on his nametag. Dr Kimura is small, neat and, I'd guess, of Japanese descent, his face dominated by a huge moustache.

'Um, I was expecting to see Mr Winger?'

'Mrs Jarvis, pleased to meet you. Mr Winger has now retired.'

Dr Kimura extends a hand and we shake.

'Please, take a seat,' he says. 'How are you?'

'I'm … I'm wondering why I'm seeing you? Why I'm seeing an oncologist?'

'Because I'm the most appropriate doctor for your care,' he replies softly.

My stomach drops and I lurch forward and grip the desk.

'Hold on, hold on, I'm trying not to panic here,' I say. 'What are the results – is it bad news?'

'The results show that within the ovary that was removed there was a small tumour, Stage I.'

'What does that mean?'

'We categorise cancer in different stages, from one to four, with one being the least advanced and four the most.'

Dr Kimura smiles sympathetically.

'Where is Mr Jarvis today?' he asks. 'I understand he accompanied you to some of your other appointments. We do advise patients to bring someone with them, for support.'

'I don't know where he is.' Probably making love to his beautiful, young girlfriend. Chiselling away at a twenty-foot egg. Lying stoned and unconscious in a wood somewhere. How the bloody hell should I know?

'Oh,' says Dr Kimura, 'I thought he was your husband.'

The last bit was supposed to remain in my head; did I actually say it?

'He w-*was* my husband,' I stammer, 'ten years ago, but not any more. I'm sorry. I just didn't expect this.'

'I understand. Now, let's take a look at you.'

I lie on the hard, narrow bed so that Dr Kimura can perform a pelvic examination. He's actually very gentle and explains what he's doing ('just palpating the abdomen') and why ('now checking for any irregularities') as he goes. Or perhaps he seems gentle because I am not actually in my body, but floating about the ceiling. They found cancer, I have cancer – is that what he just said? Surely not. I don't think Kimura is a real doctor anyway. With his incongruously large Zapata tash, I fancy him to be a bandit from a Sergio Leone film; give him a suntan and a big hat, and make him sweat and snarl, and I'm certain he could pull it off. I'm aware my mind is being flooded with increasingly ridiculous, moustache-related fantasy-thoughts, but anything that can distract from the rectal examination I'm now undergoing has got to be a good thing.

Re-dressed and sitting opposite Dr K, I'm having difficulty focusing on anything other than his moustache. Christ, Gina, get a grip. Listen to what he's saying, it's going to be important, possibly the most important information you've ever been given. But it is an impressive moustache … silky, luxuriant; sumptuous even. Although, personally, I would recommend that Dr K cultivate some form of just-under-the-bottom-lip hair to balance out the tash, *à la* Frank Zappa. Oh, I think he's asked me a question. He's stopped talking and is looking expectant.

'Sorry?'

'Mrs Jarvis, did you understand what I was saying?'

'Yes.'

'Can you repeat it back to me?'

'Um … no.'

'I'll try again. Perhaps if you look directly at me, rather than at my top lip, then you will take it in better.'

I connect with Dr K's small, bright eyes.

'The tumour that was removed during surgery is classed as Stage I cancer because it was contained within the ovary. As far as we know, there was no cancer outside of this area.'

'That's good then, isn't it?' I ask, marvelling at how I can refer to any news of cancer as 'good'.

'Yes. However,' says Dr K, intense and serious, 'I have detected a slight fullness on the left of your abdomen.'

'Maybe it's still swollen from the operation,' I say.

'The left side, Mrs Jarvis, not the right.'

'Oh, yes, of course.'

'We will get a better look with a scan.'

'Another ultrasound? Okay.'

Dr K scribbles something on a form, then hands it to me.

'I need to go now?' I ask.

Dr K nods, 'Then come straight back here after.'

4

ATOMIC

So, here I am again – this time with three young, expectant mothers – in the Ultrasound Department. They probably think I'm some freak of a granny who's had IVF and is now expecting triplets. I wish I was. I'm ushered in before them all. Not a good sign.

I look at the screen, but can't make out a thing; it's all a fuzz of black and white, like an old-fashioned, out-of-tune telly.

'Is there another lump?' I ask the sonographer, a middle-aged woman wearing a headscarf. 'You found the last one, on my right ovary.'

She carries on working the probe over my abdomen, and clicking the mouse on the images on the screen.

'There does appear to be something, on or very close to the remaining ovary.'

'What do you think it is?' I ask, when of course I shouldn't.

'I really couldn't say. The doctor will speak to you as soon as he's examined the results.'

'How long's that likely to take?'

'He'll have them later this afternoon.'

She checks that my phone number and address haven't changed, before directing me back to Oncology. I make a detour, telling myself that I need to find a loo. But I don't. I walk out of the hospital, get in the car and drive home.

I make it back in one piece, but with no memory of the journey. I feel so peculiarly high. I make coffee. I want a cigarette. If I have cancer, what difference will one more make? If I'd never smoked, would I still be in this situation? Oh God, they've found a cancerous lump in the ovary that was removed. But at an early stage, at least. But now I have another lump, on the other ovary. Perhaps it'll turn out to be another cyst. They can swell up and go down like mad during a woman's monthly cycle. But 'just a cyst' was what the last one was supposed to be, and now I'm minus an ovary. And a cancerous tumour. Surely another one couldn't grow that quickly? But then ovarian cysts do and they're just a different form of tumour – a benign type. I'm still struggling to sort out the fact that benign-equals-good-but-malign-equals-bad, which keeps becoming confused in my mind. How inconsiderate for such a harmless word and such a deadly word to sound so similar. Then there's negative-equals-good-but-positive-equals-bad. No wonder it's hard to think straight. I wish I'd had someone with me. Okay, maybe not Olly, who was as supportive as a three-legged chair during the other appointments, which I had to cajole him into attending due to his imaginary 'hospital phobia'. If someone like Leon had been there he would have asked all the right questions and known what everything meant. He probably would have taken notes. I should have gone back to Oncology, instead of running away like a dreadful coward.

The ground begins to open up beneath me. No, I mustn't fall. Leon said I should let him know how it went. Should I go next door and tell him? No, no, he'll be with patients. I know he wants us to be friends, to move on from the past, but I can't burden him with this.

I resolve to behave normally. There's no point in worrying about anything until Dr K has looked at the scan results. It could be really obvious it's a cyst and I've been panicking unnecessarily. I'll ring the hospital later and see when I should come in again.

Unusually, I didn't tidy the house before going out this morning. I'll do that, then get on with what I'd planned to do today. Keep busy, busy, busy, with no time to think. But what I'd planned to do today was be given the all-clear by the gynaecologist, then go into town and treat myself by way of celebration. But there is nothing to celebrate. Or is there? If I hadn't had the cyst and ovary removed, then the cancer would still be inside me, instead of wafered between glass slides in a laboratory somewhere.

Looking down at my hands as they unload the dishwasher, I wonder what's propelling them into action. Life force perhaps? Or autopilot? I'm grateful to it, whatever it is.

'They're not going to know what this new lump is until they take it out, are they?' I say out loud, as I get on with the chores. 'I might have to have more surgery. A hysterectomy even. Such a horrible word. If it was called a "spanella" or a "floofy" I might not mind having one. What I've already had done is a unilateral salpingo-oophorectomy. Oophorectomy – now there's a great word! One that looks surprised by its own ostentation, with all those open-mouthed 'o's. Hysterectomies, on the other hand, are what our mothers could only whisper about in corners. And it takes forever to recover. Mind you, I'd rather have a hysterectomy than ... than die. Am I really going to be fifty in eighteen months' time? Mind you, I sure feel it today.'

I continue to mutter to myself as I reload the dishwasher and wipe the worktops.

'Can't deal with you yet,' I comment to the laptop, as I pass the dining-room table.

'Bloody hell. Life was difficult enough. And now this,' I say loudly, as I go up the stairs, warning my mother not to put in an appearance.

I go into my bedroom and shake out the duvet and plump up the pillows.

'Chemotherapy. Will I have to have that? Doesn't everyone with cancer have to have that? Or radiotherapy? And why's it taken them so long to get back to me, to tell me this awful news? They must have known weeks ago. How could they be so lackadaisical about such a thing? Lackadaisical – what a preposterous word. Like serendipitous. But not a patch on onomatopoeic or dodecahedron.'

I hang wet towels on the banister, then bleach the toilet.

'Actually, I'm beginning to think mathematicians get all the best words. Should have been one of them, or a medical researcher, doing something useful, like finding a cure for cancer. Wonder if I can get parallelogram into my next *Eurotica* story. It's a … oh!'

As I go into the back bedroom, I'm surprised to find Moya stretched out on the bed. She's as rigid as a dead starfish and staring at the ceiling.

I approach with caution.

'Are you okay?' I ask gently.

'Nowhere else to go,' she sniffs. 'You'd left the back door open. The French doors, too. All the downstairs windows.'

Well, I had been in a hurry this morning, after Leon left. I sit on the bed.

'Moya.' I touch her hand; it remains frozen. 'Is it … is it …?'

I always forget her partner's name. Despite meeting her a dozen times, only a vague sense of a plain woman in her fifties forever chattering on about baking and petting their toy dog remains.

'Jocasta,' says Moya (I remember now that Jocasta's name is the most interesting thing about her). 'She. Has fallen. In love. With another. We've been together fifteen years.'

I want to hurl myself on Moya and sob my heart out for her, because I know she can't do it for herself. But Moya couldn't stand this. She hates displays of emotion, even genuine ones.

'Didn't want to be in the house,' Moya says. 'She's packing. You don't mind?'

'Of course not. Stay as long as you want.'

Moya nods her silent gratitude.

'Did you hear what I was saying just then,' I ask, 'when I was, um, talking to myself?'

Moya shakes her head.

'Good,' I say, suddenly aware that I'm going to have to tell people about my health news. But not yet, I want to hold on to normality a little longer.

'Oh, it's awful,' I say, as I sit on the edge of the bed. 'I do feel for you, Moya. It's like what Olly has put me through. When you love someone and they reject you, it's a slow crucifixion every day. The amount of times I've tried to make sense of it, tried to pretend it didn't hurt, but it does. Never stops hurting. The years I've wasted, tears I've shed, over him. Love is a terrible thing. Let's face it, it can kill you. The times I've thought about throwing myself in the river. I even went as far as buying a wheelbarrow. One of those Mr Dyson invented. Because the river's quite shallow, you know, and I wondered how I'd get a heavy weight down there. Not to mention tie it round my neck. That was another problem. If you want to drown yourself, but can swim, then you need something to keep you down at the bottom, don't you? So, it's literally got to be like a millstone. And where on earth do you get one of those? Mind you, Virginia Woolf managed it with stones in her pockets. I gave up on the idea in the end. The logistics. The wheelbarrow's still in the shed. Actually, I think it's called a ballbarrow. They're good, though, aren't they, the Dyson vacuum cleaners? Have you got one?'

I look at Moya. Her eyes are shut. In fact, her lids are squeezed together with such force they look as if they might flip inside out at any moment.

'Coffee?' I suggest gaily.

Moya nods.

I go downstairs and put on a six-cup espresso percolator, which Moya can put away all by herself, no problem. I sense Moya's always been unhappy in love. The unknowable motives that draw one person to another, then wrench them apart. How many times have I witnessed various friends collapse under the agonies of unrequited, lost or disastrous love? And how many times have I listened, sympathised and sometimes advised (a case of the blind leading the blind, if ever there was one), usually while thinking 'but he's *so* thick' or 'but she's *so* boring' or 'but he/she is *so* unattractive'. How I've wished I could flick a switch and turn off love's irrational, blinding beam, and allow the torment to evaporate. If only. And how many friends must I have stupefied with tales of Olly? I would state in my pathetic defence of staying with him after yet another humiliation 'but I love him' and they'd look at me equally pityingly, while no doubt thinking 'but he's *so* thick, boring and unattractive'. The workings of the human heart are a mystery, and an eternal one at that.

For a moment I'd forgotten, but now it hits me again, and the kitchen begins to disintegrate – the walls, floor and ceiling threatening to zoom away to infinity, till I'm left standing on nothing, nothing surrounding or supporting me. You're in a state of shock, I tell myself. But the cancer's been removed, and this new lump is bound to be another cyst. Don't worry. I blink hard a few times and the world returns to normal. See? Everything is as it was and should be. And you will be, too.

When I bring her coffee, I find Moya tucked up under the covers reading *Everything You Ever Wanted to Know About Poo*.

'Joy came round earlier,' she says. 'She waited a while, then had to go.'

I hear my mobile beep and return downstairs to find it. Sure enough, there's a message from Joy asking where I am because she needs to talk, badly. This latest crisis will no doubt have something to do with her nineteen-year-old son, Aiden. So far this year we have dealt with him smoking cannabis at college and being threatened with expulsion, his girlfriend telling him she was pregnant when she wasn't, and him crashing his dad's car. Joy spoils her son terribly and he is the source of much friction between her and her husband, Tim. When I bump into Aiden in the street he appears intelligent, articulate and witty, but in front of his mum he reverts to a grunting halfwit, incapable of threading the shoelaces through his new trainers or cutting a slice from a loaf of bread (I have witnessed Joy doing both these things for him in the past few months). He causes a lot of stress, and stress induces one specific reaction in Joy.

I glance around the kitchen. Joy, so Moya reported, 'waited a while' before leaving. This is suspicious. I open a cupboard. Chrissy's squash has disappeared, as have her biscuits. I look in the bread bin. Empty. I go through the fridge and inspect more cupboards. The microwaveable treacle puddings and carton of instant custard (in case Olly comes round) have also gone. I sigh. I know Joy has some kind of uncontrollable, compulsive eating disorder but, over the years, she has cost me a fortune. She came for Christmas dinner once, when we were both single and Susan was about five. Susan developed a terrible earache so I rushed her off to the emergency clinic, where we spent three hours waiting for antibiotics. By the time we returned, Joy had eaten the entire turkey, bar one leg, the bowl of nuts and the tin of chocolates. I swear she would have started on the stocking-shaped selection pack if Susan hadn't gathered what was left of her strength and wrestled it from her. Joy's other unfortunate, automatic response is to laugh hysterically at shocking news. She is mortified every time this happens, but can't stop herself. She giggle-shook-shrieked continuously for two days after her mother died.

I look in the bin and see my two-for-one jars of chocolate spread lying empty; one still has a dessert spoon in it. Things must be really bad. Just as I'm about to ring Joy on my mobile, the landline goes. My heart pounds; will it be the hospital? No, a receptionist from the opticians tells me this is a 'courtesy call' to remind me that I have an appointment in half an hour. I'd completely forgotten about the sight test, which I booked after Moya pointed out that I've been doing that stretching arm thing when reading small print. Just as I'm about to tell the receptionist that I'm sure my eyes are fine, she reminds me that if I don't turn up they'll still bill me.

I text Joy on the way to the opticians, telling her to meet me there in an hour.

All cancer-shock-turmoil vanishes as soon as I'm seated next to the optician, due to his awful breath. Every creeping, cringing, neck-twisting second in his incredibly close proximity is unspeakably dire. I didn't realise how intimate an eye test is: you hear and feel the optician's breath. Unfortunately with this one, I can smell it, too. I am inhaling through my mouth only, certain the stench is contaminating me. Breath that bad must contain dozens of contagious diseases. I'm convinced it's causing my skin to blister and crinkle, as if paint stripper had been applied.

'Look left.'

Gasp.

'And right.'

Urgh.

'Now down.'

I feel sick.

I leap from the chair as soon as it's over and bolt from the room. I check my face in a mirrored spectacle rack in the reception area. I thought I'd be down to bare skull and a few ragged strands of hair by now, but no, I look normal. I smell Mr Halitosis approaching. What is it with these health professionals and their ridiculous, stuck on, Mr Potato Head moustaches and putrid breath. Surely some specialist organisation should sort them out before unleashing them on the public? Years of training, but still unable to use a razor or a toothbrush. I almost rush into Joy's arms when I see her friendly face. Well, perhaps 'friendly' isn't quite the right word.

'I've been waiting for you for *ages*,' Joy complains.

'I'm sorry, I'm sorry.'

'Where shall we go? I need to talk. You won't believe what Aiden's done.'

'Mrs Jarvis,' calls Mr Halitosis, as he strides towards me and I back into a carousel of sunglasses. 'Don't you want to choose a pair now? Your prescription for reading spectacles is rather strong. I don't know how you've been coping without them.'

'I need glasses?'

'Yes. You have a classic case of presbyopia. Most people over forty need reading glasses.'

'I don't need glasses! How can *I* possibly need glasses? My eyesight is perfect.'

Joy and The Malodorous One exchange looks. Are they in on this together, trying to persuade me I need specs? When I clearly don't, when nothing has been wrong with my eyesight, ever, in my whole life, perfect twenty-twenty vision since the day I was born.

'Oh, stop making such a fuss,' pipes up Joy. 'I've had to wear them since I was sixteen. And they're only for reading. You're so vain.'

'I most certainly am not. Anyway, you don't wear glasses, you use contacts, so who's the vain one? And look at the price tag on these so-called designer sunglasses. Now that's vanity, that's more money than sense. Nearly two hundred pounds! And how much did they cost to make, I wonder. A few pennies at the most. Daylight robbery, that is.'

I have suddenly turned into an embittered old woman.

'Such rubbish,' I continue, 'such consumer, capitalism-gone-mad trash. And what's with those funny coloured lenses – the blues and yellows and stuff? That's just weird, that's a government plot to, to …'

Now I've transmuted into Olly, midway through one of his drug-induced, conspiracy-theory freak-outs.

'Plus, glasses are not a fashion accessory, they're a sign of disability, of physical deterioration. Glasses tell the whole world there's something wrong with you. Sat right on your face, looking stupid and ugly. I hate glasses. *And* I don't need them.'

I 'eave the shop, the rotten optician, my turncoat friend, and stomp home.

When I step through the front door, while wondering who else I might find lying, unasked, on one of my beds, the phone is ringing. A wave of sickening anxiety breaks over me. I'm beginning to hope, rather than dread, it'll be the hospital, so I can get it over with and avoid having a panic attack every time the sodding phone rings. Is this what my life will shortly be turning into: a series of excruciating waits for more bad news?

'Can I speak to Mrs Jarvis, please?'

'Speaking.'

'It's Mr Phelps from the opticians. About your –'

'I don't need a prescription. I've already told you. There is nothing wrong with me.'

'Whether or not you decide to purchase a pair of spectacles is up to you. It's a free country. But you left without paying for your sight test.'

'Oh.'

'So if you would be kind enough to pop in and –'

'I'll send a cheque. Goodbye.'

Now there's a knock at the door. Joy's shape looms through the glass. I answer anyway.

'What's wrong with you, Gina? Have you gone mad? Are you on drugs?'

'What's wrong with *you*, Joy? You seem to have turned into my mother.'

Joy eyes me venomously. She never could stand me criticising my mother when hers was taken from her so young in life. She thought I should be permanently grateful mine wasn't dead. And then when Mum did die that I should establish a shrine to her in my house – of photographs, mementoes and fresh flowers – with which to console myself every day, just as she does.

'That was a fab little speech you gave before running off, about glasses being horrible and ugly and awful. Just what a shop full of people who have to wear them want to hear. I bet you really made their day.'

I walk into the front room and crumple onto a sofa. Joy sits next to me.

'Is it Olly? What's he done now?'

'It's … it's me. I've just been to the hospital for my check-up.'

'Oh my God, Gina, I'm so sorry,' says Joy, reaching out and grasping my arm. 'It completely slipped my mind, what with all the stress Aiden's been giving me.'

'It's okay.'

'Is … is it bad news?'

'You know when they removed the cyst, they took the ovary, too? Well, they found a lump in it, a cancerous tumour. The doctor said it was small, not advanced. But now there's another lump, on my other ovary. I mean, it might turn out to be okay, another cyst, but …'

Joy begins to make strangulated noises at the back of her throat. Her eyes flicker and twitch and her mouth spasms. Then her breath comes rapidly, as if she's unable to catch it. Soon, her whole body is shaking to a crescendo, until it erupts into short, manic laughs. They continue to escape, despite the fact she has clamped both hands over her mouth. I give her a hug and tell her it's alright. I know she can't help behaving like a bloody imbecile. And nor, so it would seem, can I.

5

PING

Oncology is amazingly busy. I didn't seem to notice last time. I can't believe this many people are finding out if they have cancer, are being treated for cancer, are recovering from cancer, are supporting someone with cancer. Dr Kimura's secretary called to summon me back to hospital the following day and in the last week I've had more scans and tests. I'm here to find out the results, but am beginning to regret bringing Joy with me. After a frenzy of Internet research, she has turned into a walking, talking encyclopaedia of medical facts, procedures and protocols. But at least she's stopped laughing. The hysteria took a day to subside, which I suppose I should take as a compliment.

Dr K quickly sums up the results: all the scans show a lump on my remaining ovary, yet blood tests remain clear.

'Why did it take so long for Gina to be told about the cancer?' asks Joy.

'This has been most unfortunate,' replies Dr K, 'and is due to computer and communication problems, as well as Mr Winger retiring, and the reorganisation of departments to establish our new, multi-disciplinary team, meaning paperwork has been lying on desks.'

'Do you think this new lump is more cancer?' I ask.

'I cannot say. Once it has been removed and analysed, and comprehensive surgical staging completed, we will know much more.'

'Staging?' I say.

'Meaning thorough examination, during open surgery, of the nature and extent of the tumour, and the taking of biopsies from all adjacent sites.'

'I don't understand why this wasn't done in the first place,' says Joy, 'why she wasn't referred to you, to a cancer specialist, straight away.'

'Evidence of cancer was not detected by Mr Winger, Mrs Jarvis' blood test results were negative and she was not post-menopausal. Gynaecologists cannot refer all such patients to an oncologist. It is always a difficult balance between causing unnecessary worry for the patient and not being cautious enough.'

'So the original scan didn't show any evidence of cancer?' asks Joy.

Dr K hesitates; Joy's on him in an instant.

'What was there?' she demands.

Dr K pauses.

'Examination and discussion by all relevant members of a multi-disciplinary team – which we now have in place – *may* have led to the identification of other irregularities in the ovary, as well as the presence of the large cyst. Two or three heads is better than one.'

'Right,' says Joy, her voice quivering, 'so something *was* missed.'

'Not exactly, because it was not at all clear. And it is easier to see something when you know it is there.'

Dr K turns to me.

'I want to assure you, Mrs Jarvis, that Mr Winger was a very experienced and well-respected gynaecologist and surgeon. Out of thousands of laparoscopic procedures performed for ovarian tumours, less than one in five hundred will turn out to be cancerous.'

'Bad luck, then, is that what you're saying?' I ask.

'That is not how I would put it, but ...'

'What would have been done differently, if someone *had* spotted the "other irregularities" on the scan?' asks Joy.

'Another ultrasound to clarify, perhaps. More tests pre-surgery, giving a more comprehensive picture of what we are dealing with, possibly making us take a different treatment pathway.'

'Which would have been?'

'Open surgery, for example, rather than keyhole. A different surgeon may have been considered, one being a specialist in gynaecological oncology. Or one may have been made available for consultation during the procedure, as is now the policy of our multi-disciplinary –'

'Yes, we know all about the damn multi-disciplinary team you have, now it's too bloody late,' declares Joy.

I bet Dr K's regretting his 'bring someone with you for support' advice. But he remains calm, and continues.

'Gaining full consent of the patient would also have been a priority.'

'Full consent?' asks Joy.

'Yes, prior agreement to more extensive surgery, if deemed necessary, during the procedure.'

'Of course Gina would have consented to more surgery if she'd had any inkling that cancer was a possibility.'

'Mrs Jarvis gave her consent to conservative surgery only.'

Joy looks at me aghast.

'Mrs Jarvis,' says Dr K, 'given the presence of a cancerous tumour within the removed ovary, the relatively minimal extent of the initial surgery, the quick occurrence of another growth on the left ovary, and that you are likely to experience the menopause soon, I recommend the removal of the other ovary, a total abdominal hysterectomy, and full surgical staging. Have a think and, if you are in agreement, we shall book you in immediately.'

Joy and I are sitting in the ominously named Quiet Room, mulling over Dr K's recommendations before making a decision. I'm sipping coffee while Joy has her head in her hands. Shouldn't it be the other way round?

Joy lifts her head slightly and peers at me though her fingers.

'I can't believe what I've been hearing – this catalogue of errors. First, the gynaecologist doesn't look at the scan properly, no matter what excuses Dr Kimura is prepared to make for him. Then the path results lie unread on a desk for weeks. And now it turns out you didn't even sign the normal consent form. I just don't understand.'

'It all happened very fast. One minute I was having a cyst removed and then, when I was going through the consent form with Mr Winger, he said you couldn't be totally sure about anything until you opened a patient up, and would I agree to any other surgery considered necessary. When I asked what sort of surgery, he said in the worst-case scenario a hysterectomy. I said no. I just couldn't accept the prospect of having such a major operation for what was supposed to be "just a cyst", and on my ovary, not in my womb. He asked about the removal of the ovary if it was too badly affected by the cyst to be saved and I agreed to that.'

I drain my coffee cup.

'We didn't discuss it properly, not really. I suppose I didn't trust him either. I had a sudden fear that he was only suggesting more surgery because I was middle-aged and "better out than in" would be the easiest way of dealing with whatever problems I had. Whip it all out now so he doesn't have to do another operation in five or ten years' time. Better for him, but not necessarily for me.'

'But why didn't you agree, when it's something so serious?' asks Joy.

'The thought of cancer didn't even cross my mind. I mean, it had earlier, when I was waiting for blood test and scan results, but not after I was told the lump was a cyst. I was going in for relatively minor keyhole surgery and then it was like, "Oh, and by the way, we might take your entire reproductive system out while you're unconscious, if that's okay with you. Perhaps a kidney or a lung, too."'

Joy manages a weak smile.

'I didn't even think that much about it, just said, "No, can't consent to that" and he nodded and didn't appear fazed either.'

'You're going to agree to the full works now though, aren't you?'

'Of course.'

Because I trust Dr Kimura, I will take his advice. Because I didn't trust Mr Winger, I couldn't agree to his consent form. Because Dr K has consulted with two other colleagues in his much-bandied-about multi-disciplinary team – and they are all in agreement that this is the best course of action, that the lump looks 'suspicious', but they can't be certain of anything until after surgery and path results – I'd agree to anything.

Oh Gina, what vanity led you to want to keep your womb, your womanhood, when you're of menopausal age anyway? Submitting to irrational desires has always got me into such trouble.

I'm letting everyone know about the imminent surgery. I have apologised to Mr Halitosis for my erratic behaviour in the opticians, and chosen some flattering reading glasses. Moya's being an absolute rock, a cliff face of calm, and has offered to be my 'designated carer' after the hysterectomy. This is so kind of her and suits us both, as she is still unable to face returning home after Jocasta's desertion. Olly hugged me, cried and said, 'Don't leave me, baby.' I haven't told Susan the real reason for the surgery yet, due to our less-than-optimal relationship at the moment, let alone Chrissy. Strangely, telling Leon was one of the worst. I downplayed it all, saying that at least the cancerous tumour has been removed and this other lump might turn out to be a cyst. He was genuinely choked up and said he wanted to be there for me in any way he could.

The operation is booked for Monday 17 May, a week's time. I feel like I'm starting from square one, but under the care of the right doctor and medical team this time. Leon's investigated Dr K's credentials for me, and it turns out he's one of the best in the field, which is a relief. I can't believe the Spokes' barbecue was less than two weeks ago.

I'm keeping extra busy – working, seeing friends, trying to do normal life. Just get through this next week and then, well, worry about what comes after when I get there. I have a date with Ralf, the building surveyor, who returned to deliver his report, then invited me to dinner. I'm also moving ahead with plans to do up the house, employing Marty, Olly's builder brother, to manage the job. I asked him when I saw him busking up town on Saturday morning. I told him about the cancer-hysterectomy-worry news first, hopeful of a discount.

Marty certainly hasn't fared as well as Olly in the looks department, but he does have an intangible resemblance to him. He is my age and everything seems to have become blubbery and pocked, like perishing rubber, leaving his face sort of chewed-looking. The joys of ageing. Marty is short and squat, with a bit of a pot. Despite balding drastically, he still maintains a long, thin, yellowy-grey ponytail. In twenty-six years, I have never known him to wear anything other than cowboy boots. I've always felt sorry for Marty because he is a genuinely nice and unassuming person, and has therefore been walked over all his life. Despite having to spend his days knocking down walls and filling skips, he is an idealistic musician at heart. He's got a one-man, John Martyn-like guitar and echoplex thing going on, which he does at the drop of a hat – in pubs, at local festivals, busking; he even turned up at Susan's eighth birthday party (uninvited) and did his stuff. Marty spends a lot of time avoiding his family: Tessa, his depressive partner, and his two grown-up sons, who still live at home and can barely be bothered to get out of bed, let alone work.

I even found myself telling Phyllis about my health news, on the phone this morning. I was only calling to distract myself from pressing work responsibilities. Phyllis is a cat obsessive who, like so many of her kind, relates more easily to animals because humans are too difficult, though I don't blame her for that. She is the editor of *The Cat Lover's Monthly*, for which I do a regular feature; a fact, it goes without saying, I rarely admit to. Rather than being shocked or sympathetic about my health worries, Phyllis used them as an excuse to go on about her fifteen-year-old tom's inoperable tumours. Despite having written for *The Cat Lover's Monthly* for ten years, I have never met Phyllis. The magazine is a specialist publication (I specialise in them) and mainly consists of factual pieces about breeding, grooming, showing, healthcare, and so on. I write a light-hearted series called *The Adventures of Monty*, about a swashbuckling cat hero who gets into many humorous (I use the term loosely) scrapes, but who always comes out good, and is never actually described tormenting his prey, depositing worms on the carpet or shitting in freshly dug flowerbeds. Stories tend to go on a seasonal theme. I've already done the June and July issues so the next is August, which clearly demands that Monty go on holiday somewhere. I dread September, when I have to create an amusing tale around booster vaccinations.

On the telephone, Phyllis asked if I'd received her letter about the additional article she'd like me to write. Not wanting to appear disorganised or lose the chance of extra money, I said yes. Rashly, I also claimed it was nearly done. I flick through the small bundle of post that has been gathering on the dining table, until I find the envelope addressed in Phyllis' spidery hand. I determine to make a start on the article, no matter how banal the contents will have to be or how pointless it seems in the current circumstances.

Phyllis has enclosed a reader's letter, which she says has been the inspiration for the proposed article. My mind empties even more rapidly than usual when I find that she wants it for the next issue – meaning it will need to be finished in three days – and her request that it be written in 'your usual comic style'. I examine the reader's letter; it is of a familiar type. Composed in the first person – as if the writer is the cat itself – it asks for nutrition and healthcare advice for 'a retired, deservedly high-maintenance, prize-winning feline in my sunset years'. The letter is 'signed' with a paw print, which could be genuine. In the middle of shouting 'you sad arse' repeatedly, I hear someone come down the stairs. Olly walks through the dining room and into the kitchen. He is naked.

'Writing anything good?' he asks, as he pours himself a glass of water.

'Where have you come from? Where are your clothes? What are you doing?'

'Moya's been sketching me, in the back bedroom, for some painting or other.'

Olly passes back through the dining room and up the stairs. After fighting off the desire to follow him, pounce, lash him to the banisters and chew on his buttocks until he begs for mercy, I switch on the laptop. I sigh a lot as I write. In fact, I am so distracted by the brief vision of Olly's naked form that I have to leave the cat article and work on one for *Eurotica* instead. I am just at the point when the doomed lovers turn out to be not so doomed after all and are about to be reunited when Joy rings. I have to concentrate hard to decipher what she's saying through the furious chomping and rustling noises; it's like being in the cinema waiting for a film to start.

'Gina, I'm on a website. I've been doing more research into, you know, ovarian cancer.'

'I have heard of it.'

'Can I read you something?'

'Go ahead.'

'It's a proper website, by the way, for a medical research and treatment centre in the US.'

'Yes, go on. I didn't think you'd be on cure-cancer-with-garlic-dot-com.'

'Okay, okay. What it says is, "The quality of the *initial surgery* is the single greatest predictor of survival."'

'I know. You told me that already, last time you phoned.'

'There's definitely a case for medical negligence. Dr Kimura as good as said so. That bloody gynaecologist didn't even look at the scan properly, get more tests done, or discuss treatment with you as he should have. He knew he was retiring in a few weeks and if there was any come back it wouldn't be on him. You didn't consider the possibility of cancer because you couldn't face it. You've always lived in a fantasy world, blotted out the truth, ignored things that are staring you right in the –'

'Back to the point, Joy.'

'He should have been more thorough. That's why you're getting the kid-glove treatment now, getting booked in for surgery so quickly – because they messed up. I *know* they did. I'm not having it. It makes me so angry! It's like what happened to Mum …'

After trailing off, Joy hastily ends the call with a tearful, 'I'll ring back in a while.'

I can hardly wait.

No longer feeling inspired by my erotic story, I decide to get on with the aging cat article instead. I am writing in the first person, and am supposed to be a pedigree, pampered queen and perfect mother, but seem to be coming out more flea-bitten mongrel with chequered history. The writing is terrible, but it's making me laugh. My only hope is that it's so bad it's good, an aspiration which frequently accompanies my work. Luckily, Phyllis is quite techno-phobic and if I email her anything inappropriate or just plain crap and she queries it, I can usually get away with claiming that the Internet must have done something to it in transit.

Don't get me wrong, I like cats. Mum always had cats and we got brother and sister kittens (who grew to hate each other when adult) when Susan was about five. In fact, my first writing success came with a series of children's books about Ruffles the cat. It was right at the end of the seventies and Ruffles had hallucinogenically large pupils, a permanent stupefied grin and a penchant for chewing so much catnip, which grew in abundance in the gutter of his rooftop home, that he'd fall asleep at the most inappropriate times. This made him a bit of a cult figure with leftover hippie types. I realise now that Ruffles was modelled on Olly. Ruffles was the laziest, stupidest, fluffiest cat but, like for Monty, like for Milady Manors and, of course, unlike real life, things always turned out well in the end. But I never tampered with the minds of the young: Ruffles' adventures always ended with a sound moral and he was a spotless hero. Twenty-five years later and I am still writing about imaginary cats; hardly career progress.

The phone goes again. I know it's Joy. If I don't pick up, she'll ring my mobile.

'Sorry, Gina, sorry. An emotional outburst from me is the last thing you need right now.'

'It's okay. I know you're just trying to help. What else have you discovered?'

'A gynaecological oncologist should perform surgery for suspected ovarian cancer.'

'But it wasn't suspected at the time, was it?'

'No, but it should have been, if they'd looked at the scan properly. And even if it is suspected, it says here that only up to fifty per cent of women in the UK will actually be operated on by a gynaecological oncologist.'

'So it's not just me getting the rubbish treatment?'

'No, and listen to this, "Laparoscopic surgery of an ovarian mass which later turns out to be malignant can cause considerable and early spread of cancer, due to the shedding of cells during the procedure."'

A horrible image of my ovary bursting like a toxic balloon, spreading deadly cells throughout my body, appears in my mind. And won't go away.

After I get Joy off the phone, I unplug it, and switch off my mobile. Joy; hardly an appropriate name. I feel sick. Joy is raging mad on my behalf, but I don't know what to think. Can they really have made that much of a mistake with my treatment? Is this a common experience? Am I to turn into another news story, an unfortunate statistic, a medical negligence claim pursued by a grieving relative? And what about me? I would only consent to minimal surgery, so how responsible am I for this situation? Would Mr Winger have done a hysterectomy if I had consented? I can't see why, because the path results seem genuinely unexpected. And if an oncologist is the best person to remove suspected cancer, is it a good thing that the gynaecologist didn't do more surgery? I can take Joy's brutal honesty because I know she is on my side, but I'm beginning to believe that things are even worse than they first appeared. One of those 'I never thought it could happen to me' scenarios has happened to me. And this wouldn't be the first time that mistakes at the local hospital have cost patients dearly. Over thirty years ago, women died because an incompetent pathologist misdiagnosed test results. Joy's mum was one of them.

I go outside and pace about the garden. I don't know what the truth is about the treatment I've received because I don't know all the information. I don't know what the truth is because I'm not a medic. I don't know what the truth is because the facts keep shifting. Not because they are changing, but because they are still being tracked down. As an adult, I have known, or know of, about half a dozen people who have been diagnosed with various cancers and survived. A friend's father and a friend's sister died from it. In both cases, what appeared to be early diagnoses, successful operations and treatment, and the all-clear, turned out not to be. What was initially thought to be skin cancer was actually a secondary cancer from another site in the body. And after what was considered to be a complete recovery, breast cancer killed my friend's sister within six months. It wasn't so much that the cancer wasn't cured, but that the extent of it was never fully uncovered, remained hidden in the uncommunicative body, like wicked secrets waiting to be revealed.

I've just got to get through the next six days as best I can, and then the surgery. I cannot think beyond it.

When I go back indoors, I find Moya and Olly (both clothed) in the kitchen.

'Simone's dumped me,' Olly announces.

'Really? Are you ... feeling okay about it?' I ask.

'Yeah. She was too …' Olly struggles to find something to blame her for.

Intelligent, I could suggest, talented, beautiful, young.

'… complicated.'

I nod sympathetically, then go into the front room and close the door. I run round the coffee table mouthing, 'Yes, yes, yes!' I then slip back into the dining room, happy at the prospect of eavesdropping on the end of the affair.

'She's so beautiful,' I catch Olly saying to Moya in the kitchen, as I settle in front of my laptop.

This isn't what I expected to hear. My fingers hover over the keyboard.

'She's … sparkly,' he carries on enthusing.

I can't believe it; he must be on to another woman *already*.

I feel my heart slowing, my blood cooling, as I become physically frozen while, simultaneously, my mind fizzes, sparks, then ignites. I bet *he's* dumped Simone because he's met someone *even better*. He just said she was sparkly. What can this mean? She can't be more than twenty, nobody older than that wears body glitter.

I lean back and crane my neck so that I can hear more clearly.

'Caen. That's her name. It's French,' Olly is saying, dreamily.

Moya's not saying much, but then she rarely does.

'I know I can work so well with her, break new ground,' Olly continues. He sighs. 'I'm smitten, love at first sight,' he adds.

Everything pings apart. All the threads and springs and screws that kept my head on my shoulders, my joints in their sockets, my eyeballs fixed within my skull, fly apart, and I fall backwards in the chair, my head hitting the floor with a crack.

I'm sure I'm knocked out cold for a few seconds, but this may be wishful thinking.

When the world comes back into focus, Olly's face is over mine. I turn my head away. I cannot bear to look at him ever again.

'Gina?' I hear Moya call, as I try to raise myself up. 'What's wrong? What happened?'

'Olly,' I croak.

'I'm here,' says Olly, reassuringly.

'I heard what you were saying, about this new woman, about Caen, about it being love at first ...' I manage to whimper, before collapsing back on the floor.

Now Moya's face appears above mine. She is not wearing a sympathetic expression. In fact, she looks quite scary.

'Gina – you ridiculous woman – Caen is a type of *stone*.'

I'm lying in bed with the curtains drawn, recovering from today, from this last week. I've tried to carry on as if everything is normal, and that's not been a bad thing to attempt, but it's no longer possible. Olly is downstairs making me what we've always called 'gypsy bread' for tea – slices dipped in egg and fried. He's burnt it twice already and is on attempt number three. Ten points for effort, zero for attainment. I might see if I can go back into therapy with Leon to help me through all this. I know we've been making an effort to put the past behind us and get on as friends and neighbours, but I wouldn't have to explain my life afresh to him and I'd only have to go next door. Plus, Leon reminding me of why I ended therapy so abruptly has brought home that I still haven't moved on from Olly. I mean, I slept with him a couple of weeks ago, he's here now and even Dr K asked where my husband was, when we've been separated and then divorced for ten years. And I'm still smarting with embarrassment from the Caen incident. I must stop doing this to myself.

I realise I've been quite hyper since the shock of finding out about the cancer and this new lump. Now I've stopped rushing round and am remembering to breathe, memories – in the form of disconnected, soundless images – are running, unbidden and unstoppable, through my mind. It's as if my life is passing before my eyes, but slowly.

The prickly wool texture and warm, damp smell of my cream-coloured mittens as I sit up in the old-fashioned boat of a pram, a huge thing by today's standards, which was invariably left outside shops. Or is it a photograph I remember? I view myself as an observer would, as you often do with memories and recalled dreams. Burning my tongue on the boiling, bubbling sweetness of homemade jam tarts that Mum has just lifted from the oven. It hurts and I have tears. Mummy is softly cross. She *told* me to wait; patience was never my strong point. Joy telling me 'my daddy ran away before I was born' and me telling her 'mine died from a heart attack when I was a baby'. Fatherless, sibling-less, we swear to be sisters to each other, and for every birthday and Christmas make and buy 'sister' cards and gifts.

School holidays at Milady's. Unlike my mother's house – a sterilised 1950s semi in a non-descript suburb – my grandmother's mansion-cum-drama-school-cum-retirement-home is inexhaustibly exciting, appearing to reinvent itself every day in new and fantastic ways. When I'm about nine, I discover a narrow, winding staircase, accessed from what appears to be a cupboard on a main stairway, which opens into an attic room. It's crammed full of old props and costumes. I spend the whole half-term playing in there. When I tell Milady about my discovery of the room, she says, 'I wondered where that had gone,' as if she'd mislaid a hatpin. Ancient thespians people the top floors of the house: withered ladies with badly drawn-on eyebrows, faces thick with powder and blobs of cold cream, and shrunken men with limp wrists, long purple-rinsed hair and paisley cravats. Best of all, children people the lower floors, due to the constant ebb and flow of students. From toddlers to adolescents, from effeminate boys to vivacious girls, from the absurdly shy to the indecently extroverted – in fact, any kid who wants to play, to fantasise, to tell tales, to change shape and escape from dull, dull reality – find their way to *Milady's Academy for the Performing Arts. Milady's Players* offers a similar escape to adults.

More memories. In a home economics room in secondary school, aged twelve, shaking the flour sprinkler over the table and drawing patterns in the fine, dusty layer. Being sent to the headmaster. Suspended for two days for 'wanton despoliation of school property', when all I was really doing was *playing*. Mum can't meet my eye, such is her shame. She keeps repeating 'and what with me working in the cake shop', as if this is somehow ironic given my scandalous activity with baking ingredients. Trying to talk to Mum about friends, boys, her youth, how she fell in love with Dad. Her remaining tight-lipped and ill at ease, unable to answer me, or doing it only in generalities. A growing sense of being alone, isolated, with no one, or no adult, to talk to, to connect with meaningfully, to help me make sense of myself as I grow.

Rushing off to Milady's every possible weekend, now I've hit my teens, catching the first train out of dullsville straight after school on Friday. It's becoming increasingly difficult to return to colourless, lower-middle-class suburbia on Sunday nights, with its suffocating routine and predictability; a place where nothing goes unnoticed, though nothing ever appears to happen. I resent life at my mother's more and more: the same evening meals each day of every week, household chores done like clockwork, no visitors, no outings, no conversation other than the everyday and mundane; nothing to look forward to, nothing to celebrate, nothing to break the monotony, not even a sibling to pinch or play with; just the two of us and the weight of the terminally leaden sky.

Joy's mum dies and her auntie moves in. We don't talk about it, not once while we're growing up, nor does my mum, nor does anyone at school. It's as if we're pretending Joy's mum never existed, when everyone knows she did, when everyone knows there's now a hole in the world where she should be. Joy grows angry, bossy, and turns against the things she used to love: sport, ponies, being silly. The weight piles on, and stays there. We start to talk about boys, and how we couldn't possibly go out with any from our school, they're so uncool; but we spend ages in front of the mirror every morning getting ready.

Summer 1970 and, as usual, I'm spending the holidays at Milady's. I am fifteen. Neil arrives. He appears inordinately older than me. He has sinewy arms, van keys in a back pocket, competencies. I fancy him to be an aspiring actor who will fall in love with me. In fact, he is a married electrician with two small children and, it transpires later, homosexual. Looking back now, it appears that he was little more than a terrified adolescent, trying to bed any female he could to prove he wasn't gay, knowingly and yet not knowingly creating mistake after mistake: three children by the time he was twenty-two. That summer I ended up doing one of the most predictable things any young female can do:

having sex to feel grown-up, falling pregnant straightaway and being left holding the baby. Milady tells me to get the pregnancy 'sorted out at the doctor's', but I can't. Despite the shock and the shame, amazement that my body has created new life is stronger. I instantly feel as attached and connected to it as I do to my right arm or left foot – I am part of it and it is part of me.

Susan's little newborn face, peachy and fine. Such a bonny baby. I fall in love with her immediately. So does Mum. She can't help it. She stands by me. We continue to live at Mum's until I turn eighteen and then Susan and I move into the attic flat in River Street. Mum doesn't want us to leave, but I need my own space, my own life. With part-time work, Joy babysitting and some benefits, we get by. Every day Mum brings round unsold items from the cake shop; it's amazing Susan and I have any teeth left.

Mum. There she is again, at my wedding, in one of her matching hat, gloves, shoes and handbag ensembles. She could be very artistic with her baking. My wedding cake has five tiers and pear-and-rum-flavoured icing, and is decorated with sugar ivy leaves. Mum's smiling for me because I'm so happy, but is unable to take Olly seriously as a husband, as a human being probably. There I am, in the lizard-green dress. Can Olly and I ever have been so young? Olly had turned twenty only two days before. He's stoned. Those were the days when he smoked a chillum before getting out of bed. Those are still the days, although now he has to go to the loo first. And there's Susan, scowling because I requested she wear the most fabulous pistachio-coloured bridesmaid's dress with co-ordinating crochet hat. Mum's trying hard to jolly her out of her bad mood, without success. Oh, I am crying. I am crying then and I am crying now.

I try to get my brain to change the subject, but it refuses and lots of faces from the wedding – some I've barely thought about since – stream in. There's Ruth and Frank, aspiring actress and photographer, but actual drug dealers. Jim, Jane and Paul, who are involved in a three-way relationship. Jim looks like David Gilmour from Pink Floyd and Paul like Oliver Reed; lucky Jane, I say. A snapshot of a large, white-painted, Victorian house. It's summertime. Look in the bay window at the front and see right through the French doors at the back and into the garden. The living room is huge, knocked through, and it, too, is whitewashed. Giant, shiny-leaved plants, their roots escaping from their pots, sit beside sofas draped with thin, ethnic throws. These are pushed back against the walls to make floor space for large squares of foam, used to protect residents when they practice their yogic flying, which is known to damage knee cartilage. It can only be one place. The commune Hippie Richard set up, and which just about everyone we knew joined, then left, over the course of a couple of years.

The Mune, as it came to be known, was a meditation centre and ongoing experiment with self-sufficient, earth-friendly living. Everything was shared, what with our eschewal of personal possessions, not that Olly and I had many possessions to eschew. Susan had just turned ten and I was finding her difficult, which I put down to something I was doing wrong (having yet to conclude that we are incompatible as personalities, that it's impossible for us to get on). I can't remember exactly what principles we were trying to follow in the Mune, but I do recall long conversations involving ideas such as enlightened consciousness, crystal therapy and healing channels. I don't think most of us knew our auras from our elbows. But the idea of sharing and caring together in a big group –

work, meals, chores, social life – appealed. Susan would have other children to play with (there never would be a 'right time' to try for a baby with Olly, our relationship being such a series of ups and downs; okay, mostly downs) and, after a solitary childhood with Mum, I believed the more the merrier. What could be better for Susan than living in a democratic community where everything was discussed and voted upon? But life's not as clear-cut as that. It all became so intense and involved that most of us ended up incapable of making a cup of tea without forty-five minutes of deliberation beforehand. Only the few children retained a sense of normality and continued to play, fight and make up. Susan still keeps in touch with one of the kids from the commune – Caroline (formerly known as India) – and they occasionally get together to discuss how ludicrous their parents were. But at least Caroline has had the decency to become a singer-songwriter, rather than a council tax assessor, like Susan.

Looking back, I seem to have become involved in a series of experiments on how to live. Having grown up in an incredibly dull, respectable household with my mother, escaping to Milady and her artistes whenever possible, I moved on to the constraints and responsibilities of early motherhood, dabbling in a vaguely underground, artistic bohemia along the way. I then found myself trying out a decidedly wholesome lifestyle at the Mune. But it turned out to be a lot less, well, interesting, than I had anticipated. Hours and hours of meditation, of boiling lentils, of strumming folk songs. Month after month of trying to grow organic vegetables in poor soil. Week after painfully earnest week of quasi-group therapy. I may not have felt bad or confused in the Mune, but I didn't feel excited or positive either. But that's not why we left.

Olly comes in with the gypsy bread.

'Third time lucky,' he grins.

'Olly, why did we live in the Mune for nearly two years?'

'The Mune ...' Olly ponders, 'can't remember.'

'Try.'

'Erm. Was it cheap? Did it mean there was less to do around the house? Were we homeless?'

I roll my eyes, 'I thought it would be good for us, especially Susan, that it would make us healthy, happy people.'

Olly looks thoughtful, though he may just be spacing out.

'The road to hell, eh?' he says, eventually.

'Yes.'

'It was a crap commune though, wasn't it?' he comments. 'All I can remember is the farting from the veggie food. No free love, free drugs or anything. Free farts. That's what it should have been called – The Free Farting Commune.'

'Who was that woman? You know the one. Always wore a kimono. French.'

Olly shrugs.

'Françoise, that's it,' I say, as her name suddenly comes to me. '*That's* who I've been trying to remember.'

A year or so after we arrived, Françoise – ex-model and Face of France 1969, ex-actress, ex-free spirit, ex-heroin addict, traveller, drug trafficker, life lover and liver – moved in. She had turned her back on the fashion and narcotics industries and taken up her own form of pseudo-Buddhism at the Mune. Françoise seemed inordinately glamorous – older than any of us, in her early thirties, an already-fading beauty who had experimented wildly with life. But she had an ever-present hint of insanity, of self-destruction. She was so on the edge, even without drugs, that Olly made no attempt to sleep with her. Françoise couldn't believe it when, following a move to clean living after a life of debauchery, she discovered a breast lump. Hippie Richard thought it might be due to blocked channels or fuzzy auras. Various communards and friends of communards performed cosmic rituals over the lump and prescribed alternative remedies. It got bigger; another appeared under her arm. Françoise kept on with the alternative cures. Then her mother visited from France. She told us that two of her sisters, her own mother and an aunt had all had breast cancer. She declared that if Françoise didn't receive proper medical attention she'd more than likely be dead within a year. Hippie Richard tried to persuade Françoise against medical treatment, to keep up with the alternatives, but Françoise's mother prevailed, no doubt saving her daughter's life. There was a hefty price to pay: double radical mastectomy, chemotherapy, sickness, baldness. Françoise continued to live at the Mune and was almost regarded as having sold out because she'd chosen to undergo conventional medical treatment. That's what made me leave, that's why we moved back to River Street. I don't think Hippie Richard was a sadist or megalomaniac, but someone who genuinely believed in the power of his alternative approach. But he was playing god, and the commune became more of a sick joke than an idealist's dream come true. I wonder what happened to Françoise, I wonder if she's still –

Olly coughs.

'What's going to happen, Olly? What am I going to do? How am I going to cope?'

Olly bites his bottom lip.

'Erm … anything else I can get for you, Gina?'

'Do you know what I want, what I want more than anything?'

He shakes his head.

'I want my mum.'

6

FRIGGIN' IN THE RIGGIN'

I'm probably being overly optimistic about how easy it'll be to live in a building site post-hysterectomy, but at least the house plans are taking my mind off everything, and encouraging the belief that life will continue after surgery. Since the Caen debacle and the day spent in bed, I've calmed down and slowed down, although it's made me realise how scared I am. I may not have Mum to make things better, or a loving husband to help me through, but I do have good friends and a life to return to once this is all over.

Marty – Olly's builder brother – has been round to discuss the house and is going to start work on the bathroom while I'm in hospital. I'm being ruthless about the refurbishment. No 'I suppose it'll do' or 'just paint over it'. No. Ancient, bashed-up skirting that has been glossed over a dozen times will be replaced, the damaged ceiling roses will be restored, patched plaster walls will be skimmed. The windows that stick, the guttering that droops, the cracked paving slabs: it's all to be sorted. I only have to instruct Marty, choose any replacements and supply the money.

It's Thursday, and I have a date with Ralf the building surveyor this evening. The surgery is on Monday and I need to do various things to prepare for it in the preceding couple of days, so this is my last chance to go out before the op. I don't think I'll tell Ralf about my health problems; after all, it's only a first date and I'd like to spend an evening not talking, worrying and thinking about them. I'm feeling quite buoyant, and I'm not sure why. It's probably just another high in the bipolar disorder I seem to be developing. Perhaps it's because I feel well, apart from the sudden lurching panics that knock me sideways. I keep pressing my abdomen to try to feel where the lump is but, really, I can't tell. I've been reassured by Dr K's use of the word 'we', because it makes me feel we're in this together, and by Leon's conclusion that he's 'one of the best'. I've told everyone who needs to know about the imminent hysterectomy, including Susan. I've told some people about the cancer that was removed and the possibility there might be more, but not Susan; I seem to fear her sympathy more than her disapproval. Of course, I haven't told Chrissy about the cancer either. But, if things go well, if it's good news after surgery, she won't ever need to know.

I did a bit of unsuccessful shopping this morning. I began early, in search of a new outfit for tonight. But all I managed to purchase was a three-pack of light-bulbs and a toilet duck. I also had an impulsive colour and cut at a new salon (opening week, half price), so at least my hair looks good. On the way home – walking, to be healthy, ha ha – I called in on Olly. I know I should move on from him, and I certainly shouldn't sleep with him, but I can't imagine us not being in each other's lives. And we are Chrissy's grandparents, after all. Maybe I'm just making excuses, the same excuses I made ten years ago. But I'm going on a date with Ralf, which at least shows I'm trying to find someone new.

Olly has indeed fallen for Caen, a type of stone he's not worked with before, and love it is. He's beginning to swing between euphoric exhilaration and dark, depressive doubt. The stone he's using was imported from France nine hundred years ago, to be used for the sculptural decoration of a church in a nearby village. But its exquisite and unusual yellowy-pink colouring and natural sparkles were considered unsuitably frivolous by the religious leaders, so it was discarded. But it has now been delivered, by crane, into Olly's back garden-cum-studio. It is beautiful stone and Olly shows all the signs of entering into one of his 'inspired' periods. Like all true artists, he moves in and out of such phases. They can be frightening, inducing a manic high and total obsession, the world narrowing and narrowing until nothing else exists. World War III could be declared, a marching band parade through his studio, even Donna dancing on his dining table stark naked would have no impact (maybe I'm kidding myself there).

It's only when inspired that Olly appears to come fully into being, as if his life force is concentrated into these months of intensity, leaving him sucked dry and semi-comatose the rest of the time. The work has been commissioned by the council to sit on the forecourt of the new museum and gallery complex, which is being developed in the city centre. Its subject is at Olly's discretion, although everyone expects an egg. But Olly has had an artistic breakthrough. It is simultaneously scaring the hell out of and elating him, and he's unable to talk about it coherently. He can only repeat the words 'irregular organic form'. We must wait and see.

I return home with armfuls of rhubarb from Olly's garden, which I don't particularly like. I could make a crumble, but you can buy them in Asda for 90p. Despite the threat of disease and death, I'm worrying about what to do with surplus fruit (or is it a vegetable?), the profound and mundane rubbing shoulders ever more closely. Of course, I have an urge to do something deeply meaningful with my life, while I still can. But what?

I flick on the laptop. Perhaps work can distract me. Luckily, the deadline for the extra *Cat Lover's Monthly* article has been extended because it's being moved to the following issue. There's an email from Phyllis requesting I tone down the more raunchy aspects of the draft I sent and stick to actual advice. I search the Internet for information on the principles of geriatric cat care. It's all a bit half-hearted because I'm waiting for Joy to arrive. She promised to call in this afternoon to help me put together an outfit for tonight. I haven't had a proper date for ages. I don't know why I'm making such an effort. The symbolic Last Supper perhaps.

I hear the front door open (Joy has a key, but usually knocks first) and the rustle of a carrier bag, which sounds as if it's stuffed with at least twenty thousand calories worth of confectionery.

'Gina!' Joy cries in surprise as she walks into the dining room. She tries to hide the bag behind her back. Joy claims to hardly eat a thing and have some unspecified metabolic problem. Everyone knows this is rubbish and that she simply can't stop over-eating, but she will not or cannot admit this. And, being quite beautiful, she has been subject to 'you're so pretty, if only you weren't so … big' comments all her life.

'Oh, sorry. This *is* your house,' she says. 'I don't know why I was so surprised to see you there. Thought you'd be out – still shopping up town. Hair looks nice. Any more news from the hospital?'

Joy's really pushing the medical negligence issue, but I'll be under their care next week, my life literally in their hands. Perhaps it's just cowardice, but I can't countenance confronting and criticising the medics I'll be relying on to treat and look after me – not at this point, anyway.

'No, no more news. Same as before. Total hysterectomy, more cancer a possibility, then, maybe, the joy of chemotherapy. Forget piña coladas, sunburn and sand in my knickers this summer, I have only surgery, nausea and hair loss to look forward to. Fancy some lunch?'

'No, I'm not really hungry,' Joy says nonchalantly.

'Well, there's a carton of soup in the fridge, I thought I might –'

'Actually, I've brought some goodies. Let's eat these instead and cheer ourselves up,' declares Joy brightly, but shamefaced.

I don't know why she's so embarrassed about her eating; we've all got our props and comforts. Olly has been perma-stoned for decades; I doubt it's ever crossed his mind to question if it's the right way to live, let alone feel guilty about it. I doubt he's even got much of a mind left to be crossed.

'What's he like then, your date?' asks Joy, while unpacking a boxed cream-cake selection onto plates.

'Tallish. Own hair and teeth. I think. He's a building surveyor, but harbours ambitions to be a writer, apparently.'

'Not another one.'

'What do you mean, "not another one"?'

'What about that freak you picked up on that TV script-writing course, the one who was doing a sci-fi drama.'

'He wasn't a freak. Well, he may have had mental health problems, but I couldn't tell at the time. I thought he was just getting in touch with his characters. And he did have very shiny, glowing eyes. Perhaps he *was* an alien.'

Joy smiles upside down.

'And what about Ivan?'

'What about him? He wasn't a writer.'

'Oh, a wrestler, that was it.'

'I know writer and wrestler both begin with "w", when they should perhaps begin with "r", but that hardly makes them similar.'

'He was … unusual.'

'Yes, not every woman can experience the thrill of being taken out to dinner by a man wearing a leotard and silver lamé boots.'

I really shouldn't pander to Joy's vicarious enjoyment of my disastrous love life. She's been happily married, or as happy as it's humanly possible to be, for over twenty years. Cow.

'Do you remember your homosexual phase?'

'What? I've never slept with a woman.'

'No, I mean falling in love with gay men.'

'Hmm … it all started with Susan's dad, didn't it? I seemed to develop a repressed-homosexual-man-pretending-to-be-straight homing device for a few years.'

'Then there were the alcoholics.'

I remain silent.

'And what was that really awful guy's name? Dean, was it, or Gene? The fact he counted badger baiting as a leisure activity should have warned you. No wonder you kept going back to Olly.'

I look Joy in the eye.

'Yes, Joy. It's a shame not all of us can have a husband like Tim – honest, faithful and adoring. A bit like a well-trained dog.'

Joy glowers at me, but says nothing. We eat cakes in silence (I have two, she has six), then I go into the kitchen to make tea. When I return, Joy has placed more cakes on my plate. She actually bought a dozen, fibbing to the bakery girl that they were for a colleague's leaving do.

At least I have a date. With a fairly fit, handsome (well, he qualifies as normal-looking which, believe me, some of them haven't), professional man, even if he is a would-be writer. Quite frankly, if he appears halfway decent, I'll consider going to bed with him. The operation is in four days and who knows what it'll do to my body and libido. I wonder if I'll still be interested in men, in sex? Could it be a relief not to be? I push my plate away. There is a point at which all pleasurable things become painful and, as far as chocolate éclairs go, it's three and a half.

Joy's promise to 'run me up something special' for tonight soon diminishes to altering items she sells on her stall so they fit better. So much for *haute couture*. She eyes my body as I stand in front of her in my underwear, before slipping a dress over my head. It's candy-pink silk with a wide, cream-coloured, lace trim. I'm not convinced; I don't want to look like an ageing fondant fancy.

'I can let it out a touch at the bust, bring in the waist, definitely leave it skimming that belly. And long enough to cover the thighs.'

Joy says the words 'the thighs' in the same way she might say 'The Alps'; for a twenty-stone woman, she's got a nerve.

'What about something a little less … shiny? I'm not a teenager. I'm not even young. I'm …'

I've only just got used to being middle-aged, next will come elderly. If I'm lucky.

'You know I wouldn't put you in anything awful. It wouldn't do my reputation any good. You can still get away with it, honest.'

Joy retrieves her portable sewing machine from the car and makes a few adjustments. She also 'advises' on accessories and make-up. Joy's always been a tyrant when it comes to fashion, forgetting the person inside the clothes. Still, she does know her stuff.

'And a magenta bolero with peacock feather trim.'

Or maybe not.

'We're only going for an Indian.'

Joy gives me her disdainful look.

'Okay, okay.'

She continues to boss me about over my refusal to switch handbags for the evening or dye my favourite strappy white sandals a co-ordinating pink. Talk about obsessive. I'm so worn out by the time she's finished with me, I feel like flopping into bed. Moya's much easier to have about the place, partly because she hardly speaks. And she does such useful things, like replacing washers and pruning trees. But Joy's right, I do look fab and feel confident. I have scrubbed up well, as they say, even though it's taken all day.

'I'm sorry, Gina,' Joy whispers as she hugs me goodbye, 'for all my stupid comments, for going on about the hospital, for bringing up old boyfriends, for telling you what to wear. I just want you to get the best treatment, to be well, to feel good about yourself and meet someone decent. But it always comes out wrong.'

'Don't worry about it. You've always been the same – a bossy, insensitive cow. I don't know how Tim puts up with you.'

'Nor do I. I hope you have a wonderful time tonight. Ralf could turn out to be the man of your dreams.'

As I wave goodbye, I try to shake off the feeling that Joy's optimistic comments have jinxed the evening. For, nine times out of ten, dates – like parties, holidays, jobs, marriages, whole lives – turn out worse than anticipated, rather than better, in many and unpredictable ways.

I drop the remaining cakes off at Olly's before walking down to the restaurant, knowing he won't have eaten all day. Like the small child he is, Olly is overjoyed at being brought the gift of free food, especially because it has coloured icing and sprinkles. Before I go, we kiss. Olly tells me I look gorgeous. It makes me immeasurably happier than it should.

The date begins okay. Ralf says I look good enough to eat, which makes me smile and cringe in equal measure, and again causes worry about my resemblance to a synthetic pastry. He's keen to buy me lots of drinks, which means that either he's generous or he wants to get me drunk fast. I'm happy to accept, regardless of motivation. Things take a turn for the worse after the poppadoms, however, when he brings out a huge manuscript and says he'd like me to read it. Three hundred and fifty thousand words over the main course might be a tad optimistic.

'I know what sort of stories *you* write,' he says, with an unhealthy gleam in his eye.

'What do you mean?'

'You know, nudge, nudge, wink, wink.'

Oh dear, here we go. Ralf is transforming from potential partner into repellent knobhead before my eyes.

'You mean *The Adventures of Monty* in *The Cat Lover's Monthly*?'

'No.'

'*Arts and Crafts Today*?' (Got that through a potter friend.)

'No.'

'Articles and interviews for the Art College's interactive website and gallery?' (Got that through Olly's mate Bob.)

'No.'

'*The Wonderful World of the Wurlitzer*?' (Okay, I made that one up.)

'No, the erotic whatsit. I thought you'd be more than qualified to advise me on a certain scene.'

'Oh, alright.'

'The novel's called *Fortune's Logbook*, and it's an eighteenth-century, seafaring adventure.'

Audible sigh.

'That's not exactly my area of interest – I mean, expertise – but go ahead.'

He hands me the manuscript, having opened it at the scene he's having trouble with.

Goodness, it's absolute filth. It's set on a merchant ship bound for India on which a young, naïve girl and her family are travelling in search of a suitable marriage match in the colonies. The young woman is the object of desire for a number of randy sailors into whose quarters she persists in stumbling due to seasickness, sleepwalking, darkness, fog, and so on. It's Patrick O'Brian meets Stephen King ...

'Euw! I mean, um, what do you want help with exactly? Apart from your psychosexual problems. Ha, ha, ha.'

Ralf frowns for a half-second, before the comment bounces off his numbskull.

'The metaphors. I want the sex scenes to be of the period and to reflect the setting.'

'Let's see what you've got so far.'

I skim-read a few pages. Mates One, Two and Three are described as 'standing proud as a yardarm' and having 'mighty masts of oak', while Four, Five and Six are at various levels of 'hoisting', 'raising' and 'bringing to the fore'.

'Maybe it's not so much the nautical metaphors themselves, but the phrase "standing proud as",' I suggest. 'I did count it six times in one paragraph. They certainly are a virile crew.'

'All young men, these sailors, on a voyage for months, with no female c-c-company.'

Ralf suddenly reeks of a man who has been unwillingly celibate for years, and I become a woman rapidly understanding why.

'What about this bit?'

Ralf flicks forward to a scene in which the Purser and two Ordinary Seamen ... I rapidly lose my appetite and any attraction to Captain Crusty himself.

The date's been so awful, I'm now horribly drunk. Ralf didn't appear deranged when I first met him, so how could he turn out like this? I'm either a terrible judge of character or incapable of attracting anyone but a freak. Perhaps both. I ask the waiter to ring for a taxi. I tell Ralf I'm feeling unwell and must get home. And that I'm going in for major surgery in a couple of days, which will take months of recovery, so there's really no point in pursuing this. I have to say he looks more disappointed that I'm leaving without his manuscript than at the prospect of never seeing me again.

I wait outside the restaurant, hopeful the fresh air will sober me up. It doesn't. And who is it who finally comes to pick me up, just to round the evening off? Dougie Spokes. All this surgery and cancer crap, yet I still have to deal with all life's regular crap as well.

'Oh, it's you, Gina,' says Dougie, leaning out of the cab window. 'Sorry about the Doc. I never laid a hand on him. It was the girls what done it.'

I open the passenger door and stumble-fall-flail onto the back seat. I have started blubbing.

'Cheer up, it might never happen.'

'It has. They found a cancerous lump, and now they're worried there might be more.'

'Do you remember when I was shot? They thought I was a goner, but I'm still here. You'll pull through, don't you worry.'

Dougie turns round from the front seat and treats me to a broad smile, which coincides with a sudden swell of nausea. As he drives he recounts the lurid details of being shot. He glosses fairly incoherently over the why or who, but makes frequent use of phrases such as 'bad blood' and 'what goes around comes around'.

'Where was it you were shot, Dougie, in the head?'

'Nah, me chest, like I just said. Weren't you listening?'

When Dougie pulls up at River Street, I notice Leon standing outside my front door, as if he's just knocked. The last thing I need is another altercation between him and Dougie, so I keep Dougie talking in the taxi until I see Leon push something through my letterbox and then go into his own house. Even after I've scrambled out of the taxi and am standing, albeit unsteadily, on the pavement, Dougie is still going on about his gunshot heroics.

'Look, here's the evidence,' he says, and he disentangles a gold chain from his copious chest hair, then runs a thumb and finger round it until he finds the pendant. It's a bullet. 'They couldn't believe I'd survived up at the hospital. When I came round that was one of the first things I wanted to know – if they had the bullet. They said yeah, but they'd have to give it to the coppers. But I says to myself, I know what I'll do with that. So I swiped it. Had it gold plated. Twenty-two carat.'

'Well, it makes a change from a St Christopher,' I say, peering at the blinged-up bullet through the driver's window, my hand clamped to the car roof to prevent the pavement from tipping upside down.

Dougie grimaces again.

'I'm a tough old bugger. And so are you. You'll get through this.'

He refuses to let me pay the fare.

'Couldn't come in for a quick coffee, could I?' he asks; I wish he wouldn't keep smiling, it really has the most unappealing, knock-on effect on the rest of his face. 'I'm on an all-nighter, got another six hours to go. Tar wants one of them new sunbeds, what you stand up in. It's gonna cost thousands.'

'Oh, okay, Dougie. But you'll have to help me up the front path, you'll have to make the coffee yourself and there's every likelihood I'm going to vomit.'

'Fine by me.'

While Dougie sticks the kettle on, I open the card that Leon put through my letterbox. It contains words of encouragement, reiterates that he wants to 'be there' for me and a cheerful, sunny landscape is depicted on the front. I suppose 'get well soon' is hardly an appropriate sentiment when you might be dealing with cancer. As I automatically go to put the card on the mantelpiece, on display, I hesitate. I really don't need any more reminders of what I'm having to face, no matter how kind the intention. I push the card back in its envelope and leave it on the table.

After coffee and chitchat with Dougie, during which I try, unsuccessfully, to persuade him to apologise to Leon for his behaviour at the barbecue, I say it's time I was getting to bed. Dougie stands suddenly and squeezes his hand into the front pocket of his jeans. After much unpleasant straining and grunting, he manages to extract a little sheet of pills. He throws it onto the table in front of me.

'What are they?'

Dougie's eyes twinkle; he looks like a menacing Tellytubby. 'Viagra.'

Despite the offer to show me his bullet-wound scar and the promise that he'll be 'a real gentlemen in the bedroom' and 'go like the clappers all night long on that stuff', I decline Dougie's offer of no-strings-attached sex. But I do manage to get a Viagra off him before he leaves. After the disastrous date with Ralf and with my only other prospect being Dougie, I guess it's back to Olly. Is it any wonder I haven't moved on from him, considering the alternatives? I am determined to get in a night of passion before the operation. Hope seems to be rapidly thinning to desperation, but when was it otherwise?

Knowing someone you can have sex with as and when you like is no bad thing, and Olly never fails to oblige, although the favour is not exclusive to me, of course. And it's always been remarkably easy to get him going. I only have to say something fairly innocuous, such as 'frilly knickers' or 'sweaty breasts', and he'll be unable to concentrate on anything else. Having sobered up a bit, I walk round to his bungalow. He's still at work in his studio, unfazed to see me arriving, unannounced and dishevelled, in the small hours of the morning.

'How'd it go?' he asks.

'Bloody awful. I spent all day getting ready for nothing. I've got to have a hysterectomy in – God, now it's Friday – three days' time. I want to have sex with someone I love. Or at least like. Or at least fancy. Or who isn't fucking repulsive.'

Olly looks blank.

'That means *you*.'

He throws down his chisel and rubs his hands together. I unbuckle his tool belt and fling it wantonly to one side.

Having had second thoughts about spontaneity, I tell Olly to get in the bath first, what with him being caked in stone dust, and I'll bring him a glass of something. And a Viagra.

'These drugs they keep inventing, Gin,' he says, after he's swallowed it, 'they just get better and better.'

There speaks a man who greeted the invention of ecstasy in the same manner as doctors did penicillin.

Olly's bath is so hideously wonderful it's almost impossible to describe. Probably because it's so hard to believe that someone designed it, that a company produced it, then that people actually bought it. It is circa the early seventies and made from a deep burgundy-purple plastic, a colour previously unknown to man and which many people have spent many stoned hours trying to invent a name for. It is a massive scalloped shell shape, works as a whirlpool and has a huge, gilt mixer tap that requires the strength of both arms to turn. Olly discovered it being thrown out of a hotel renovation and brought it back to Sycamore Gardens. But being so large and awkward a shape it wouldn't fit in the bathroom and so he and Marty spent a very speedy weekend plumbing it into the conservatory in a way that I am sure does not comply with safety regulations. Olly has been known to spend days on end topping up the hot water and experimenting with the whirlpool functions, while chain-smoking joints of hallucinogenic skunk. I get into the bath with him.

'Shall we smoke a little spliff?' he suggests.

'No. But you can massage my back.'

After five minutes of gentle pummelling I feel a persistent pushing against my spine. I look round. Olly's grinning, eyes downwards.

'Look at my knob, Gin. It's enormous.'

'Yes, it is looking rather large and … um … persistent.'

We get out of the bath and get to it. Again, and again, and again.

As I have remarked before, there is a point at which life's pleasures become life's pains. And for sexual intercourse, as for chocolate éclairs, the number appears to be three and a half.

7

THREES

'Mr Bummalo will be your anaesthetist today.'

'Pardon?'

'Mr Bummalo, here, will be putting you to sleep for the surgery.'

Ten minutes later and I'm still shaking with laughter. I have just got myself under control when Moya informs me that a bummalo is a small fish, often used dried in curry dishes. She drove me to the hospital for 7 a.m., the operation being scheduled for nine o'clock, and is now sitting at my bedside trying to calm my hysterics. This light-headed mania may be partly due to the pre-surgery bowel preparation of liquids only and copious laxatives: weight-loss heaven! Hopefully, the pre-meds will have a sedative effect. These are administered by ...

'Nurse D'you Mind My Retard.'

'Pardon?'

'D'you Mind My Retard. I am your key nurse for today and will be with you before you go to theatre, and here on the ward after you come round.'

Either stress is causing auditory hallucinations or I have checked into The Hospital for Clinically Ridiculous Names.

Moya explains, as I sit on the bed in an oversized, cardboardy surgery gown, that it's Nurse Jemima Rittard.

The Registrar's name is Mr Bloomer and the woman in the bed opposite is Helena Peaswell. Thank goodness for Dr Kimura, with his sensible name and consistently enormous moustache. Reassuringly, he remembers who I am, makes the horrendous-looking black-marker line across my belly in what would appear to be an appropriate place and puts a hand on mine when talking.

I thank Moya and tell her she should go. I just want it to be over. Waiting reminds me of trying to while away hours in an airport, only without the shops and over-priced coffee, but with the same overshadowing fear of death. Will the plane fall from the sky? Will I come round from the anaesthetic?

I'm wheeled to theatre by two porters. I manage not to scream, 'Don't let me die!' at Mr Bummalo and breathe deeply to relax as the anaesthetic chill creeps into the back of my hand and up my arm. I count one, two, three, four …

Olly's in a dinghy on a sun-shiny sea. I'm sitting on the beach, watching. He's wearing a pirate hat, brandishing a cutlass and shouting 'land ho me hearties', 'shiver me timbers' and other nautical nonsense, while nearly tipping into the water and swigging from a bottle of beer. Chrissy's in the boat behind him, drawing in a sketchbook. Moya is beside me, buried, not very well, in the sand. Her feet are sticking out, but her hands are well covered, and she's managing to lie perfectly still while puffing away on a cheroot, without getting smoke in her eyes. I wince. I feel sore all across my stomach. A jellyfish sting, it must be. I try to move my head to look, but connection between brain and body appears broken. I try to tell Moya, but my mouth's not working properly. A crab is nipping my ears.

'You're just coming round from the anaesthetic, Georgina. It's all over now.'

Praise the Lord, I've survived!

'Can you hear me, Georgina?'

I hiss 'yeth' through my teeth.

'Good, good.'

I leave Olly, Chrissy, Moya and myself at the beach. I realise the jellyfish sting is the operation incision, and the crab nipping my ears the nurse rubbing the lobes to bring me round.

'Are you in any pain?'

'Sore. Cold.'

'I'll get another blanket. You can go back to the ward in a while and rest. They'll sort out your pain relief and make sure you're comfortable.'

My eyes focus on the clock. I was wheeled into theatre at a quarter past nine and now it's coming up to half past three. I'm not able to add up the hours properly, but I know it's a long time.

I'm back on the ward and feeling dreadful, much worse than after the previous surgery. It's as if someone's reverse parked into my forehead. There's pain all through my hands, my arms, my torso. I keep shaking uncontrollably. My jaw feels wired together and everything's stiff, like it's rusted up. As I become more alert, the pain increases. There are drips and tubes and needles, a catheter, and a wound drain coming out of my stomach. I slip in and out of consciousness. Staff come and go, check things, lift up a blanket, look at my bandaged middle. One of the theatre nurses comes in and asks how I'm doing. I nod and wave my hand about, unable to talk. I try to reassure myself: you can't expect to feel great after hours of surgery and oceans of anaesthetic.

My poor body. Do I resent it for going wrong, for letting me down? No, I feel sorry for it, I mourn for it, for the bits of me that have been removed: the diseased bits, but also the essence of life and essentially female bits. I hear nurses talking over me, quietly bitching about other members of staff and chatting about where they're going on holiday. Normal life continues.

'"You will not be able to eat or drink at first,"' reads Joy the following afternoon, from a printout from one of the million health websites she's been trawling. '"But as soon as you are fully awake you will be able to wet your mouth with sips of water. Your doctor will listen to your abdomen with a stethoscope to see if your bowel is working normally. Sometimes the bowel goes on strike for a bit after abdominal surgery. As soon as it is —"'

'Hold on a minute,' I croak. 'Can a doctor really tell if your bowel is working with a stethoscope?'

'That's what it says. Has someone done that, Gina?'

'I don't know. I can't remember much from yesterday.'

'"As soon as it is working normally you will be able to increase the amount you are drinking and then progress to something light to eat. You should be eating and drinking normally again within a couple of days at the most."'

I have a hand-held morphine pump for pain relief – a palm-sized disc about the size and shape of a tin of shoe polish – which I control. I feel like the White Rabbit holding his pocket-watch. I was really nauseous earlier, so I'm trying to go easy with it. But Joy's making me want to bring on a fresh wave of opiates.

'"A hysterectomy is a big operation and because it affects a woman's hormone-producing organs will have profound consequences. If the patient is still menstruating and has had her ovaries removed, she will experience an instant menopause.'"

Joy continues, but I zone out, closing my eyes and nodding occasionally. The significance of what I'm going through is hitting home. Now the surgery is over, there's the wait for the pathology results. And for instant menopause to kick in. I've known, theoretically, that it's going to happen, but now I've not only got the surgery to deal with but the change of life, too. And chemotherapy, maybe. They say it comes in threes.

'Gin.'

'Ooh, yes please! Ha, ha, ha.'

I don't need to open my eyes to recognise Olly. Despite it being only two days after major surgery, I hope I don't look too ghastly and my catheter isn't too visible (oh, the humiliation!). Olly has brought coffee cream chocolates (my favourite, not that I could stomach them at the moment), cartons of strawberries and cherries, magazines, and a book of short stories. I can't believe he's been so thoughtful and has chosen all this himself; I stick to saying thank you and not asking questions. Olly's deeply uncomfortable in hospitals. He hops about from one foot to the other, while glancing around fretfully, as if someone might rush up and spray him with deadly viruses. A nurse comes over and ushers him away, to his visible relief. She says he can wait in the reception area until she's finished with me, but I let him off the hook and tell him he can go. Susan's away on a training course for work this week so she won't be visiting, and I've told Graham not to bring Chrissy in; I don't want her to see me in this state. I'm actually feeling worse than I imagined, so I'm glad I won't see them till I'm out of hospital.

The nurse wants me to try to walk. I can't say it's an appealing prospect. My legs are very shaky, I'm worried I'll faint, and my stomach is swollen to six months pregnant. I manage to shuffle up and down the ward. It's hard to believe this can be good for me, but the nurse reassures me that it is: it helps prevent deep vein thrombosis. The raw, brutal truth of mortality is appalling.

Moya comes to visit and helps me back into bed, even though the nurse says I should sit in a chair instead. I nearly lose my temper. I know – from everything Joy's read to me and everything the hospital staff have said – that being mobile aids recovery and helps prevent complications, but I feel so awful. Moya pulls the curtains round my bed. I weep on her sturdy chest and she pats me reassuringly. Even this is difficult due to all the fucking tubes tangling me to drips and other medical equipment like a demented octopus. I'm so frustrated and angry, but with no one to blame.

By evening, I'm in a private room, which you can request if one's available and you're willing to pay, but Dr K has assured me it'll be free. He came in earlier. It's the first time I've registered seeing him since the operation. I was honest and said I'm not coping well with being on an open ward and would prefer to weep, swell up, leak urine (had catheter removed earlier, can't seem to feel anything and might have a bladder infection) and top myself up with morphine in private. He said that would be fine, seeing as I'm making a good physical recovery from surgery and don't need constant monitoring. We haven't really talked about the surgery, or anything else, yet, and I've been too out of it to take anything in. I know the morphine is killing the pain, but it's also addling my mind and emotions. Dr K said he'd be round tomorrow morning to discuss my path results and, as ever, that it would be advisable to have someone with me.

After a heavily sedated sleep, I feel fairly with it the next day. I've said goodbye to the morphine pump and hello to Voltarol pain-relieving suppositories. I can't help thinking that Harry Potter's nemesis, Voldemort, is being pushed up my arse in pellet form. Unbelievably, the disastrous date with Ralf was only one week ago today.

Moya is with me when Dr K arrives to recap that the operation went well and I'm healing up nicely, and to tell me that all major, and visible secondary, tumours were removed. Tumours; major, secondary. These words said smiling to me. The vain hope that Dr Kimura would say the lump was a cyst, a benign mass, evaporates. Of the thirty biopsies taken, only one lymph node was cancerous, but that's what's given me the Stage IIIC rating on the cancer scale, something I am now fairly *au fait* with. Dr K is at pains to point out that any cancer found outside the original site – the pelvis – immediately raises the rating to Stage III. He says that the cancerous lymph node was in the groin area, near the site of the original tumours, which is better than it being farther away. He recommends six cycles of chemotherapy, each one being a day of drug treatment in hospital, followed by three weeks recovery at home. Leaflets are placed in my hand. If I'm up to it, the first chemo session will be administered on Monday, before I've even been discharged from the hospital. And the last one, assuming everything goes according to plan, will be around the beginning of September. Well over three solid months of treatment. I wish I could be knocked out and brought round again when it's all over.

Stage IIIC. I know that once classed as Stage IV, the next one up from mine, surgery and chemo are largely done to prolong life and ease symptoms, rather than cure. I also know that the majority of women are diagnosed at exactly the same stage as me, and that nearly one in three will have no reoccurrence in five years, after going through surgery and chemotherapy. I've never been a lucky person, but, perhaps, this time … Joy has informed me that new research shows that a positive attitude in the face of cancer makes no difference to outcome. I find this reassuring, being such a miserable old pessimist.

After Dr K has delivered his news, I persuade Moya she can leave, that I'm fine. And I am remarkably calm and chipper, given what I've just been told. I feel like I'm on a conveyor belt and will be guided through this whole process by people who know what they're doing, who deal with this every day. Or maybe it's not really sinking in. I read my leaflets while eating half a sandwich for lunch, the first solid food since the operation.

As I finish, a woman of about sixty, wearing a hospital name tag that says 'Margaret MacDonald – Senior Administrator', approaches and hands me a flyer. It's for a cancer survivors' support group. She smiles and leaves. I stare at the word 'cancer'.

Unmarried mother groups, feminist consciousness-raising groups, discovering your aura groups, writing and reading groups, meditation groups, a cancer survivors' group. The last one sounds the least appealing, and I've joined a lot of crap groups.

It finally registers that I may be, potentially, seriously ill. Not may be, but am.

After a reasonable night's sleep, I decide I'm not doing too badly and resolve to be positive, even if it doesn't 'impact on outcomes'. Dr K has been nothing but pleased and encouraging about how it's going: surgery successful, healing well, all tests indicating I'm 'healthy' enough to tolerate chemotherapy. This is the first day

I've felt markedly better physically, and it has raised my spirits. It's hard to believe things could be worse, but it's possible: I could have a more advanced stage of cancer, complications from the surgery, and no friends and family to help. I could have untreatable cancer, an inoperable tumour, a lot less hope. The bladder infection is clearing and the sensation needed to wee is returning. It feels good to make some decisions, like to reduce pain relief. But one problem seems to be immediately superseded by another. I haven't had a bowel movement yet and they are keen for me to eat as much as possible to 'get things moving'. The nurses' euphemisms make me feel like I'm in a comedy sketch playing Les Dawson's Cissie to their Adas.

Margaret MacDonald, the hospital administrator who handed me the cancer support group flyer yesterday, returns in the afternoon.

'Alright, hen?' she asks, in her strong Scottish accent, and then, without waiting for a reply: 'I work at the hospital, but also go to the patient support group. I know what it's like, you know. So if you feel alone, well, you don't have to. If you want to discuss anything with others who know what you're going through, or just sit and listen, do come along. It's every Thursday evening, up here at the hospital. The counsellor's a great guy, keeps us all in order. Just, you know, make a bit of contact if you want to. Don't be a stranger.' And she leaves.

Then she comes back and perches on the edge of the bed.

'It will get better. You're going through a terrible time, physically and emotionally. But you won't feel like this forever, just remember that.'

'Thank you.'

'I'm not really supposed to approach people myself, but ...'

Margaret's voice rises and her accent thickens, as if she's retaliating against a critical authority figure, 'for God's sake, we're dealing with people's lives here. It's all very well giving someone a leaflet, but I think personal contact is much more effective.'

I nod.

'You know,' she says, lowering her voice again, 'I don't mean to overstep the line, what with patient confidentiality and all that, but I know you've had a hysterectomy, and there's no use pretending I don't because I booked you in for it.'

I nod again.

'I've had one, too, but before the cancer. Just, you know, be prepared, expect a few symptoms,' and she hands me another leaflet with 'menopause' in the title.

The next day, five days since the surgery, life's a mixed bag of better and worse. On the positive side, I am sitting on a bench outside the hospital, in the sunshine, eating. On the negative, Dougie Spokes is seated next to me, spouting endless platitudes: 'It's true what they say, innit, you ain't got nothing if you ain't got your health.' He coughs as he smokes, while shifting uncomfortably around the weight of his belly. At least I'm now totally cured of my nicotine addiction; the very thought makes me want to heave. I am wearing a huge, caramel-coloured, velour 'relaxation suit'; that's the last time I send Moya out to buy clothes for me. It's two sizes too big, enabling me to stretch the elasticated bottoms above the operation incision and under my breasts. I hoped it would be a step up from nightwear, but I look disturbingly like a middle-aged woman in a toddler's romper suit. Dougie has just, I'm ashamed to say, brought me a mega-burger from a fast food drive-thru, which I had a sudden, intense desire for. Dougie is used to such requests, providing regular runs for patients and staff for food, fags and any other requirements, as he also does for the driving-banned alcoholics, depressed stay-at-home mothers and the housebound obese on his estate. I manage to eat the whole burger while Dougie smokes three fags.

'How long ago were you shot, Dougie?'

'Seven years ago now, before Britney was born.'

'Did it make you reassess life? Did it make you want to change anything?'

'Not really. I already had everything a man could wish for – a beautiful wife, great kids, a nice house. The job's a bit boring, but isn't everyone's?'

The messages coming through loud and clear on Dougie's taxi radio are getting louder and clearer – 'Dougie, you fat, lazy bastard, we're rushed off our bleedin' feet, where are you?' – so he says goodbye, telling me he'll get me anything I want, I only have to say the word. He doesn't let me pay, even for the food.

'You can owe me one, darling,' he winks. 'Give you something to look forward to when you're back in working order again.'

I know the naff innuendos are Dougie's way of being encouraging, and I'm grateful, even though I'm having difficulty keeping the burger down.

By Sunday, I'm desperate to get out of hospital and back to my own house and bed, back to normality. I don't want to constantly think about illness and disease, which is impossible to escape in here. The last couple of days I've been walking around regularly, eating more, have finally produced a poo (a significant achievement), and the surgical clips have been removed. Hallelujah. To be able to get up and out without thinking of my body would be a luxury, like a night's sleep with a newborn baby. Dr K has insisted I remain in hospital until the first chemo session, which is tomorrow. He also suggested staying in the night after, but I'm determined to go home and, if there's an emergency, the hospital is only a ten-minute drive away. I thought I was running a fever – suddenly overheating, my body boiling from the inside out – but I spoke to a nurse earlier and she said it's likely to be hot flushes. She mentioned HRT, but there's going to be so much else going into my body I'm not sure I should have that, too; another thing to discuss with Dr K. I have a stack of leaflets, advice sheets, website downloads and even books about chemotherapy and cancer, but spend the afternoon reading through six months' back copies of *Hello!* magazine instead.

The morning of the first chemo session and I've moved into passive patient mode. I've only been in a week and I'm institutionalised; I'm like the nodding dog toy in the rear window of a car. I'm taking so many pills and having so many tests, now in preparation for chemo, that I can't keep track of it all. There are a few people waiting in the chemo suite reception area, but I'm brought through to the small ward before everyone else. A nice nurse runs through all the things that are going to be administered through the drip: the chemotherapy drugs, anti-sickness drugs, more stuff to flush out the previous drugs. I lie back in the bulky reclining chair with a blanket over me. There are eight identical set-ups lining the light, modern ward. I want to sleep to blot everything out. I remember feeling the same in the middle of childbirth: maybe if I get up on this hospital bed I can lie down and sleep. As if.

The drugs descend into my body, through my veins: icy, spreading, itchy. I try to tell myself this is good for me, that it's killing the killers within. There's a middle-aged woman opposite with very thin hair. I can't look at her directly. I don't think I can face the support group, can cope with mirror images of myself, my body, what I'm going through. The woman seems angry, unhappy and ill, but also, perhaps oddly, strong. She's not sitting there passively, looking depressed. Rather, she appears very very pissed off, and reads through magazines as if it is an unsavoury, but unavoidable, chore.

The nurses are in and out, hour after hour, checking and re-checking. They say that treatment needs to be administered slowly, and that it's essential to monitor me closely, especially for the first cycle. Putting all the drugs through takes nearly seven hours. I feel like cancer is turning into my full-time job. I feel like I live in the hospital. Does River Street still exist, the busy city centre, fresh air and breezes? Yes, all that remains. It's the old, healthy(ish) Gina that's gone.

By 5.30 I'm sitting in Joy's car being driven home. So, that's it then, the first session of chemotherapy is over. It doesn't feel particularly momentous, and nowhere near as major as the hysterectomy. Maybe the significance needs time to sink in, and no doubt the side effects will bring it home, too. It's lovely to be driven up the dear old street and to see my house again, the house at which I first arrived, over thirty years ago, as a single teenage mother with a singularly unimpressed two-year-old named Skylark. I've probably lived in this street longer than anyone else now. There's Mr Winston walking his dog, and the kids from three doors up in their football kits heading to the recreation ground. It's warm and sunny, the cherry trees that sprout from the pavement at regular intervals are heavy with frothy pink blossom and the front gardens are in bloom. I hug Joy goodbye, say hello to Moya, then hobble about the house, still less sure on my feet than I thought I'd be.

Considering there's been building work going on, it's amazingly orderly. The garden is neatly trimmed and watered, courtesy of Leon, who's offered to do it till I'm fit enough again, and the house is tidy and clean, with fresh cut flowers in the dining and front rooms. God bless Moya, who hovers in the background, a robust, comforting presence. Marty has worked flat out to finish the bathroom refit and it looks fantastic: freestanding bath in the middle of the stripped floor, a separate shower cubicle in one corner, beautiful tiling, and he's made a brilliant job of renovating the open fireplace. I have a quick shower, doing my best to avoid the angry scar down my belly, then get into bed. I imagine life can be good again.

8

HOMME SWEET HOMME

Despite being tired and happy to be home, I find it difficult to sleep. I feel wired, as if I've just downed the contents of Moya's six-person espresso percolator. I want to open the bedroom sash wider to let in more air, but can't due to the surgery. No lifting, driving or doing anything that could cause strain for six weeks.

I examine the scar, something I've not allowed myself to do before, even while washing, knowing how upsetting it's likely to be. It's healing well, but looks dreadful: long, lumpen and red. I resemble a Christmas turkey that's been roughly tacked together to keep the stuffing in. Although the incision is less painful, I can't move about normally and am ever conscious of it. The biggest shock is not being able to find my belly button. I can find this weird, wonky, skin-flap thing, but not my neat little button. I consider ringing the hospital's out-of-hours, cancer care line to demand its return. I haven't cried yet about the cancer *per se*. Well, only when drunk after the date with Ralf, but I'll put that down to the alcohol and poor literature. And after surgery, but I'll blame that on the combination of sudden hormone loss and morphine. Now I have a good blub about my missing navel. That once connected me to my mother, now also missing. I contemplate Susan's button, and Chrissy's. I wonder how Milady's ninety-nine-year-old one is doing; I bet it's still present and correct. I consider all the buttons linking female belly to female belly backwards and forwards throughout time. It's a long night.

When I wake, Moya brings me a cup of tea. In fact, I summon her by ringing the landline from my mobile: what decadence! I'm tempted to play the proper, old-fashioned invalid and bash on the floor with a walking stick. Judging from the contents of the fridge, Moya intends to cook me hearty, nourishing meals with lots of red meat and veg. I appreciate her kindness, but don't reckon the escalating temperature and chemo side effects will allow me to eat them. I have hardly any appetite and can only face frozen yoghurts, lollies and ice cream. At least the weather might disguise my hot flushes. It's good to be home, although, when it came to it, I was apprehensive (okay, scared) about leaving the security of the hospital. But, after a couple of days, I feel safer: more sure of myself, less fearful of developing some grisly medical complication, more accustomed to balancing all the drugs to help my body cope with chemotherapy. I tell Moya she doesn't need to stay in the house all the time; that's what mobile phones were invented for.

For the rest of the week, I don't do much else other than rest, read, listen to the radio and potter about. I can't judge what's going on with me physically: what might be the result of major surgery, the effects of sudden menopause, the chemotherapy, having cancer in the first place, or the stress of all the previous. Marty and I agreed that he wouldn't work on the house for the first week after I came out of hospital, but I've still been making plans. I've been researching all manner of things on the Internet – tracking down reproduction tiling, locating salvage yards for old floorboards, even comparing brands of environmentally friendly paint, after significant arm twisting from Marty – but I can't seem to type the words 'ovarian cancer' into the search engine.

At the end of the week, Joy visits with Aiden's webcam, which we fix to my laptop so I can chat with Milady Manors, who's keen to see how I'm doing. I've got to hand it to Milady, who may be fairly immobile and hard of hearing but is totally with it. She tells me she had breast cancer in 1946, suspected ovarian in 1953 (I ask her what stage, but she merely waves her hand dismissively and comments, 'In those days they whipped everything out at the drop of a hat, dear, and never told the patient a damn thing'), and various skin cancers throughout the seventies. Her closing words are, 'Bloody nuisance, but you'll no doubt get over it.' Hope raises its head more visibly.

The weekend is busy with visitors. Susan thrusts a pot plant into my hands at one point and apologises again for not visiting me in hospital because of being away on her training course. She asks what she can do to help, but I say that I already have everything covered by Moya and other friends. She looks a little put out, but I tell her she has enough on her plate with both her and Graham working full-time and looking after Chrissy.

I don't get a chance to tell her about the cancer and chemo, just recount that the hysterectomy has gone well, but it takes a while to recover. Susan also gives me a hand-made 'get well soon' card from Chrissy, with a picture of a grandma and granddaughter dung beetle happily rolling a giant dung ball together (I'm the one with the blonde bob and lipstick and she's the one with sunglasses and roller-skates). Chrissy's also made me a gift bag and filled it with sweets, drawings and stickers, a plastic bracelet, a ball made from elastic bands, a bookmark decorated with flowers that we pressed last year, and her favourite rubber, which is in the shape of, and smells like, a watermelon. I'm so looking forward to spending time with Chrissy again, but don't want her to see me in bedridden, sick granny mode, so will wait a bit longer.

Due to the weather and hot flushes, I'm actually looking relatively rosy and healthy. But by Sunday afternoon I'm so worn out I can barely move. Leon knocks round in the evening, but Moya refuses to let him in. I text an apology, saying we'll meet up soon. Moya orders me to rest and, sure enough, by the middle of the following week I feel much better again. Despite my initial aversion, I read some of the health info I've got stacks of, and it's reassuring to know that what I'm going through – the lack of appetite and energy and the overwhelming exhaustion after minimal activity – is normal.

Sitting at the dressing table in my bedroom window trying, not very successfully, to do some work on the laptop, I wonder, as I observe various people arriving and leaving, what miseries and traumas are propelling them through Leon's front door and into therapy. Leon does a mix of NHS and private work, the former being mainly assessment and short-term, focused therapy, and the latter allowing him to enter into long-term psychotherapeutic relationships with patients, which I know he values most. A few teens and younger children with parents also troop in, as well as the typical older adult. Therapy is not self-indulgent nonsense for the micro-obsessed, as some may think, but a long hard slog through the past to try to make sense of, and hopefully improve, the present. Hmm … the present. That can inflict its own difficulties. Maybe therapy could help me cope with cancer and chemo, as well as move on from Olly, though that hardly seems important now. I decide to broach the subject of going back into analysis with Leon. I text him, saying I'd appreciate it if he could call in soon.

That evening, while Moya and I are in the front room watching telly, Leon calls round. Moya shows him in, then goes to make drinks.

'How's it going? How are you coping?' asks Leon, while hovering in the doorway.

'Um, okay. As well as can be expected. And do sit down.'

He takes a seat.

'Thanks for doing the garden and stuff,' I say. 'It's really good of you.'

'It's no problem,' says Leon, gazing at me earnestly. 'It's a pleasure. I know it's been awkward with me moving in next door, but, now we've got over the whole therapist–patient hang-up, things will be easier. I'm so glad we've discussed it all, and moved on.'

I try to return Leon's smile as Moya comes in with the drinks.

The three of us spend a pleasant-enough evening chatting about this and that, and with Leon offering to do what he can to help: lifts to the hospital, shopping, anything, just say the word. But all the time I'm restraining myself from screaming that I just want him to sit and listen, like he used to. I want him to contain all my pain and not crack under the pressure. I want him to reassure me that I'm not alone, that I can cope. I want the therapist–patient relationship back again, with knobs on. Please.

At the end of the evening, after closing the front door behind

Leon, I feel bereft, an intense pinprick of loneliness piercing my core.

Having cancer is like anything else, in that it soon becomes part of daily life. It moves from the realms of anguished fantasy into routine reality. I mean, I can't just sit around worrying about cancer, wondering if it's all gone, wondering if it'll come back. Well, I do sit thinking these things, but then I have to think about something else. And life here on River Street is certainly providing a fantastic distraction. It is alive with tanned, bare-chested workmen who can, surely, only accelerate my recovery. They have multiplied and flourished in the last couple of weeks, no doubt due to the rocketing temperature. Practically every other house has piles of bricks, timber and bags of sand cluttering its pathways and gardens.

Working on the laptop in my bedroom window becomes inspiring. Soon I'm able to categorise workmen from their builds, like athletes. You know, lean and wiry for long-distance runners, broad and beefy for rugby players, young and muscular-thighed for footballers; I could go on. Bricklayers come in a wide variety of shapes and sizes; men with diggers aren't much cop, no doubt due to sitting on their arses all day; carpenters have a certain sensitive demeanour, but not enough physical exertion to put them in the Class A category. This is largely reserved for roofers, although scaffolders turn out to be the *crème de la crème* of workmen. It must be something to do with the leather tool belts and gloves. This really must be a fetish of mine, in the same way that stockings and suspenders are for the hetero male. Of course, all illusions are shattered when you hear them swearing into their mobiles and exchanging affectionate greetings such as,

'Ow's it goin', you tosser?' It's like hearing Donna speak for the first time, but I'm sure you can tune out anything with enough practice.

Moya cautions, in a rare not-strictly-necessary conversation, that I'm turning into the female equivalent of a pervy old taxi driver, safe behind his glass shield, with nothing better to do than salivate over passing women. I reply that I would do something worthy – like plant an organic vegetable patch or run a marathon for charity – if I hadn't just had half my bloody insides removed.

Joy has warned me of the 'anger stage' of serious illness, which is inflicted on those nearest and dearest who are only trying to help. I'm looking forward to being extravagantly rude to people, then blaming it on the appropriate psychological phase. Frankly, as regards the workmen, I'm relieved I can experience anything resembling desire, although appreciation tinged with nostalgia would be a more accurate description.

'God, Gina, is it just me? Maybe I'm showing my age, but I'm sure men were never this good-looking when we were young.'

'Hmm … they were certainly hairier.'

Joy has taken a couple of days off work in order to 'support' me, but it's largely turning into an excuse to ogle the talent. Husband Tim is, of course, none the wiser, and simply thinks his wife is even more of a saint. Joy is wearing such a low-cut top to display her huge bosom to best effect that even I'm distracted by it. At one point, the large, disc-shaped pendant hanging round her neck is completely lost in her cleavage for several minutes.

Joy heaves open the sash window in my bedroom and gazes out brazenly. We take a short break from discussing the menopause, shopping and our children, to bask in the full glory of a bleach-blond scaffolder. He has an angelic face, an incredibly lithe, muscular torso, and just enough swagger to reveal that he suspects he's being watched. With several metal poles balanced on one shoulder, he pauses dramatically, then wipes his forehead with the back of a hand.

A knock on the front door interrupts our reverie; Joy and I exchange wide-eyed looks. We both belt downstairs (okay, the best I can manage is a slow hobble step by step), hopeful that ... well, I'm not sure what we're hoping for. Certainly not Marty, who it turns out to be.

'Forgotten the key again,' he shrugs.

Marty's not even started work for the day (and it's twenty to eleven, I might add), although this is no doubt due to him tracking down environmentally friendly, ecologically sustainable building materials, rather than just popping into Jewson on the industrial estate like a normal builder. His faded-to-almost-colourless Genesis 1983 tour T-shirt is patched with sweat under each arm and across his belly, and his usually limp ponytail is even more stringy than usual. Maybe his mate is better. No. I spot Gary – bottle-bottom specs, wire thin, missing front teeth – shuffling up the path behind Marty, just in time to see him flick his cigarette butt into a potted fuchsia. How come number twenty over the road gets an old fag's dying dream and I get Little and Large?

'Sorry we're late,' says Marty. 'I was having chest pains, my breathing going all funny again. Gary said I should get checked out at the hospital. All fine now though.'

Gary coughs violently, hacking up a good dose of phlegm, which he then snorts up his nose and billows into a well-used scrap of tissue. I suppose I should be glad he didn't flob it onto my doorstep. He smiles. I race upstairs and vomit down the loo. It's the first time I've actually been sick and it comes as a shock.

'Gary,' I say to him later – jokingly, of course – when I've recovered, and as Joy hands him his tea (three sugars), 'you have the same effect on women as chemotherapy.'

Despite feeling nauseous, I sit on the front steps with Joy under the spurious assertion that we're 'getting a bit of afternoon sun'. Due to chemo causing photosensitivity, I have to wear a wide-brimmed hat, huge sunglasses and a long-sleeved top.

Joy lights a cigarette. If anyone asks, she gave up fifteen years ago. Poncing other people's (Marty's, in this instance) doesn't count. I'm now so utterly repulsed by cigarettes, I can't believe I was addicted to them. Hopefully, one day, I'll feel the same about Olly.

'I wish I wasn't so old. I wish I'd appreciated being young, when I was young,' murmurs Joy wistfully, as she exhales. Hold on a minute, I'm the one with the life-threatening disease: aren't those supposed to be my lines? 'So much time worrying, so much time struggling, so much hard work just to make ends meet.'

Here we go again. Joy didn't marry until she was twenty-seven or have Aiden until she was nearly thirty.

'I wish I hadn't wasted my youth angsting over things, about what I was going to do. Should it be photography or fashion or just working to earn as much as possible.'

I remember Joy living a full and interesting life all through her twenties, and having a pretty nice time after, being adored and supported by Tim, although unhappiness with her weight has always been a black cloud. Joy inherited her mother's house when she was eighteen and has never had to worry about keeping a roof over her head. And when she decided it was time to find a husband and have a baby, she came up with the most successful chat-up scenario ever. She would approach a man she fancied, tell him she was a photography student, that he was blessed with a remarkable face and she'd love to take some pictures of him. The men were always flattered, and Joy could tell if there was any mutual interest in seconds, and she had created the perfect excuse for exchanging phone numbers to arrange a photo session or send a copy of the snapshot she'd taken. This is how she met Tim. If I hadn't been with Olly, I may have given it a go myself. By the time my marriage was over, claiming to be any sort of student had more chance of making me appear suspect rather than sassy. I have been trying to think of an equivalent chat-up scenario for the older woman for years.

Maybe it's Joy's self-indulgent chatter, the sun or, let's be realistic, the effects of chemotherapy, but I soon retreat into bed, feeling sick and tired. Having endured eight months of cold, grey skies and a paucity of light, now that summer's in full bloom I'm confined to bed in a darkened room. I hate this about illness: the world shrinking to the size of the hospital ward, your own house and bed, the small circumference of your weakened body; life folding in on itself. Although, as I'm a writer, and therefore prone to escapes into vivid flights of fancy and with a preference for the imaginary over the real, this should be less of a psychological strain for me than for most people.

When I wake, it's dusk. I've lost a chunk of the day, but don't feel too bad. I'm hungry. It's great to have an appetite. Listen up all you dieters and flab haters: it is w-o-n-d-e-r-f-u-l to want and be able to eat. I sit up into the early hours, snacking and writing.

I'm not sick again after the day that Gary came round and it's reassuring to feel my body slowly recovering. I also realise that I'd forgotten to take my anti-sickness pills, so they must have been doing an effective job. I find myself constantly counting the days and weeks: since surgery, since chemo, to the next chemo, to when I can drive again. The highlight of Friday (three-and-a-half weeks since surgery, two-and-a-half weeks since chemo, three days till the next chemo) is the arrival of a fire engine on the street in order to, quite marvellously, rescue a kitten from the very high branches of a tree. Within five minutes, every female from teen to geriatric has remembered essential tasks to do in her front garden: clean muddy boots, poke weeds with a hoe, wash windows, vacuum the car. It's the mix of bravery and competence that can explain the effect of firemen on women. And the big hoses. I can't understand why I've yet to write a fireman rescue story for *Eurotica*; what's wrong with me?

The weekend pours in like a waterfall over the street, putting paid to all interesting outdoor activity. Leon's been texting – asking if I need him to do anything, if I'm well enough to go out – but seeing as all I really want to do is corner him and offload what I feel, I decide it's best to avoid him. Perhaps mistakenly, I trawl the Internet for information on ovarian cancer. It's reassuring to read the personal stories of women who've gone through what I'm experiencing, have coped and survived, and are still living full lives. Are still living, full stop. But some accounts are frightening, especially when a woman's been given the all-clear and the cancer returns, months, most often years, but occasionally a decade, later. There are also pieces written in loving memory by bereaved family and friends, claims about miracle and alternative cures, cases of the medical professionals getting diagnosis and treatment wrong, and many technical papers on screening, treatment, outcomes and clinical trials.

As the physical discomfort eases, psychological effects kick in. I worry. I sit transfixed, unable to concentrate on work, not knowing what to do. How can I make life more meaningful? How can I live with this uncertainty? How long have I got? Should I make contact with other women who have gone or are going through the same thing, join an online support group? Should I go to the hospital support group? Why haven't I told Susan? Should I tell Chrissy? When I phoned Chrissy a couple of days ago, she asked when I was going to pick her up from school again, when I was going to be 'properly better'. I said I wasn't sure, but, with chemotherapy lasting months, I'm not going to be 'properly better' for ages. I hate not telling her the truth, but would being honest be worse, cause unnecessary worry? And what is the truth? Nobody knows if or when I'll be better. I have no answers, only questions, and intensifying anxiety and confusion. I close my laptop and go downstairs; to do what, I have no idea.

'Ahh!' My God, someone's just appeared outside the French doors in the dining room. Hold on, they're carrying arms of foliage and smiling. It's Lara, who lives a few doors down with her husband and children. I let her in.

'Georgina!'

Lara addresses everyone by their full name, pronouncing them with reverence. She squashes me into a soggy hug. Lara looks and smells as if she has just been rinsed in invigorating spring water, like a freshly dug and scrubbed root vegetable. She's in her early forties, with a pretty, make-up-free face, long red hair and what is probably a very trim figure, underneath all those ankle-length, hippie skirts and tie-dye smocks.

'Just gathering some of your *super* nettles,' she enthuses.

Lara's always so positive. It's a rare person who uses the word 'super' to describe a bunch of weeds. Not that my garden is full of them, but there's a patch at the bottom I leave wild. Bees and butterflies appreciate it, and witches. That's what Lara is. I'm not sure what it entails exactly, but she regularly invites me to stand around moonlit bonfires in her back garden and, as she often culls weeds from mine, I'm all for it.

Moya stomps through the dining room and into the kitchen. She's not very tolerant of this sort of stuff and, being a generally morose character, finds Lara's shiny-eyed enthusiasm wearing. Lara lays the nettles on the table. Then she clasps my hands and gazes at me intently.

'She's here.'

'Who?'

'Shirley.'

'My mum?'

'Yes.'

'Where?'

'Under the tree, by the nettles.'

I glance down the garden. Nothing.

'She's all around, in spirit,' says Lara.

'What's she wearing?'

'Wearing?'

'Yes.'

'Well, she's more ephemeral, Georgina, more of a sense of a figure than an actual figure, a light, a colour, a –'

'What colour?'

'Pale blue, mostly. Although, now you ask, she did appear to be wearing a hat, and matching –'

'That's her alright.'

I sink into a chair. Lara asks if I'd like some nettle tea. I nod.

Moya noisily fills the coffee percolator, while muttering 'utter nonsense' and 'poppycock'.

'I'm having treatment for ovarian cancer, Lara.'

'I know.'

I wonder if someone's told her or if she's divined it through a witchy sixth sense; one doesn't like to ask. I watch Lara as she busies herself with the tea making. Although I'm slightly wary of alternative belief systems, after my experiences at the Mune, if I see Lara as anything, it's a good fairy. We've chatted about her perspective on life before, which basically involves respecting the earth and its natural cycles, and living a wholesome, conscientious existence. Although she does have a pathological need to set things on fire, and has already produced two candles from somewhere and lit them. She's like a 'back of a lorry' spiv, but instead of knock-off watches and jewellery, she retrieves incense and crystals from her clothes. I fill her in on the details of disease and treatment.

'What's a witch's view of cancer then? A test? Bad karma? A curse?'

We sit opposite each other at the dining table, while the nettles stew.

'Sometimes we search for logical reasons, and there are none. Things live, things die. They flourish and they become diseased. That's how it is throughout the natural world, how it's been throughout all time.'

Moya makes use of her impressive smoker's hack during

Lara's words. She hesitates on her way back through the dining room, holding her mug of coffee. 'All very well, means nothing. Throughout time and across the natural world there are causes and effects. Hundreds of years of scientific research and medical developments give us knowledge. "That's how it is" never helped anyone.'

'That's not what I mean, Moya,' says Lara. 'Yes, our lives and health and understanding are improved by advances in medicine. But, why Georgina, why this cancer, may be unanswerable. In fact, they may be the wrong questions to ask in the first place.'

Moya moves away. I'm sure she doesn't agree, but cannot bear the personal nature of the conversation. But I don't mind. It's a relief to talk about it in a way I haven't been able to with anyone else. Due to her spiritual convictions, I'm pretty certain Lara sees death as another stage on our 'journey'. I don't share such beliefs, but her presence is heartening somehow: her openness, her honesty.

Lara turns her attention back to me.

'What I'm trying to say is don't waste time and effort searching for unknowable reasons or apportioning blame.'

'I've been looking on the Internet, at alternative cures. I seem to have coped with the first chemo okay, but I'm scared of being really sick, of not getting better. Part of me wants to believe, but part of me knows, really knows, that this alternative stuff is rubbish. You read the testimonials, the theory behind it, and then, of course, comes the order form for hundreds of pounds worth of life-saving herbs. Or details of how much treatment will cost in centres abroad. It makes me angry, and hopeful, in equal measure.'

'Yes, it does give hope. Maybe for those who have none left. Unlike you, Georgina. Maybe even false hope is better than no hope.'

'I'm not much of a cold, hard facts of reality fan, but "false hope" at a profit? No. Some of it makes sense. You know, we all have malignant cells and our immune systems destroy them. Cancer cells multiply when your immune system is below par, so doing stuff to boost it should help, should –'

'Should, should, should. It's not your fault you've got cancer,' says Lara.

'But I've smoked, you know that, I –'

'Everyone hit by a traumatic event asks "why me?", which is what you're asking, isn't it? You know my beliefs, Georgina, and maybe I should tell you where they come from. I'm not a fool, much as Moya may think me one, but I do need spiritual fulfilment in my life.'

Lara's right hand comes to rest over her heart as she talks.

'You know that our first son, Danny, died, when he was just four, before we moved here?'

I nod.

'I've never told you why, have I?'

I shake my head.

'He was born with a genetic disorder. He was diagnosed early and received the best possible medical care and treatment. But he didn't live. Some children with the condition survive well into adulthood; some don't make it past a year. It depends. How did we cope with that? Not very well. Why was he born with it? Both Simon and I are carriers of the gene – we found out after Danny was diagnosed – but each child born to us only had a one-in-four chance of inheriting the full-blown condition, not just being a carrier, or being totally free of it. Why was our Danny – the brightest, the sunniest, the most easy-going and sweet-natured child you could imagine – the one-in-four? There was no rhyme or reason to it. I mean, there was – genetically – but not emotionally, not spiritually. There was no moral dimension, either. It just was, and we all had to deal with it.'

Lara takes a deep breath, then continues.

'Our beliefs gave us a way of dealing with what couldn't be changed, a way of seeing Danny's existence as a blessing, however short his life was. Paganism may be an earth religion, but I don't see nature as some freshly sprung, romantic garden. It's birth, life and growth, but also disease, decay and death. It's as much a mid-winter wasteland as it is a springtime wonderland. Seeing human life and death as part of the natural world's cycles of regeneration makes me feel part of something bigger, gives me solace, a sense of oneness, and replaces a Christian God I never could believe in.'

Lara gets up to check on the tea.

My head is whirling with everything she's told me. I rub my hands over my face and lean back in the chair.

'I'm so glad your beliefs bring you comfort. I can't imagine anything worse than losing a child. And I think I hear what you're saying, that there's no point in blaming myself for having cancer. That the "why me" won't get me anywhere either. But it's not just the treatment getting to me, or the alternative cures. There's other stuff, too: your negativity has caused your cancer, open yourself to God and he'll cure you.'

'How do you feel?' asks Lara, setting out the cups and teapot in front of us.

'Mixed. All the clichés. I want to wake up and find it's all been a bad dream. "You don't know what you've got till it's gone." I want to be brave and protect the ones I love. I want to shout and scream and rage that life's so unfair. I want it to be over. I just want to forget about it. But it's there all the time. And there's so much information now. I've realised there are thousands, millions, going through it across the world. You read their stories, and at first it's a relief, because you realise you're not alone. And then you read so many it all becomes too much, too recognisable, too confusing, unbearable. I want to retreat indoors, into myself. Then I want to go out and do mad things. Sometimes I feel at peace with it all, sometimes I'm terrified. And so … so alone. Perhaps that's the saddest thing. Everyone's been fantastic, they really have, but I am alone.'

'What about Susan?'

'I still haven't told her. We're just not close.'

'Won't she find out from someone else?'

'I don't know. The people I told about the first cancerous tumour, I asked them to keep it to themselves, you know, until I knew for sure if there was more. Susan knows about the hysterectomy, of course, but I haven't got round to telling her about the cancer yet.'

'Maybe you're worried about breaking the news to Chrissy?'

I nod.

'Children are more resilient than you think,' Lara reassures. 'What about Olly, is he supportive? I can never tell if you two are together or not.'

I shake my head.

'No, we're not together, not really. And Olly was never the supportive type. He usually caused the traumas. And what can I expect from him anyway – he's my *ex*-husband. Friends have been brilliant, but there's no one special. No one who loves me and will, if it happens … be there till the end.' I sigh. 'I feel like Smike from *Nicholas Nickleby*, wanting to call another person home, afraid of dying alone.'

'But I'm here, I can –'

'I know, Lara. Thank you. And thank you for everything you've shared with me. But you have your children, your husband, your family, and I can't, I won't, impinge on that. You understand, don't you? This illness makes me feel like a child again. I want a big, strong parent to look after me, to make it all better. Sometimes, I even want a god to find comfort in. I'm not very good at being brave.'

Lara gives me a fresh-as-a-daisy smile, then pours out the steaming nettle tea and hands me a cup.

I take a sip, then splutter.

'That's disgusting! Are you trying to poison me, on top of everything else?'

I feel better after my conversation with Lara. I really have communed with her. Joy means well, but her worry and fear for me are palpable, not to mention the fact that she tends to bash me over the head with statistics and boss me about. And 'chatty' could never be used to describe Moya. But, although I don't see Lara that regularly, I'm totally at ease in her company, and conversations are a real two-way street. She told me to call in or phone anytime. I appreciate her offer, but really don't want to impose. She also told me she'd like to hold a séance for Mum, an offer I'm not so sure I appreciate.

But it is true, what came out in our conversation today, and unexpectedly: I do wish I had a partner who loved and would want to look after me. I'm sincerely grateful to all my friends, especially Moya, but there's no one I have a 'right' to call on, a husband who has sworn in sickness and in health, till death do us part. This is why I want to go back into therapy with Leon – so I'm not such a burden on my friends, so I can be honest and open about anything and everything I feel without worrying about the effect it's having on him, because it's his job to deal with it. Maybe I should ask him outright. The worst he can say is no and, even if he does, he's bound to be able to recommend someone else. At least I feel less confused after chatting with Lara: calm, balanced, accepting. It's not something I expect to last, of course, so I will enjoy it while I can.

9

BLINDSIDE

I take a taxi to the hospital first thing on Monday for the second cycle of chemo. I was tempted to drive, but it's only been four weeks since surgery and I'm supposed to wait for six. It's amazing how busy the hospital is at 8 a.m., as crowded with traffic and people as a town centre on a Saturday morning. I'm dropped off at the main entrance and, despite being given directions to the chemo suite, take a wrong turn into Physiotherapy. I'm about to backtrack, when I spot a large, leaf-filled tank in a corner of the waiting area and decide to take a closer look.

Rustling slowly over the foliage, according to the label on the tank, are two Giant African Tree Snails as big as my hand, with large conical shells worn at a rakish angle. Small, yellowy-orange blobs litter the floor of the tank, which must be their poo. I feel sick enough at the thought of chemo, without contemplating snail shit. But – Giant African Tree Snails – how cool is that? I remove the lid, then use a scrap of paper to quickly scoop a few blobs into one of Chrissy's pots. After replacing the lid, I fill out the date, time and 'where fond'.

We're all sitting quietly in the chemo suite reception area before going through to the ward for our treatments. I can't seem to make eye contact with anyone and force myself not to scan faces and bodies for signs of side effects: thinning hair or wigs, unhappy skin, puffiness or emaciation. I pick up a magazine and stare at photographs. Nurses call names and usher us through to the ward, where bloods are taken. A few patients jolly each other along with a 'here we go again' or 'sooner it starts, sooner it's over'. Maybe I should have brought someone with me; Moya offered, but I can't expect her to sit about doing nothing for hours on end.

Routine tests show that my red and white blood cells and platelets are high enough for the chemo to go ahead, then everything's set up and the session begins. It's difficult to relax in the reclining chair, what with hours of being drip-fed poison stretching ahead. I close my eyes, but can think of nothing but ripping everything from me and running away. I wish I could knit – it would be something to occupy my brain and body, but not too taxing. I don't remember the treatment being so slow and tedious last time, but I suppose I felt a lot worse. I try to sleep.

After what feels like thirty minutes, I open my eyes to see that less than ten have passed. I haven't brought anything to read. What did I imagine I'd be doing for seven hours? Don't tell me I'm going to be reduced to doing word searches. Or Sudoku. But now I'm hooked up, I can't even move.

'Everything alright?' asks a well-spoken man of about seventy. 'Can I do anything? You look a bit flustered.'

'No, no, I just … didn't bring anything to read.'

'I can get you something from the shop. I'm just going there myself as I seem to be last in line today.'

Rather than um-ing and ah-ing or are-you-sure-ing, I say thanks very much.

The man, who introduces himself as Ron, returns with a fiver's worth of puzzle books. An eight-year-old could do them, but they keep my mind occupied and help to pass the time. Survival is the priority; not thinking is a close second.

I overhear the nurse talking with Ron as he's hooked up next to me. He's polite, but obviously fed up at being the last to get started. It's his son's fortieth birthday and he plans to join his family to celebrate, so wants to be 'done and dusted' as quickly as possible. He asks the nurse if his drugs can be put through faster. She says she'll give it a go.

After a while, I raise my eyes from the puzzle books and look around the room properly. Apart from Ron, who is reading a newspaper, there are two other men; one is asleep with his mouth open and the other is staring into space. There are another three women, apart from me, who are all doing something: reading, chatting quietly to a friend, pawing over a jigsaw. Never again will I view puzzle enthusiasts with disdain. One of the eight reclining chairs is empty. I can't shake off the feeling that the person who should be reclining in it is dead.

The afternoon goes quicker with the end of treatment in sight. After a final drip to flush through, various checks and note writing, I then wait for drugs from the pharmacy to take home. I feel a bit spaced out, but not horribly unwell. I'm so preoccupied with myself that it takes a while to register that Ron is waving a hand in the direction of the nurse, trying to attract her attention. I call her over. He says it's too much, he can't take it, and asks her to slow the drip down. Ron's eyes have sunk into his colourless face, and he seems to have diminished in size. The nurse is sympathetic, commenting that it's a tough treatment, and easier to tolerate if administered slowly.

'But, but, I wanted … my son's birthday …'

The nurse can only shrug in reply.

I pat Ron's hand when I leave, say thanks and good luck.

'Take care, my dear,' he replies.

I sit in the reception area waiting for Marty, who's agreed to pick me up today. Moya did offer, but I didn't fancy the sidecar.

Leon comes through the automatic doors.

'Oh, hello,' I say, surprised. 'How are you?'

'Fine, fine.'

He stops and smiles. I smile back. It goes on too long.

'Sorry, Gina, I'm here to collect you, I should have said straight away. Marty got a call about a delivery and asked if I could check it over and sign for it. But I thought it would be better if he dealt with that and I came up here.'

'Thanks, Leon, that's good of you.'

Leon tries to chat in the car – about the weather, the building work, Chrissy – but I can't concentrate. It's as if he's so determined to be normal, neighbourly and 'non-therapy', he's pretending that I'm not practically nodding off next to him. It's clearly not the ideal time to ask about going back into analysis.

When I get home I eat ice cream, then curl up in bed. Day over.

I wake the next morning feeling more positive, and run through a list of things to do. But when I get up, everything spins. It's not too bad when lying down, but as soon as I attempt to do anything, I feel awful, so feeble, my body leaden and achy. I try to get up again in the afternoon, but dizziness forces me back into a horizontal position. I'm hungry, but nauseous, and my stomach feels strange and sore. Moya tells me off.

'I'm not doing too much, Moya, I'm just trying to get out of bed!'

'Rest and recuperation, that's what you need. Push it and you'll regret it, set yourself back.'

'But I've got so much to do, so much I want to do. And there was this man, yesterday, having chemo next to me. He was really friendly and helpful, came in all cheerful and well turned out and wanting to go to his son's birthday. And by the time I left, he was a wreck, he looked at death's door, and yet he told me – he still told *me* – to take care.'

'Chemotherapy can kill a person before it cures them.'

I shoot Moya a 'Well that's hardly an encouraging comment, is it?' look.

'You must keep well enough to tolerate it. Those are the facts. You've got to get through as best you can. Day at a time.'

She's right. I feel so frustrated and angry and sick, but so loved and looked after and grateful to Moya.

Moya reads to me from *The Wind in the Willows*, and I am there. I hear the lapping of the river on the bank, I feel the sun, breathe in springtime; I am in another world, sailing along in Ratty's boat.

I doze off and when I come to it's eight in the evening. Despite a night's worth of sleep, I still feel exhausted. The freezer is now stocked with every imaginable dessert, as that's all I want. After a bowl of raspberries and ice cream, I do something I haven't done since my Art College days in my early twenties and draw my dreams. In a vivid one I had earlier, I was in my bedroom, but it was a hundred floors up, and the windows were double doors and cast open, the floor sloping down towards them. The furniture kept sliding away, threatening to slip out and spin to dizzying destruction below. I had dreadful trouble trying to keep a fancy French cabinet from flying out. There was also a huge, dark wardrobe, which remained fixed against one wall. As I draw, I realise the French furniture is Joy, and that I'm worried about how she's coping with my illness. She phones, texts or emails most days, and a sense of intense anxiety underlies her casual cheeriness. I laugh out loud when I realise the enormous, immovable wardrobe is Moya!

The week following chemo is one of rest and recovery, as Moya predicted. After a couple of days of fairly constant nausea, occasional vomiting and no appetite, she forces me back to Oncology and the pharmacy, where I'm given different anti-sickness drugs to try, as well as blood checks and more tablets to help counter the negative effects of chemo on my 'good cells'.

By the beginning of the second week after chemo, and despite the appearance of decidedly more hair in my brush than usual – which I'm doing my utmost to pretend isn't happening by using pointless thickening shampoos and pinning it up – I feel more normal again. If you can call this normal: I've agreed a date for a séance with Lara. It's to be held at her house, not mine, in the middle of next month, because the moon will be in whatever state it needs to be and she's certain Mum will 'come through'. Lara says she needs others there, too, for it to work. Moya has agreed to join in; she's humouring me because I'm ill. And I've left a message on Olly's answerphone telling him he's got a date with his mother-in-law in the middle of July. That should terrify him nicely. At the time – about twenty minutes ago – and after talking about life, death and cancer with Lara, arranging a séance seemed a perfectly everyday, reasonable thing to do. Now I'm wondering if I've lost the plot, having dismissed all alternative cures as dangerous nonsense but agreed to a good dose of table tapping in the hope (perhaps not the right word) of communicating with my long-dead mother. I need to get this in perspective.

I run my finger over the name engraved in the shiny brass plaque: Dr Leon Comiskey. I bite my lip and knock.

'Leon.'

'Gina.'

'Do you have a minute?'

'Er, just a few, until my next patient's due.'

'May I?'

'Come in, come in.'

I realise I haven't had a proper look round Leon's house yet, which is surprising, given how nosey I am. I'm very familiar with it, having lived next door for over thirty years, but he's had quite a lot of work done. This was carried out by competent-looking men in smart overalls, who arrived at 8 a.m. on the dot in clean vans with company logos on the side, i.e. the opposite of Marty, who appeared at midday yesterday and had to reattach the rusty exhaust to his even rustier van with a length of wire before he could leave again at nine in the evening. Leon's downstairs is the mirror image of mine, but has been restored to its grand Victorian pretensions, the walls being clad in dark wood panelling, sombre oil paintings and heavily patterned paper. It's just as a psychotherapist's should be. I can quite imagine having therapy here.

I edge into the front room, obviously a study. It's lined with old photographs of dour men in beards and frock coats; even

I recognise Sigmund in half a second. I've never seen so many books crammed into one room, but I sense they're all in perfect order; Leon is definitely the type to catalogue meticulously.

'Can I have a look upstairs?'

'You can, Gina, of course. But another time. I'm expecting –'

Right on cue there's a knock on the door.

'Oh, sorry. Better get out quick. I know us patients aren't supposed to meet each other coming in and out. That's one thing you therapists hate, isn't it? Not that I am a patient, of course, but, but …'

Leon's frowning at me, obviously wondering what I'm blathering on about.

'I know we're neighbours now, and friends, and we've made an effort to move on, and blah, blah, blah, but … could I go back into therapy with you?' I blurt.

Leon shakes his head.

'No, that's out of the question. I'm fully booked. I –'

'Never mind, forget I asked.'

I return home to find Moya rinsing out the coffeepot in the kitchen sink.

'You alright, old girl?' she asks. 'You look a bit peaky.'

'I'm fine. I just need to be alone for a bit.'

'I understand. A friend's invited me fishing. I'll go, if you'll be okay on your own?'

'Of course.'

Once Moya has left, I sit at the dining table feeling sorry for myself. It's stupid, but all those things I've given up without any effort due to chemotherapy making them repellent – smoking, drinking, drug taking – I now miss. There's nothing to ease what I feel. I can understand why Leon said no, I can even recognise that he was a hundred per cent right to, but I can't understand why I'm so upset. These easy tears mean it must be hormonal, my emotions all over the place due to the hysterectomy. I feel as if I've been cut from my anchorage, that I'm drifting away, bobbing about in half a barrel with a broken paddle flung high on the seas of ... no: disease, the shadow of death and now this rejection are still no excuse for metaphors worthy of Ralf the building surveyor's awful seafaring novel. I dry my eyes and blow my nose. I'll just have to cope on my own or find another therapist. Or maybe I'll try the hospital's cancer support group.

I finally locate the flyer that 'Margaret MacDonald – Senior Administrator' gave me. At least the group's free (only a voluntary contribution for refreshments being specified in a friendly, 'handwritten' font at the bottom). It's not quite six weeks since the surgery, but I feel up to driving and should be just in time, if I put my foot down, for the start of the meeting.

The counselling 'suite' turns out to be a portacabin in an out-of-the-way car park on the hospital grounds. It's not that bad, but life continues to be disappointing in its mediocrity. It's all women, bar one elderly man with a long white beard and walking stick who appears very drowsy. They are mainly middle-aged ladies, wearing wedding rings, with growing or grown-up children, no doubt. Margaret smiles at me and says, 'Glad you could come.' They are warm and friendly, but I feel cold and depressed. I don't want to be a middle-aged lady. With cancer.

The counsellor arrives. He has a young, round, bland face, sore with shaving rash-cum-acne, terribly old-fashioned clothing – corduroy jacket with elbow patches, beige slacks and slip-on shoes – and thick, gold-rimmed specs.

Margaret begins to rib him. 'Still no luck getting a date with one of those young nurses, Harry?'

He blushes, and others chip in with light-hearted comments in a similar vein. Everyone smiles and relaxes as Harry lets them tease him. But, after five minutes, just when I'm feeling really at ease, he cuts the crap and turns to me.

'Would you like to introduce yourself and say something about what's brought you here today?' he asks.

Before I can reply, someone else arrives: a woman in her mid-twenties, with a long, heavy drape of dark hair, attractive and slim, but with a prominent, pointy, pregnant belly. She takes the empty seat next to me as the older women cluck around her.

'Perhaps,' says Harry, 'rather than putting our new member on the spot, we should introduce ourselves to her.'

I hear various cancers being attached to various names as we move around the informal circle. Margaret, bowel cancer, for the second time, recently finished treatment. Wendy (plump, about forty, Brummie accent), breast cancer, strong genetic link, first occurrence, had surgery, going through chemo. One woman, the youngest bar the pregnant one, stares at the floor, doesn't say anything and is moved over quickly. Heather (well-spoken and turned out, mid-fifties), breast cancer survivor. The elderly man says, 'John, prostate,' although I thought he was asleep. Shockingly, the young pregnant woman says, 'My name's Stacey, and I have cervical cancer. It's not treatable.'

It's all too much and my eyes fill and spill, even though I'm acutely aware that blubbing at someone's misfortune, however understandable, is hardly helpful when they're in the room with you. I apologise, but Stacey smiles and says not to worry. Someone pats my hand, a box of tissues appears in my lap, Margaret says,

'I wish we could smoke in here' and a mug of tea is magicked up. Somewhere in the middle of all this, I manage to introduce myself.

'I'm sorry,' I say again, when I've recovered. 'And I know how awful some big crying fit is when you tell someone you've got cancer. But you're so young, Stacey, and pregnant … and, I know if you say it's untreatable, it must be untreatable, but …'

Stacey's holding my hand to comfort *me*!

'Don't feel sorry for me,' she says. 'I've accepted it. Everyone here has helped me to come to terms with the decisions I've made. I chose to keep the pregnancy. My husband's just about coping. He wanted me to have a termination, but I couldn't. He's still hoping for a miracle. Mum will help him with the baby.'

'How old are you?'

'Twenty-six.'

I don't do much else but sip sweet drinks and fiddle about with damp tissues for the rest of the session. Much of it is given over to Stacey, the fact the baby is likely to be delivered early – in the next couple of weeks – due to the growth of the cancerous tumour, and how her mum and husband are coping. Stacey sometimes talks as if she's already gone. Can she really have come to terms with her imminent demise so easily? It seems ludicrous that she, and everyone else, believes it's inevitable – this beautiful young woman, literally bursting with new life. I don't say anything because she must have experienced this reaction dozens of times before. If people dissolve into tears when I tell them about me – well, okay, not that many have, but Moya had to leave the room to regain her composure and Joy became hysterical – then what on earth must their reaction be to her? Not only shock and upset, but disbelief. She's the youngest, fittest-looking one here. Margaret is very skinny and sinewy, her skin an unnatural yellowy-brown, Wendy is pale and puffy, which, I've heard, can be a side effect of steroids. But maybe I'm seeing signs of illness where there are none. Perhaps Margaret is a thin person and Wendy a fat one, and neither has been blessed with a lovely complexion. And none of us, apart from Stacey, is young, although the silent woman only looks in her early thirties.

The session isn't exactly enjoyable, but I do feel better by the end of it. I can't explain why because I've done nothing but snivel for an hour and a half. Maybe it's because I don't feel so isolated; the lonesome 'I' is now a tangible 'we'. A couple of the women, Margaret and Wendy, are going to the pub and ask if I want to come, but I say I'm too tired, and I am. I don't – but I know I could – tell them I'm feeling pretty rough due to chemo, and they would understand. Stacey makes a point of saying she hopes to see me at the next session. I nod and smile, but can't reply. Phrases such as 'take care' or 'see you soon' seem all wrong.

When I get home, I lie on the sofa and sleep for a couple of hours. I rise through a deep, dark sea of dreams into the consciousness that something terrible has happened. I run through possibilities in my head. Is it Susan? No. Chrissy? No. Olly? No. It's me. I'm the person the terrible thing has happened to. And so is Stacey, and Margaret, and all the others at the support group. For all my reticence and reservations, these people, and especially Stacey, have stripped me down, scrubbed me raw. My heart's been thrown into a pot of boiling reality and left to stew. Now it's back in my ribcage: wet, scalded, pinkly painful. Why did I initially feel repelled by these good, ordinary women, with cancer, and in need of support? Because I'm one of them, and I wish I wasn't. To be with them is to be forced to face my own misfortune and fragility and, hopefully, courage.

Friends and family spin through my mind. Usually, I'd feel less than sympathetic when thinking about Joy and her bossy, controlling tendencies, Leon and his ultra-logical micro-examination of everything, Olly and, well, just being Olly is enough. Now I see them differently. Joy is a girl who lost her beloved mother and never recovered; the bossiness and control are her protection, her armour. Leon's endless analysis is him trying to make sense of his own confusing and unhappy upbringing; although he's clearly a tosser for not agreeing to be my therapist again. And Olly – is it his fault he didn't turn out to be everything I wanted him to be? Of course not. It was actually all me, me, me, seeing what I wanted to and ignoring reality. Am I any different from, any better than, Olly? Susan still feels all the things about me as a mother that I used to feel about him as a husband: disappointed, frustrated, angry. Why is life like this? And who can I blame? What is one left with? Just a futile raging. But now, perhaps, the beginnings of acceptance. And a recognition that I must tell Susan about the cancer. I just need to find the right time.

10

HEAVEN IN A WILD FLOWER

Moya rings the next morning, just to make sure I'm okay, and to let me know that she won't be back till later. I can't believe I have turned into someone who needs to be checked on, like a frail old lady. I notice the light on the answering machine flashing, so press the button. It's Leon, who left the message yesterday, saying he thinks we should talk about 'what happened earlier' and asking me to get back to him.

Luckily, Chrissy phones before I have a chance to seriously consider whether or not I should call him. She asks if it's okay to bring a friend back with her for tea. I'm picking her up from school today, the first time since the surgery, nearly six weeks ago. Familiar anxieties raise their heads: should I tell Chrissy about the cancer? I wonder how long I'll be able to get away with it, especially if my hair starts shedding more obviously. I'll try to find a suitable moment to let Susan know today, when she comes to collect Chrissy.

Waiting outside the classroom, ignoring Mrs Hatcher, I notice that Chrissy is one of the first to come out, for a change, and is talking intently with another child. I'm a little surprised to see that the friend is a boy, with fair, curly hair and plump, rosy cheeks. I say hello and ask his name. He regards me with small, pale blue eyes and gabbles in a high-pitched, put-on voice, something I can't make out, but which includes the word 'princess' a lot. I'm sure his chubby body and rasping, girlish voice will mark him out among other boys his age, making him a target for bullies. I sense that this is a child not destined for a conventional, or easy, life.

As we walk home, he tells me they are playing Princess on the Silver Horse. I eye Chrissy. She's never been one for girly games. I soon gather that he's the Princess and she's the Wicked Queen. That's more like it. Although Chrissy's shouting and Princess' screeching and squealing hurt my head, I love their sheer, unselfconscious joy at make-believe, their complete absorption in their game. With Princess' constant petting and fussing of the imaginary Silver Horse, plus his accompanying whinnying, neighing and galloping noises, I begin to think it's real. Chrissy relishes the role of diabolical tyrant, creating new and terrible tortures for Princess: 'You must eat marshmallows made of slugs and clean the whole castle with one cotton bud.' It is Chrissy's job to play all other roles apart from Princess and the Silver Horse. In the fifteen-minute walk she transforms seamlessly into a Handsome Prince, a Cunning Stoat, a Wretched Peasant, a Helpful Fairy and the Old Man at the Castle Who Is Always Grumpy; Milady Manors would be proud.

Once home, they continue their game in the garden while I go upstairs. I lie down in the back bedroom with the window open and listen to: Chrissy and her friend at play, birdsong, sawing and hammering from along the road, cries from the odd seagull drifted in from the coast, barking, a car door slamming, a bicycle bell, kids playing on the nearby recreation ground, a ball being thwacked, a train moving out of the station. I catch the scent of summer on the balmy air: fresh mown grass and warmed blossoms. It's one of those timeless instances when the world's beauty is brilliantly illuminated, intense and suspended. But I can't make it mean any more than it does. I can't make it last any longer than it will. I can squeeze no more significance from it, other than existence is perfect at this moment and I love my granddaughter and hope she will live a good and fulfilling life.

The rapidly escalating racket of a drum kit being played, badly, soon ends all transcendental contemplation. I look out of the window. I can't see clearly into Leon's back garden, but the bushes are rustling and that's definitely where the noise is coming from. Chrissy and Princess have incorporated it into their game and are performing a jerky dance to the beat. I go downstairs, determined to ignore it. After all, I am having all this hideously noisy building work done.

'What would you like for tea, Princess on the Silver Horse?' I ask.

'Wotsits.'

I prepare a sensible dinner of pasta and take it out to them in the garden, despite Princess' claim that he only ever eats crisp sandwiches or cheesy footballs with tomato sauce for tea. The drumming persists. Even the children begin to hold their ears. Now the person is 'ugging', in the manner of a tennis player straining to return a difficult ball. It must be that Biodynamic Body Therapy woman he rents a room to trying out some kind of anger expression therapy. What's wrong with a stiff upper lip? Or Prozac? Or both? As usual, rather than tackling my annoyance in its early stages in a reasoned, controlled way, I wait until I'm ready to erupt.

'For Christ's bloody sake!' I yell. 'Some people are trying to enjoy a peaceful dinner in their garden.'

Chrissy admonishes me with a very stern frown; Princess doesn't appear to have noticed my outburst. Then Leon's pink face appears over the top of the fence.

'Sorry, Gina, didn't realise you were outside.'

'And I didn't realise it was one of your patients. I thought it was –'

'No, no, it was me. Just getting out a bit of frustration.'

'Oh. Right.'

'You sounded like a mad slave driver beating out drums on a ship,' declares Chrissy, who instantly dives back into her make-believe.

I nod goodbye to Leon and his head disappears behind the fence again. Nutter.

After dinner, the children continue to play. Princess on the Silver Horse, now draped in an old net curtain, eyes screwed tightly shut, is being led onto Happiness Island by Bestfriend Bodyguard, who picks a careful path through the plant pots, cups and plates. The whole thing is like a post-feminist pantomime, with a female bodyguard heroine and boy-in-drag princess.

'We are here now, Princess on the Silver Horse,' says Bestfriend Bodyguard, manfully. 'You may open your eyes.'

Princess gasps as he looks about. He stretches out his arms in wonderment and gasps again, then he twirls around joyfully.

'It is *so* beautiful. I never knew such a wonderland could exist.'

'I told you it was true,' says Bestfriend Bodyguard, with

Roger Moore raised brow. 'Everything you see is yours. We shall live here together with the Silver Horse. Forever. Although I will have to go saving other people sometimes.'

After a combined bout of staring and gasping, gasping and staring, they frisk and frolic with increasing hysteria, batting the overblown peonies and throwing the petals into the air. They hold hands and spin round, laughing and shrieking, until they collide and collapse on the grass. I have become so engrossed in their play, I have forgotten cancer.

I'm summoned from the back garden by a knock on the front door. I wonder who will be picking up Princess on the Silver Horse. I anticipate an earnest, misinformedly liberal, middle-class, middle-aged single mother. But it's Keanu's scowling face that greets me.

'What do you want?' I say, rather rudely, immediately fearful that he has come to do Leon over and has mistaken my house for his.

'Picking up Brad.'

'Who?'

Keanu makes a 'doh' face at me, popping his eyes and thrusting his tongue under his lower lip. Those pale blue eyes, just like Donna's, just like … Princess on the Silver Horse's. Well, who'd have thought it?

'Farewell Bestfriend Bodyguard,' Brad waves daintily to Chrissy. 'And to you, too, Old Woman People Say Is Horrid but Who Turns Out to Be Nice.'

Okay, I admit it, I gave myself a bit part in their game.

Keanu spits before telling Brad to 'Bloody shut up that silly crap or I'll kick your arse all the way home' in a remarkably affectionate tone.

'Good afternoon, Mother,' says Susan, when she comes to collect Chrissy.

'Hi Susan,' I say. 'She's playing upstairs at the moment. Um, shall we go out in the garden for a bit?'

Susan frowns.

'You should see the flowers – they're looking lovely,' I add.

'Oh, okay,' replies Susan, and she follows me outside.

In reality, the garden is not looking particularly lovely, due to all the building work, but I didn't know what else to say to prevent Susan from immediately rushing off.

'The roses have been great this year,' I comment, 'they've flowered non-stop.'

'They are rather nice,' says Susan.

God, how do I introduce the subject of me having cancer? And what if Chrissy joins us in the middle of it? Maybe now isn't such a great time, not with Chrissy here. I don't know what I was thinking.

'How's the recuperation going?' asks Susan.

'Well, it's, um … going fine,' I reply, slightly thrown. Maybe I *should* tell her now.

'That's good,' says Susan.

There's an awkward silence as Susan glances about the garden and I stand paralysed, not knowing how to say it.

'Has Chrissy been okay?' Susan asks.

'Yes. And she really enjoyed playing with her friend.'

'I'm not sure I approve of that Brad boy. He's such an odd child. I think he might prove to be a bad influence on Chrissy.'

'Oh, I think he's a sweetie,' I say, as I realise the moment for telling Susan has already passed. 'Anyway, it's Chrissy who bosses him about, if anything.'

'I'm not sure about that,' says Susan, bristling slightly. 'I'm just not keen on the boy, he –'

'Look, Mummy,' calls Chrissy, as she bounds out of the kitchen door and up the garden. 'Grandma got me this for my collection.'

She holds out the plastic pot containing the snail droppings, which I presented her with earlier. Oh dear, this is not good timing.

Susan's face blackens.

'Go and put it upstairs with the others, Christine.'

'Aren't you even going to look at it?'

'No.'

'But it's from Giant African Tree –'

'Put it upstairs!'

'But, but, Grandma said the snails were as big as my hand and –'

'*Now*, Christine! Don't make me tell you again.'

Chrissy's little face screws up, pink with outrage, as she strides back down the garden, muttering under her breath.

As Chrissy goes indoors, Moya comes out, just returned from her fishing trip. She looks at me, then Susan, and retreats back into the house.

Susan exhales loudly through her nose, reminding me of a bull about to charge.

'I'm trying to remain calm, I really am,' she says, 'especially with you just having had a hysterectomy. But I cannot *believe* you have given Christine that, after everything we're going through. You are *encouraging* her unhealthy obsession.'

'I didn't do it to spite you, but because Chrissy asked me to,' I say mildly.

'Oh really. Christine asked me if she can have a baby elephant as a pet and live in a tepee, but she's not going to, is she?'

'I know it's an odd interest, but I reckon it's harmless, that she'll grow out of it, as kids do. You don't need to worry so –'

'And you're an expert in child psychology now, are you?'

Good grief, here we go again.

'Why can't you be a normal grandmother?' Susan says.

I look her in the eye.

'I thought picking up my granddaughter and her friend from school, making them tea and playing with them were quite normal things to do.'

'Why do you have to pretend that Chrissy's obsession is acceptable? You're too old to act so weird and wacky. It's … unseemly.'

Unseemly; such a Susan word. Appearing unseemly has never been at the top of my worry list. Susan stands before me, arms folded across her chest, scowl fixed.

'I don't know what you're waiting for, Susan, I don't know what you want me to say.'

'I just want Christine to fit in, to be the same as her peers, to get on. And there's no way that's going to happen if she appears … strange.'

'But she does fit in. She's got good friends; she's doing well. I don't know what you're so worried about.'

'No, you wouldn't, would you?'

'What's that supposed to mean?'

'I want Christine to be a normal girl and have a normal childhood. Just like I wanted *my* childhood to be normal, Mother. Like everyone else's.'

'But it was normal. Ish.'

'No it wasn't.'

I know I'll regret this, but, 'Why?'

'What about the name thing, for a start.'

'I'm sorry for calling you Skylark. I don't know how many times I can apologise for it.'

'I don't mean that, I mean trying to get me to call you "Gina" instead of "Mother".'

'I thought it would make us closer, more equal. None of those uneven power relations between parents and children. Olly used to have to call his dad "Sir".'

'Olly.'

Pause.

'Yes,' I say, eventually, unsure if that was supposed to be a question.

'Why?'

'Because I loved him. Because he loved *you*. He still loves you, if only you'd let him.'

'He told me that aliens built Stonehenge and bats see using X-ray vision. My homework was always wrong. He taught me how to roll a joint when I was fourteen. And he wasn't even my real father.'

'I know, but it works both ways. You aren't his biological daughter, but he still loves you. He loves Chrissy, too.'

'I always resented that you didn't give me a dad, my real dad.'

'Didn't give you a dad? I was fifteen when I fell pregnant. He didn't want to know. Everyone told me to have an abortion, to –'

'Thanks.'

'I mean, I thought I was doing the right thing, bringing you up myself.'

'What about the rows?'

'That was … living with Olly.'

'The drugs?'

'That was just occasional. Weekends, evenings, when you were in bed. Everyone did it. Half the world has a spliff or a drink once their kids are asleep.'

'I certainly don't. And it wasn't just hash.'

I sigh. I look at the metal fire escape twisting its way up to the attic flat, and up which I used to heave Susan, her pushchair and the shopping. Every day for years I'd have to explain that, no, we couldn't play in the back garden because it didn't belong to our flat, and, no, we weren't allowed to keep pets either. And, no, she didn't have a dad like most of the kids at school because, well, it didn't work out, but that didn't mean that her non-existent father didn't love her. And I loved her enough for two. Our early life wasn't easy. It was a struggle; for me, for her.

'Just because you took amphetamines and then did the housework doesn't make it alright, Mother,' Susan continues.

'I was tired, I was on my own a lot, it kept me going. Look at minor tranquilisers, they're prescription drugs and some of the most addictive.'

'For God's sake, listen to yourself, to those pathetic excuses. "It's okay to take illegal drugs because legal ones are just as bad." That's like saying it's okay to take heroin because people get morphine on prescription. Yes, when they're dying of cancer. Those are the words of an addict – the self-delusion, the absurd justifications, the *denial*. Will you ever admit that *you* had the problem, not anyone else?'

Maybe this is the moment I've been waiting for to tell her about the cancer? But I don't, of course not.

'You're not even listening, are you?' says Susan. 'All this time, all these years, and you still can't admit it. You still can't say, "I'm sorry, Susan, I could have done better. I shouldn't have –"'

'Could have done better?' I say, my voice growing louder. 'Who do you think you are – my primary school teacher?'

'What about the commune?'

'That was totally drug free!'

'I know, but why the hell did we live there?'

'It was, it's true, in retrospect, rather misguided. But we were young, we were trying to make a difference, we –'

'The swearing?'

'Oh, for Christ's sake, Susan. You hated me when I drank and smoked. You hated me when I meditated and lived off sodding lentils. You weren't exactly an easy child. Nothing was ever good enough, nothing was ever right. Nothing *I* did was ever right. You always wanted more, better, different. All you did was criticise and complain. You never wanted a cuddle, you always pushed me away. You – you were difficult. Maybe we just clashed, but –'

'*I* was difficult. That's rich. You were my mother, you should have tried harder. I was the child. Children should come first, they have a right to –'

'Just listen to you now. You've always been the same. Moan, moan, moan, criticise, criticise, criticise.'

'I can't have been like that as a child. I only criticised because you weren't the mother I wanted, the mother I needed.'

I may not be prepared to stoop so low as to tell Susan about the cancer in the middle of a row, but I'm not averse to a little honesty. She certainly dishes it out. Whenever I tried to express what I really thought or felt, she'd kick off, and so, over the years, I learned to pussyfoot around her. And where has it got me?

Here, with her yelling in my face about what a crap mother I am, after thirty years of her yelling in my face about what a crap mother I am.

'Alright, Susan, that may be true. From your point of view. But I have one thing to say to you.'

'What? "Sorry" I hope.'

'Chrissy – your relationship with your own daughter.'

Susan's face slams shut. She marches into the house, shouts, 'Christine, we're going now,' and storms out of the front door.

Chrissy comes down the stairs and gives me a goodbye hug.

'She must be pre-mental. That's what Daddy says.'

'Pre-menstrual. Yeah, maybe. See you next week, darling. Hopefully.'

I pour a long cool drink, then return to the garden with it. I sit at the patio table and try to calm down.

Susan has always responded in this way: walking out, slamming doors, shouting me down, putting the phone down or whatever was the quickest way to disengage with what she didn't want to hear. But don't I have a point? Susan clashes with Chrissy, just as I clash with her, just as I clashed with Mum and Mum clashed with Milady. We're like pieces of a terrible puzzle that can't be fitted together properly, though we keep mangling each other in our attempts to do so. Or maybe I'm kidding myself, refusing to take responsibility by believing we're inherently at odds with each other; if things can't be changed, then I'm absolved from doing anything about them. I feel a pang of guilt. Maybe giving another specimen to Chrissy was wrong, although she didn't seem that interested and is probably growing out of the obsession anyway. But if Susan objects, which I know she does, then I shouldn't have done it. But my relationship with Chrissy feels as if it has little to do with Susan. But Susan is her mother, so what she says should go. I wanted to ask Susan about Chrissy's referral to a psychologist, but doubt she'll even be talking to me now.

'Gina,' Leon calls over the fence, 'is everything okay? I couldn't help but hear the, er, frank exchange of views.'

'Everything's crap,' I call back.

'Shall I come over?'

'Oh, okay.' I know Leon won't or can't be my therapist again, but at least I can talk to him as a friend. I just hope he doesn't start going on about what happened yesterday.

A couple of minutes later, Leon walks up the garden, full wine glass in hand, and joins me at the table.

'Gina, I've been wanting to talk to you about yesterday.'

'Please, just let me forget it. It was a mistake to ask.'

'But I need to explain why it wouldn't be a good idea for us to –'

'No, this is as far as this conversation goes. You've said no. I've accepted it. That's the end of it. *You* have to accept that. And if you can't, I'm going to have to ask you to leave.'

Leon looks startled. He takes a deep breath and purses his lips, as if he's trying to keep an avalanche of words from tumbling out. He gazes at me intently. I refuse to waver, and look back at him evenly. Eventually, he exhales.

'Alright, okay, if I have no choice.'

'You don't.'

'What, what happened with Susan? But only if you want to talk about it …'

'Nothing happened. Business as usual. Another day, another

row.' I sip my drink. 'I feel I did my best for her, but she thinks I was the worst mother ever. We never connect positively. And the way she calls me "Mother", like we're in some dreadful, pre-war movie. It feels so … unsatisfactory, accusatory. I want to sort it out, but have no idea how to.'

Leon, never one for a quick or frivolous response, remains silent while he thinks.

'A lot of my patients are very critical of the parenting they've received, often with justification. But as they get older, as their own children grow, they begin to see their parents' point of view.'

I nod. 'Perhaps I'm only just beginning to empathise with my own mother – a single parent, doing her best. I can't have been an easy child. In fact, I must have been unbearable. Pregnant at fifteen. She was so ashamed. But she never said so. She blamed herself. I was her child, so it was her fault. I never told her she was wrong.'

'It's all part of the human condition, Gina. Most children feel profoundly ambivalent about their parents, hating them, as well as loving them. When they become parents themselves, they believe it'll all be different. Then their children grow up and they find it's not. Well, it is different, but not necessarily better. Too strict becomes too liberal and then the pendulum of parenting swings back again. I witness it time and again in my practice. Remember, every child is intrinsically selfish, finding it impossible to comprehend that the parent has a life beyond servicing them. And many high-functioning adults remain –'

Suddenly, everything Leon's saying annoys me. I find him irrationally, illogically, but completely, bloody irritating.

'And what exactly do you know about anything, Mr Psychotherapist, Mr High-Functioning Adult?' I ask.

'What?'

'How many children have you raised? How many successful relationships have you made? None, I'd guess. Do you have any experience of life, apart from what you've read in books?'

Leon doesn't reply.

'All you've got is work, isn't it? Lots of dry old theories, analysis and intellectualisation. But nothing real. How does it feel to live through others – to poke and pry and pass judgement on their lives – because there's nothing, *nothing* in your own?'

Leon looks into his wine glass.

His lack of response is infuriating. An acid bubble of rage rises from my stomach into my head and explodes.

'Shall I tell you why I don't want to talk about yesterday? Because it fucking hurts. Yes, you're fully booked. Yes, we're now neighbours. Yes, that's not the ideal set-up for going back into therapy. But I've got cancer. Doesn't that mean anything? Isn't that a good enough reason to make a space for me in your well-ordered routine? You couldn't care less, could you? All those sympathetic words are a patronising act, and one on which you've built a lucrative career. But inside, where it counts, and when it matters, you don't give a shit.'

Leon stands and walks silently back down the garden. His glass remains on the table, half empty.

I hate him for walking away. I want to pick up the glass and hurl it after him. I want to challenge him to a fight.

I look at the glass in my own hand, wrench my arm back and fling it against the garden fence, then stomp indoors.

'Peas in a pod,' says Moya, gutting fish at the kitchen sink.

'What?'

'You and Susan.'

I run up the stairs and slam my bedroom door.

Moya's right, of course. And there I was, criticising Susan for her infantile tempers and unreasonableness. I need an adult-sized naughty step. I need to sit myself on it and think about my behaviour. I need a time-out.

I mull over my outburst at Leon: unfair, uncalled-for, wrong. But, at the same time, true. How can he care about people if he's not willing to help an ex-patient through cancer? And the main reason for not going back into therapy seems to be that we're now neighbours and it could be awkward. But this is hardly harmonious, is it?

I keep myself under house arrest over the weekend. I manage to communicate electronically with several people, without upsetting or launching an unprovoked attack on any of them. Margaret emails to say she's glad I came to the support group, that it meets every week and is a bit hit and miss as far as who turns up, but she's nearly always there. I tell her I'll see her on Thursday. Chrissy emails an invitation to join an interactive Internet site, where we can chat, shop, make homes, keep pets, go on holiday and play games as our virtual reality selves (where, let's face it, I'm likely to be far nicer than my 'reality reality' self). I set up an account and choose to be a soppy-looking grey cat with a pink bow over one ear, while Chrissy is already established as a penguin wearing a kipper tie. It's so horribly addictive that Moya has to remind me to eat and sleep. I'd quiz Susan over the vast amount of Internet time Chrissy is allowed if I hadn't just pissed her off. Joy also emails, insisting (can any interaction with Joy be free of her insisting on something?) we do something to 'celebrate' the fact it's been six weeks since the hysterectomy, and

I can now drive, lift weights and enjoy strenuous physical activity again. My lack of enthusiasm doesn't dissuade her.

As ever, I acquiesce, and a couple of days later Joy and I head to our local zoo – my choice. We reminisce about our various outings there, such as when Joy's mum took us for the first time when we were five, and about how difficult it was to enjoy the animals when our children were young – plagued as we were by their incessant demands for snacks and visits to the gift shop, tantrums because the nocturnal animals wouldn't appear (Susan) and, years later, running off and getting lost (Aiden) – followed by the inevitable 'this is boring' comments when they were older. I've always thought it was a shame that our only children were born nearly fifteen years apart, practically a generation, so we rarely took them anywhere together.

Joy and I spend ages watching a group of long-tailed monkeys. The adolescent ones entertain themselves by tormenting the younger ones; they particularly enjoy pulling their tails, then scampering off. I remember what I was feeling last week – laying on the bed, listening to Chrissy and Brad playing in the garden – about how I couldn't make the beautiful afternoon any more meaningful than it was. I feel different now. Not that I've discovered the secret to living a meaningful life, but I'm simply not searching for it. I'm enjoying the present, a day of sunny good health, with my oldest, bestest friend.

I thank Joy at the end of the day, not only for suggesting we do something, but for persuading me to come this morning. Or rather forcing. After listening to me witter on – about being borderline mental, unsafe around other humans, hypersensitive to the sun, and what if I have a funny turn, and I might need a wheelchair because I get so tired – she ordered me out of the house and into her car. Perhaps she wouldn't be so bossy if I wasn't such a procrastinator.

Before we say goodbye, I give her something I bought in the gift shop – a dark-wood carving of a pair of the monkeys we were so fascinated by – as a memento of the day, a souvenir. She hugs me, too hard.

'Don't worry, Joy, I'll be okay,' I whisper.

After the emotional upsets of the last week, I find myself looking forward to the peculiar comfort of the cancer support group, especially with another chemo on Monday. When I stop off at a garage to fill up with petrol on my way over there, something in the racks of magazines catches my eye. I take a closer look. Donna adorns the front cover of *Bloke*, wearing little more than a tiara and a triumphant smirk; the best woman won.

Arriving at the support group, I take a seat next to Margaret. She tells me that Stacey is in the main hospital building, her baby having been delivered by Caesarean earlier in the day. We can see the floor her ward is on from the portacabin window. I want to ask more, but it's time to start. Wendy (plump, Brummie, breast cancer, going through chemo), Heather (well-spoken and turned out, breast cancer, cured or in remission), and Nadia (thirties, mute, so no idea what cancer) are also present. The old, bearded man from last time isn't here, but a new man is already seated. He's average height, with thinning hair, and Italian-looking, with dark, deep-set eyes and a prominent nose. Indeed, Harry says he's pleased to welcome Alfredo back to the group and the others murmur, as if they know him.

'Now,' Harry addresses me, 'you didn't get a chance to introduce yourself properly last time.'

'No, and I want to thank everyone for being so kind. For letting me be upset and for that being okay. I've been through psychoanalytic psychotherapy before and –'

Alfredo whistles through his teeth. I stop talking.

'Go on,' Harry says to me.

Being a bit of a therapy veteran, what with two years of group stuff in the Mune and four years with Leon, I say what I feel.

'I don't feel comfortable continuing. I wonder what you – Alfredo – meant with the whistling.'

People tut and sigh as Alfredo responds, pleased.

'Psychoanalysis, eh? Must have cost a fortune, eh? It don't come cheap.'

'That's hardly relevant, is it, to why we're here?' I reply.

'I think you'll find it is. The better off you are, the better your chances of recovering from any illness, of having better health in general.'

'For God's sake,' huffs Margaret, 'can't you let Gina talk for five minutes before sticking your bloody oar in?'

Harry holds up his hand.

'Swearing is acceptable, unless other group members find it offensive, but no swearing at each other.'

'Naughty girl,' says Alfredo, with a patronising wink to Margaret. 'But I'm man enough to take it. Carry on.'

Margaret folds her arms and fumes. I do carry on, but feel a bit silly and irrelevant, as everyone's focused on Alfredo and what's just happened.

'Um, my name's Georgina and I have ovarian cancer. I've had a hysterectomy and two cycles of chemotherapy, so far. What about you?' I ask Alfredo, uncertain why I'm addressing him.

He looks at Harry, newly respectful and cautious. Harry nods for him to continue.

'Lymphoma. Very rare, very slow growing. Probably had it from childhood. Countless operations, radiotherapy, chemotherapy. Not dead yet!' He smiles and winks at me. 'How old d'you think I am?'

I say thirty-nine to be polite, but really he looks a badly ravaged, late forties.

'Spot on!' Alfredo exclaims. 'Life in the old dog yet, eh? Can't keep a good man down.'

'I really hope Stacey's okay,' I say, though I know she isn't. I ask Harry if it's alright to talk about another member of the group if they're not here. He says yes, as long as everything can be shared with them when they return. The irony of this rule in Stacey's case weighs heavily in the air.

'I was really struck by her,' I say, 'by all of you. But she's so young, and having her first baby. It seems insane.'

'*Insane*,' echoes Alfredo.

'Maybe it's easier to look at Stacey and feel sorry for her and her family than to examine myself,' I continue.

There are a few murmurs of agreement.

Alfredo is smirking to himself and making clicking noises with his tongue. It's unclear why, and I go on despite them. I could ask him, but guess that these whistles, noises and asides are how he leads all conversations back to himself and why everyone else in the group seems uptight. This certainly wasn't how I expected it to be.

'It just seems such a waste,' I conclude.

'Fwoar! *Such a waste*,' repeats Alfredo, rubbing his hands together lustily.

'And what exactly do you mean by that?' Margaret actually shouts.

I look at Harry. He appears unfazed, as if he's used to this.

'Exactly what Georgina, here, means,' says Alfredo. 'Such a waste, for her family, her kid, her *howdy-pardner*. And – I'm only being honest here – of a gorgeous young woman. In her prime,' and he starts tongue-clicking again.

It's clear Margaret wants to kick Alfredo's head in, that he enjoys being provocative, and the session is turning into a disaster.

'How is Alfredo making you feel? Anybody?' asks Harry, gently, which is good because he's addressing what's going on, but everyone's inhibited now. Plus, responding to such a question means talking about Alfredo, and perhaps taking sides, rather than supporting each other, which I thought was the point of these sessions. In order to break the silence, I ask Harry a question.

'I'm wondering what the rules are for this group. I mean, what are its aims? To challenge and change members' behaviour?' I can't help looking at Alfredo. 'Or to support each other, to share information and stories and stuff?'

'Discussing how you feel about other members is at the heart of true group therapy, but with an irregularly attended group like this it can be difficult,' Harry replies. 'Essentially, this is a support group, designed to provide a place where members can share their feelings and experiences with others who'll understand. The primary work of the group is to prevent patients becoming isolated, to provide a safe and supportive talking environment. It's not intended to function as a traditional therapy group, the main aim of which is to bring about changes in individual members. Although this can and does happen.'

The meeting stumbles on and, in fairness, Harry doesn't do a bad job of making people feel okay again, but, when time's up, a sense of flatness and despondency prevails. The only one who appears buoyant is Alfredo. When he stands, I notice how emaciated he is, see the hard pink lumps protruding from his neck, and experience an awful mixture of revulsion and pity. He corners Harry as the rest of us leave.

'Unfortunately, wankers get cancer, too,' Margaret whispers to me, although not that quietly, as we go out the door.

It's been a disappointing session and Margaret, Wendy and I go to the pub for the support and conversation we didn't get in the group. We talk about Stacey for a while. Her baby was delivered early due to the rapidly growing tumour in her cervix, despite the fact she looked so well only a week ago. It's quite unbelievable, totally unreal. I change the subject.

'That man – Alfredo – you all seem to know him. Who is he?'

'He's one of the patients who was first involved with the support group nearly twelve years ago,' Margaret answers.

'Really? Still coming after all this time? Still alive!'

'He's had periods of remission and periods of severe illness. His cancer has responded to different treatments, but it's never been cured. But he's not got long now. Months, I swear, even though he won't admit it.'

'Maybe that's why he acts like –'

'A total tube? Maybe. Maybe making stupid jokes and passing comment on women like he's some young stud is his way of putting a brave face on it. But he makes me sick. People need to talk and he dominates everything when he's there. Yes, we can discuss how other members of the group make us feel but, like Harry said, it's a support group and some of us don't have time to sit around listening to his bullshit. I don't care if he is terminal. So are other people.'

I don't ask.

II

DEAD HORSES

When I get home, there's an email from Susan saying 'it won't be necessary' for me to pick up Chrissy tomorrow. I can't seem to reply or phone to attempt to make peace. Or call in on Leon and say sorry. It's awful living next door to someone you've rowed with, and I've been avoiding him ever since. The likelihood of such tensions was obviously one reason why he refused to be my therapist again, but I wouldn't even hear him out when he wanted to explain, or remain calm enough to ask him to recommend someone else. But, rather than plucking up courage and apologising to him, I focus on choosing a new kitchen instead, which provides a pleasant-enough distraction from the next chemo, which is looming on Monday.

Having Marty manage the work on the house is a godsend; he's a good builder, knows reliable traders and is quite artistic in his suggestions, despite his relentless environmental preoccupations.

'What do you think of these units?' I say, sliding a couple of kitchen brochures across the dining table towards him. 'And that worktop?'

It's Saturday and Marty's just stopped for his lunch-break. He eyes my brochures with trepidation.

'They're not made from sustainably sourced trees, and most granite isn't ethical. Have you considered refurbished units or reprocessed glass worktops?'

I sigh and shake my head.

'I don't understand why you're not bothered about recycling, Gina. It's so much better for the environment.'

'Well, if you can find a kitchen that's ethical, environmentally friendly, sustainably sourced, recycled and recyclable, and that doesn't look crap or cost a fortune, then I'll consider it.'

I plonk my collection of brochures in front of Marty, then go into the kitchen to make lunch.

I know Marty's right, but all this recycling stuff reminds me of the miserable, make-do-and-mend post-war era into which I was nearly born and that my mother never left. 'Put another jumper on if you're chilly.' 'You could make a perfectly good pudding from that stale bread.' 'Use the soap miser.' But I didn't want to live in a cold house, pretend warm, soggy, stale bread plus a few burnt currants was a decent pudding, or squeeze a latherless wafer of soap into a plastic container with other latherless wafers of soap in the hope that they would magically transform into a new bar; they wouldn't. Similarly, I don't want to think about all this recycling business. I just want to bung the old kitchen in a skip and choose a shiny new one to replace it. But I'm learning that my excuses for not giving a damn – such as if cows farting can harm the environment then what hope is there – will get short shrift from Marty. He doesn't say anything, just gives me a look.

'There you go,' I say, placing Marty's bacon sandwich in front of him. He may have gone green as far as construction goes, but he's still a traditional builder by habit, with his love of fried food, roll-ups and sweet tea.

'These are the most ecological of the bunch,' he says, pointing at a couple of brochures. 'If you can find something you like I can get it ordered next week. And, if it's alright with you, I thought I might stay over tonight, so I can make an early start tomorrow, unblocking that drain.'

'That's fine by me. But won't Tessa mind?'

'She'll … she'll be alright.'

I almost go to ask how things are with Tessa, but decide against it. I leave Marty to eat his lunch in peace, but can't help wondering how his home life really is as I tidy up the kitchen.

Marty and I have always got on well, in what I imagine is an easy-going, brother-and-sister way, and I have been his occasional confidante. But we gave up talking about his and Tessa's relationship after the first ten years, about the same time we gave up discussing mine and Olly's. There was no longer any point in poring over the entrails of relationships with people we both knew we shouldn't be with. Over the years, I've watched Marty give up on receiving any fulfilment from being a father and partner, learn to just keep his head down and tolerate existence, as Tessa has nagged, bullied and drained the joy of life from him. Staying with her for the sake of the children has now been superseded by staying with her because of her health, as she has emphysema, high blood pressure and the obligatory bad back. She won't even let him play guitar because it interferes with her nerves. Marty's only escapes are to Olly's to practise his music, and work. That's why he'd rather be at my house first thing on a Sunday morning, unblocking a partially obstructed sewer pipe, than at home.

Marty comes into the kitchen and hands me his empty plate. He runs a finger down the side of a wall unit, which has certainly seen better days, if not decades.

'Are you sure you don't want me to just put on some new doors?'

I shake my head.

'Or do something with the old units – make them into shelving or something?'

'No, Marty,' I say, firmly. 'Some things in life just aren't worth salvaging.'

I'm awake so early on Monday morning that I end up having a long bath, putting on make-up and doing my hair. It's ridiculous, dressing up for chemotherapy as if it were a date, although it's likely to be more enjoyable than my evening with Ralf the building surveyor. Margaret sends me a text wishing me luck. We've also been exchanging emails. It's reassuring to chat to someone who's been through something similar, someone who's survived; Margaret's had bowel cancer twice, with two lots of surgery and chemotherapy, which only ended a couple of months ago. I wonder how much longer I'll have hair. It's thinner overall, but at least it's not patchy. It's been looking a bit ropey recently, anyway, no doubt due to thirty years of dyeing it blonde, so I'm not averse to experimenting with wigs, à la Joan Collins. Although most people find them too hot and annoying and end up going for the headscarf or hat options. What if my eyebrows go? I'm a bit old for the Aladdin Sane look. I feel a sudden spiritual bond with my pubic hair.

I'm disappointed Ron's not here for chemo today, but there are a couple of familiar faces from last time and we nod to each other. I'm starting to feel like an old hand at this and have come armed with magazines, a book and even work to proofread if I can't sleep. I stayed up late last night, hoping I'd feel tired and could doze through most of it.

Lying back, with a blanket over me, I visualise myself as one of the majority of the dead, rather than the minority of the living. Which is true, isn't it? There are far more of the dead and gone than the living and present. I'm supposed to be visualising my good cells destroying the cancer cells, but I'm no good at it, my mind wandering in half a second. Death. It has to be looked at. Facing life was difficult enough: the big, empty, white room, which has to be filled with … something. I seem to have approached it from a crouching position, from which I made a few scuttling steps forward, a wild stab at something or other, then a rapid retreat. It's all been rather unseemly, as Susan would say. I shall attempt to face serious illness, toxic treatment, even my own demise, with equanimity, with good grace. If it comes to that. Of course, it *has* to at some point. One minute I believe death is imminent and try to get myself to face up to and accept it, and the next that treatment will work and this is another blip which will, one day, be over, part of the past. And I have no idea which one it will turn out to be. Perhaps I'll be like Alfredo: still alive twelve years after diagnosis, still with cancer. People say they'd rather die than grow old, ill and infirm, but they wouldn't. Think of the alternative. I'm sure for some it's a release, especially if they're in unbearable pain or have lost too much of their life to want to continue, but most cling on as long as possible. I'm sure I will. Can there ever be a right time to die? How does one prepare for non-existence? If only I believed in a god, I might have some answers. At least when today is over, I'll be halfway through treatment. And if I count the hysterectomy as part of it, then I'm well over halfway, maybe even two-thirds.

The day's chemo progresses uneventfully and I feel relatively relaxed and positive, dozing in the reclining chair as the sun streams into the ward and nurses regularly check how I'm doing. I return home feeling almost smug and believing that my body possesses a miraculous ability to tolerate this treatment. But within half an hour, I'm on my knees in front of the toilet. The violent retching goes on for hours and I'm left weak and trembly. When I shower the next morning, clumps of hair come away in my hands. It's unspeakably dreadful. My heart goes out to all balding men. Bobby Charlton, we should never have mocked your comb-over.

The previous treatments suddenly feel like the lull before the storm, as the week following chemo is even worse than usual. I'm barely able to get out of bed, eat or do anything. I occasionally come downstairs and watch an hour of telly in the evening, but that's all. I don't even have the stamina to sit through a film. The hair loss is so appalling, the harshest of realities. It's as if, until you have to remove the soggy nest of hair that jams the plughole as successfully as the bath plug itself, you can imagine that cancer is happening to someone else.

To help pass the days, Moya reads to me, a travel book written in 1877. It's not something I'd ever choose, but it's surprisingly engrossing. It's wonderful to be transported to a totally different time and world, a relief. Communing with the dead, almost. I've been thinking of all the people I have known, or known of, who are dead: my family of the no longer living. I suppose it's macabre, but it doesn't feel it. I've also been voluntarily listening to Moya's extensive collection of country and western music, which I've always detested, especially the mawkish sentimentality and twang, twang, twang guitar. Now, Tammy Wynette makes me cry; no doubt my medication needs adjusting.

Moya asks if I want her to tell Susan about the cancer, but I say no. I know it's ludicrous that she doesn't know when practically everyone else does, and with me feeling so deathly and losing my hair, but I should be the one to do it. I reread leaflets informing me that I'm likely to feel increasingly worse the more treatment I have and that this is the effect of the chemo, not the cancer. I tell myself again and again that it's helping me. I also tell myself that when I feel better, when I've recovered from this last session, I'll tell Susan. I'll need to apologise for the snail poo incident first. Chrissy breaks up for the summer holidays in a couple of weeks and she usually spends a lot of it with me, so I'll have to let her know before then.

I'm feeling so low after chemo, I even call Olly and ask him over. I know I shouldn't, but I need to feel physically close to someone – to be held, to smell another's skin, to feel another's warmth. Olly reassures me that I look 'lovely', no different than usual; it's a kind lie. We cuddle up in bed, while I talk and talk. When I ask Olly if he loves me, he replies, 'Of course I do, babes,' as he always does. But I know he loves me in the same way he loves a roast dinner or getting stoned or watching sport on TV. It's love as a general appreciation of something – in my case that I'm a woman and we have sex; non-specific and inconsequential.

Olly appears to listen to me, and occasionally makes comforting noises, but it's hard to tell how much goes in. After I pour out all my contradictory feelings about Susan, cancer, how to tell her and how she might respond, Olly's level of analysis doesn't go beyond, 'Hmm, she's always been a bit of a downer, hasn't she?' I ask him if he's seen much of Chrissy recently. He says it's difficult because Susan doesn't seem to want to encourage him.

'But that's hardly surprising, is it,' I say, 'when you're always stoned? If you stopped smoking, Susan would let you spend more time with her.'

'I s'ppose,' he murmurs.

'I'm worried, Olly, about Chrissy. Not only about her seeing me when I'm ill or how she'll cope with me having cancer, but what'll happen if I don't get better. We know her relationship with Susan can be strained, but she does get on really well with us. We're important to her. I'd like to know, if something happens to me, that you'll be there for her. But you really will have to stop smoking for Susan to trust you. She may have decided we were rubbish parents, but we don't have to be rubbish grandparents. Can you at least *try* to stop – for Chrissy, for me?'

I nudge Olly.

'Are you listening to me?'

Olly emits a gentle snore.

Oh, I give up. I don't even feel angry, just worn out and stupid. You can't flog a dead horse.

A week, practically to the hour, since the end of the last chemo session, the overwhelming fatigue eases. And, as usual, when I feel better, another reason not to tell Susan appears, which is the need to get over this next hurdle. I've decided to shave my hair off. I'm becoming obsessed and can't stop worrying about, or worrying at, what's left of it. There's no point having it cut short because that won't disguise the thin and bare patches. Being completely bald will be less awful than strands and clumps coming away day by day. I hope I feel the same after my date with Joy's electric clipper.

When I arrive at her house, Joy sits me on a kitchen chair with a towel around my shoulders. She reassures me she knows what she's doing, that this is how she does Tim's and Aiden's hair. She gives me a number one, chattering away incessantly as she does. She's more anxious than me.

When she's finished, I go in search of a mirror, while trying to avoid looking at all the hair littering the floor. It takes a few minutes before I can face my reflection. Death camps, skulls, mortality. Cancer. I'd rather have my hair back than the ten-inch surgery scar magicked away, that's how bad it feels. Joy becomes even more bossy which, naturally, means she's feeling even more emotional. She sticks a baseball cap on my head, tells me we have an appointment and she's paying, no arguments, and orders me into her car.

She drives us to a nearby town which has a wig shop, tucked away down a side street, between a dodgy-looking second-hand jewellery shop and an even dodgier-looking tanning salon. We spend a good hour trying on wigs, turbans, bandanas, hats, hairpieces and head wraps. It's amazing what effect a different head of hair can have. Long dark tresses make me come over all sultry sex siren. A grey, Ann Widdecombe pudding basin turns me into an eccentric spinster with a strong desire to go for brisk country walks with dogs. My favourites are a purple head wrap and a straight, fringed, mid-length layered wig with highlights through it. Joy's theory is that because the multi-toned highlights are very obvious and artificial it somehow makes the wig itself less obviously 'wiggy'. She's right! I decide to buy it, but Joy insists on paying. Joy's managed to turn what could be one of the most depressing days of my life into something almost pleasant. In fact, the most painful part of the wig shopping is her insistence that we listen to *The Best of David Essex* in the car all the way there and all the way back.

I ask Joy to drop me off in town. I arrange for a giant bouquet of flowers to be sent to her, as a thank you for everything she's done for me today. I also pick up a boxed set of DVDs that I ordered for Moya. I'm glad they've arrived in time. It's Moya's birthday today, although she's been keeping extremely quiet about it. I didn't say anything when I saw her this morning because I wanted to wait and pick up her present first, but now I can't wait to give it to her. I go into a café to write her card and sort out the gift bag. It's bizarre to glance in windows and mirrors and see an unfamiliar reflection; the wig makes me feel like I'm in disguise. All this stuff has happened – cancer, surgery, chemotherapy, baldness – yet I'm still walking in and out of these same shops, up and down these same streets, past these same buildings, under the same sky. I'm still me, yet not quite who I used to be. Maybe it's no different to remembering walking around these places as a small child, holding my mother's hand. I've shifted into another phase of my life, one I never imagined fate had in store for me.

I'm surprised to hear the telly blaring when I open my front door. Moya's not much of a one for viewing, especially during the day.

'Happy birthday!' I call.

I go into the front room to find Olly sprawled on the sofa.

'Hey, who are you?' he asks.

'What do you mean, who am I?'

'Oh, Gina, it's you. Cool hair.'

'Do, do you think so?'

'Yeah. What was wrong with the blonde though?'

'You know – cancer, chemo, falling out, all those things I talked about for hours when you came over the other night.'

'Oh, yeah, right, of course.'

Ollie's eyes swivel back to the TV.

'What are you doing here? Is the sculpture finished?'

'No, I just came over to have a word with Marty, then sort of … flaked out. I'm knackered.'

'Poor you.'

I wait for Olly to ask how I am, to show a flicker of concern for my well-being. He's smoking a post-food spliff (so much for trying to give up for Chrissy), having eaten something from the bakery at the end of the road. I know this because the wrapper is lying scrunched up on the floor, near the bin it missed, having left a trail of pastry flakes in its wake. Olly's also removed and left his stinking trainers in the doorway, which I have already stumbled over. To top it all, he's watching women's beach volleyball on Eurosport.

I walk over to the telly and boot it as hard as I can. The fit, tanned, bikini-clad 'sportswomen' toss their ball no longer. Having popped unimpressively, with less drama than the motor going on a vacuum cleaner, the screen spills a few chunks of thick glass. I yell at Olly to fucking fuck off, you fucking selfish fuck-face. He promptly does, jumping up from the sofa and hurrying out of the house in his socks. I run after him and, standing on the pavement, take aim and score a bull's eye on the back of his head with one of the trainers. Turning to go back indoors, I note both Leon (blind half-raised in his front-room window) and Marty (up ladder, paintbrush in hand) gawping at me. I make a digni-fied return indoors, pausing only momentarily to adjust my wig.

After I've stopped shaking with anger, I look at the smashed telly. How will Moya watch her birthday DVDs now? I decide to give the insurance company a ring because you can't be sure until you've asked. I know someone who made a successful claim for complete redecoration, new fitted carpet, rug, bed linen, and almost the entire contents of her wardrobe, including wedding dress, due to spilling a pot of paint, in what she swore was a freak falling-off-a-stepladder-in-the-manner-of-a-whirling-dervish-while-touching-up-the-coving accident. The fact she had put on two stone since ordering her wedding dress, and that the big day was in only six weeks, had nothing to do with it. She's got a cheek, Joy has. I consider ⌐honing her for advice first, but don't. Naively, I decide not to lie.

'Yes, Madam,' says the youthful male claims assistant, 'you do have accidental damage cover on your contents policy. Now, if I could just take down a few details about what happened.'

'Can't I just go out and buy a new telly? There's something I want to watch tonight.'

'I'm afraid not. We'll need to approve the claim before we agree to cover the cost of a replacement. The process usually takes three to five weeks. So, if I could just take down a few details.'

'My foot went into the screen.'

'You tripped and fell?'

'Well, I, I kicked it.'

'Oh. That doesn't constitute accidental damage, Mrs … Jarvis. That's intentional damage, isn't it?'

'But it wasn't intentional, not really. It was a momentary act of madness. I am prone to them.'

'Hmm.'

'Only since I've been ill, though. Until then I was as well-adjusted a person as you could wish to meet. It's given me terrible mood swings, you see. A bit like temporary insanity – not being accountable for your actions.'

'Let me just get this clear. You're saying you have accidentally smashed your television screen due to your illness. Some type of mental health issue, I assume? I'd better get my supervisor.'

Bumholes. Why didn't I say I was drunk and fell into it? Or dropped it? This is where honesty gets you.

An officious-sounding older woman finally comes on the line.

'I'm afraid the policy doesn't cover such events; it was intentional damage.'

'I don't see why not, my life insurance policy covered suicide.'

Silence. She cracks first.

'What is the nature of your illness, exactly? If relevant to the policy, you are supposed to inform us. I mean, that's usually for life insurance. I've never heard of an illness being relevant to contents insurance, to –'

'Well, I'll tell you. I've got cancer. My hair's fallen out. The last of it was shaved off today. I am wearing a wig. And I came home to find my husband, my ex-husband … you wouldn't believe it. And the chemotherapy seems to be having some unexpected side effects, apart from the sickness, the exhaustion, the hair loss, the weight loss. Like emotional and mental instability. But that could be due to the hysterectomy. Because that brings on the menopause. Obviously. And we all know what a nightmare that is, don't we? Or maybe you don't, yet. Or perhaps I'm just scared of dying, of being in pain. Because I don't know how to make life more meaningful or, or how to cope with the not knowing. I asked to go back into therapy with him, but he said no. Sometimes, I wonder –'

'I, I quite understand. I'll send you a claim form straight away, there really shouldn't be a problem.'

'It's ovarian cancer, which is one of the worst sorts. Apparently. Although they're all bad, aren't they? You can't have a good cancer, can you? And, I've just had a hysterec–'

'I know, I know, how much did the damaged television cost?'

'Um, um, a fortune,' I lie. 'It was a new thing, a plasma whatsit, flat screen, latest technology, dodgy – I mean, digi – thingy, ready for … ready for anything.'

'Do you still have the receipt?'

'Er, unlikely. You see, I'm having the house renovated. That's been another stress, all the upheaval and building work and –'

'Look, any claim for five hundred pounds or over will be subject to a claim assessment. However, I can authorise you to buy a new television up to the value of four hundred and ninety-nine pounds and ninety-nine pence and, as long as you send us the receipt, with a completed form, we will refund you, minus the fifty pounds excess, no questions asked. How does that sound?'

'Fantastic.'

'I'll put a note on your file.'

I think I have just played 'the cancer card', as Margaret refers to it. Was the supervisor genuinely sympathetic, thinking, 'You poor sod, of course you can have a new telly, with what you're going through'? Or embarrassed, wanting to get me off the phone as quickly as possible? Or am I so unhinged that it really is a viable excuse for 'accidentally' breaking my TV? I wonder what the note on my file will say. Mad as hatter? Do not offer to renew policy when up? Refer to Fraud Squad? I don't know, but I do nip over to ElectricalWorld Megastore and buy the best telly they have in stock for £499 on a credit card.

Moya and Marty have it out the back of the car and set up in no time. Moya has to take a number of deep breaths to recover herself, after I present her with the complete boxed set of Jacques Cousteau DVDs, Jacques being the waterborne conservationist she idolised when growing up and with whom she shares her love of everything marine-based. (She has described to me in great and enthusiastic detail – more than once – his pivotal role in the development of the Aqua-Lung.) I don't think many others – okay, any others – have remembered Moya's birthday. She seems in seventh heaven, sitting there smoking her cheroots and sipping her special 'birthday coffee', i.e. two parts whiskey, one part espresso, while viewing the underwater legend.

Later, when I tell her I'm off to bed, she earnestly thanks me for one of the best birthdays she's ever had. I suddenly feel guilty and ask if she wants me to stay up with her. She shakes her head.

'Although,' she says, hesitantly, 'I do have some news – or at least some plans – I wanted to tell you about.'

I sit back down on the sofa.

'I've decided to sell the cottage. And I'm hoping to move to Cornwall. I've got some friends down there. They run a ferry boat service and want me to help manage it.'

'Are you sure about this, Moya, sure you're not just running away because of the break-up?'

'It's where I've always wanted to live, since I was a child. We used to holiday there, crossing the creek on the boat most days to get to the bigger town on the other side. Living and working there would be a dream come true, if it happens.'

'There's no chance of getting back with Jocasta?'

'She has asked. It didn't work out with the new girlfriend.'

'Blimey, why don't you tell me these things? Don't you want to talk them through with someone?'

She shakes her head, 'I just need to think, then make a decision.'

'And?'

'If she'd asked in the first few weeks, I would have said yes. But the longer time's gone on, the more I've been seriously considering the time I have left and what I want to do with it. And this is what I want to do, if I can.'

'Would you be making these plans if you were still with Jocasta?'

'Don't think so. She never wanted to move.'

'Ha, well, she's lost you now. Serves her right. And you'll end up doing what you've always wanted to.'

Moya allows herself a little smile.

'I'll need to spend time at the cottage, sorting it out,' she says. 'Jocasta and I rather let it go in the last few years, so there'll be a lot to do before it's even ready to go on the market. I'll be here when you need me, though. Is that okay? Will you be okay?'

'Of course it is, of course I will. I couldn't have got through this without you.' I squeeze Moya to me. 'I really hope it all works out. You deserve to be happy.'

When I'm in bed, I shed a secret tear over the prospect of Moya moving away. She's been such a wonderful friend and I'll miss her so much, but I'm sure she's making the right decision.

Life feels stranger than usual, more broken up and bitty. And I'm even less sure of what I'm doing. Or even who I am, as I barely recognise myself in the mirror. I wear the wig outside, but indoors the head wrap is so much comfier, although I look a bit Molly Parkin. Life was always moving forwards to something, even if it was only the next pay day, but it's no longer clear what I'm aiming for, what I'm trying to achieve, other than getting through this treatment. And trying to keep my houseplants alive and healthy. Having neglected them for decades, I am now cleaning, pruning, re-potting and feeding. I've even bought a book. I think this is called displacement activity.

I dither about whether to go to the support group. I missed last week's because I was feeling so awful. I'm embarrassed about wearing a wig and want to hide away indoors. My bald head feels sore and sensitive, and my face has sprung an itchy red rash. Margaret emails on Thursday morning, asking if I'm okay. She says she hopes I'm not finding the inevitable hair loss too upsetting and that I'll be at the support session tonight. Either she's a mind-reader or chemo side effects really are this predictable. The email makes me want to go to the group; I know I have nothing to be scared or ashamed of.

'I feel bad, Gina,' says Margaret, kicking off the session. 'I've encouraged you to come, this is the third time you've made it, and yet we haven't really discussed you – your cancer and treatment. How's it going?'

I stare at the floor. I think we're all relieved Alfredo's not here, and the atmosphere's more relaxed, but now the spotlight's on me. Here goes.

'Um. I'm bald as a bald man. Balder. My friend shaved the last of it off for me. I've been feeling more and more dreadful after each chemo. I know it *is* the chemo, but sometimes it feels worse than the cancer.'

'I know what you mean,' says homely, mum-of-four Wendy. 'I hate losing my hair.'

'It's not a dirty secret,' says Margaret.

'And, and I've told everyone about the cancer,' I say, 'except my daughter, my only child.'

I look up and, yes, they're all gazing back at me with raised brows (those with them left to raise). Even Nadia, the mid-thirties woman who's never said a word, glances up momentarily.

'I've told my grandmother, I've told friends and neighbours, my ex-husband. I've even told my optician and house contents insurer, but not Susan.'

'Why do you think that is?' asks Harry.

I heave a huge sigh. Therapy is so weird, you never know what's going to surface.

'We see each other, but we don't really get on. We've just had a row. Another row. And now she doesn't want me to pick my granddaughter up from school, like I usually do. The row, it was really my fault, but … I don't know, I just don't want to deal with her.'

'Deal with her? Won't she be devastated to be the last to know, won't she want to help?' asks Wendy.

'I suppose she might, but we have such a difficult history, I can't imagine she'll be all flowers and sympathy.'

Wendy nods, but I can tell she doesn't really understand.

'She likes animals,' I say. 'I mean, she doesn't have pets or anything, but the only charities she gives to are animal ones. She thinks humans are responsible for their own troubles. I'm not sure what I'm trying to say. She's one of those people who can't stand humans, who prefers animals. Only she doesn't like them much either.'

Everyone laughs.

'Maybe I'm the hypercritical one. I probably sound awful,

slagging my own daughter off like this.'

'Cancer can bring out the best in those around us,' says Harry. 'They can be supportive, loving, can go out of their way to be there for a person during their illness.'

'That's true,' I say. 'Friends couldn't have been kinder or more helpful. And it's been so important for me because I'm on my own.'

'But it's not always like that,' Harry continues. 'Some turn away, because they can't cope with their own mortality or don't know what to say or do. Some become angry, angry at the person with cancer for not being there for them any more, for being ill, for impinging on their life. It can bring underlying frictions to a head, as well as heal them. What do you feel when you think about telling Susan? What are your hopes, your fears?'

'Is this okay?' I ask, worried I'm dominating the session and everyone's bored or annoyed.

'I really appreciate you talking about this,' says Margaret. 'I've found it difficult to let some people know, too. I've been scared of their reaction – whether they'd reject me or smother me in pity. You're being very open, Gina. And thoughtful, calm. Not embarrassed.'

Thoughtful and calm, eh? Not words usually used to describe me. Not embarrassed. No, not any more. I can't be. I'm too old and this is too serious.

I close my eyes as I think.

'Telling someone you're ill –'

'Try to make it more personal, more specific,' interrupts Harry, 'by referring to Susan, not just someone, and telling her about the cancer, not just that you're ill.'

'Okay. Telling Susan I have cancer implies that she should

be, well, what? Shocked. Worried. Scared of losing me. Telling her kind of necessitates a sympathy response. And Susan doesn't do sympathy.'

I pause for a second, then look up.

'I'd feel guilty, like it's all my fault, because I haven't lived the healthiest of lives.'

'Do you really think she'll blame you?' asks Wendy.

'I suppose I do.'

We talk more about telling people and dealing with their re-actions. All of us have felt responsible for how others are coping.

'I nursed my husband, David, during his cancer, years before I was diagnosed with breast cancer,' says Heather, 'so I can see things from both sides. It's inevitable to worry about how others will take it, how they'll react and cope, but you need to put yourself first and do what's right for you, whatever that is. Maybe you're simply not ready to tell your daughter yet. Just give yourself time. What David went through – what *I* put him through – made me realise that the wishes of the person with cancer must take priority.'

'What do you mean – what you put him through?' asks Wendy. 'You never did anything to harm him, Heather.'

'No, of course not, not intentionally, but … I know some of you have heard this story before, but I'd like to explain – to Gina.'

'I'd appreciate that,' I say.

'David had already been pretty ill for a couple of years, when he began to need really intensive care. I decided – we both decided – I'd give up work in order to look after him at home. It was tough being on call twenty-four hours a day and watching him deteriorate, but I wanted to do it. Anyway, after about six months, I was invited away for the night, with some girlfriends, for a hen do. It was all very civilised, not that far away, at a posh hotel with a spa. David seemed pretty good health-wise, but he had to force me to go because I didn't want to leave him. He said he'd be fine, that he had a dozen people he could call if anything happened. So I did go, and had a great time.'

I think I know what's coming.

'He was taken into hospital the Saturday night I was away and died on the Monday. By the time I got back on the Sunday he … well, he never regained consciousness.' Heather looks around at us. 'I believe David wanted me to go away that night, so he could die. He wasn't scared of dying, but he knew I was petrified of losing him. He'd already hung on a very long time, when maybe he shouldn't have. Putting pressure on someone who's seriously ill to keep going, to keep on having treatment, to keep living, can be as cruel as not caring at all.'

The conversation meanders round to various subjects I've barely considered before, let alone discussed: voluntary euthanasia, the right of the patient to refuse treatment, a case in the news in which a health authority tried, unsuccessfully, via the courts, to force a terminally ill teenager to have more medical treatment that she'd decided she didn't want. I don't get any further with working out why I can't tell Susan, but it's been a productive session. We've all spoken (apart from Nadia, of course) and genuinely empathised with and supported each other. When it finishes, I feel ten times better. I shake Harry's hand before I go.

'Thank you,' I say, 'for providing this for us. I really do appreciate it.'

He flushes and smiles as he squeezes my hand.

Walking up my front path, after driving back from the support session, I'm sure I catch a glimpse of a bare, male torso through the window. Moya opens the front door.

'Who on earth's in there?' I ask.

I follow Moya into the front room and am greeted by a life-size, full-colour, cardboard cutout of Iggy Pop. Stuck to his forehead is a post-it note with 'Sorry' written on it. Moya, who took delivery, informs me that it was 'appropriated' from the foyer of a venue advertising a forthcoming appearance. It's an apology from Olly. I look at Iggy, in all his mad-eyed, rubber-faced, bendy-bodied glory. I've always had a soft spot for him, despite, or maybe because of, his massive drug consumption, demented stage antics and inability to keep it in his pants.

Moya carries Iggy up to my bedroom, telling me that two legends – him and Jacques – in the front room at the same time might be too much and the house could explode. I think she may be developing a sense of humour.

After supper, I chat to Iggy. When it gets chilly, I wind a scarf around his rigid neck. Then I see how my wig suits him. During the course of the evening, Iggy and I work out three things with regard to Susan and cancer.

One: it's Chrissy I can't face telling, not so much Susan.

Two: I feel safer being cross with and disconnected from Susan because it's familiar; attempting change is daunting, even if it's for the better.

Three: I blame myself, at least partly, for having this disease.

Who needs a Leon when you've got an Iggy?

12

SPACE-CAKE

'You're not going ahead with this madness. Are you?' asks Moya.

'Course I am.'

I was forced into consciousness this morning by my mobile. There was a text from Lara saying vibes are good for the séance and could we get everyone together for two o'clock today. I'd assumed it would take place in the evening, not in the middle of a brilliant, sunlit afternoon.

'Come on, or we'll be late,' I say.

I organise myself, Moya, Joy and Olly to get over to Lara's. Then Lara says we need six people, so I trot back home and ask Marty, who readily agrees. I don't question why he's here on a Saturday, again. Not that he appeared to be working, but fashioning miniature wind turbines out of old cigarette packets and matchsticks and naming them 'Prototype 1', '2' and '3' in purple felt-tip. At least he was taking a break from knocking out blown plaster and covering the whole house in dust. I don't seem to know anyone who leads a normal life and isn't available for an afternoon séance.

Lara's house is just along the road from mine, in the

middle of a Victorian terrace, with long, narrow back gardens. Lara hands each of us a glass of mugwort and lemon balm tea (it tastes better than it sounds), then we make our way to a hexagonal wooden building at the end of the garden, which is largely obscured by overhanging trees and is relatively cool. It's the hottest day of the year so far. Thin raffia blinds are drawn over the windows and there are six big cushions arranged in a circle on the floor.

'Far out,' says Olly, removing a tobacco tin from his pocket.

'No smoking,' says Lara to Olly, and Marty, who has pulled the roll-up from behind his ear.

'What about in the garden?'

'No.'

We sit down. In the middle of the circle is a Ouija board and, in its centre, the traditional upside-down glass. Despite the Mune and various other hippie nonsense I've engaged in, it *is* a bit weird and I feel uncomfortable. I've never liked the idea of Ouija boards and have always refused to have anything to do with them, but I trust Lara. She instructs us to look into one another's eyes, in turn. I start from my left: first, I find Olly's beautiful green but red-rimmed ones, move swiftly on to Marty's slightly wonky hazel, then Moya's grey, to Lara's bright and blue, and finally around to Joy's warm, velvety brown on my right-hand side.

Lara asks us what we see.

'I see their colours,' I say.

'I see that Marty needs to get more sleep,' jokes Olly.

'I see that Olly needs to smoke less puff,' says Marty.

'I can't see very well at all, I must need spectacles,' says Moya.

'I see us all, behind our eyes, our souls,' says Joy, earnestly.

'Thank Cerridwen someone's got a spiritual bone in their body,' says Lara. 'I see people on their journeys though life, midway through their journeys.'

'Hang on a minute, I'm only thirty –' says Olly.

'You're forty-four,' I correct.

Lara directs us to join hands, concentrate and not speak unless she or one of the spirits asks us something.

'Are the spirits quite chatty then?' says Olly. 'Will they introduce themselves? I mean, how do they speak if they're dead?'

'Through the board and through me,' replies Lara.

'How can we tell if it's you or a spirit? Will a different voice come out of your mouth? Hold on a minute, you're not going to go all *The Exorcist* on us, are you? That film freaked me right out. The LSD beforehand probably didn't help, but I had nightmares for months afterwards, flashbacks too, especially that bit when the girl –'

'Shh,' Lara hisses. 'Someone's trying to come through. We must keep our hands joined. Now, let's close our eyes.'

I'm holding hands with Olly on one side and Joy on the other. Olly's hand begins to shake. I take a peek. He and Marty – whose hand Olly's holding – have got the giggles. Just as a snort escapes from Olly, the upside-down glass in the middle of the Ouija board flings itself into a corner and smashes.

'Don't break the chain,' orders Lara.

Olly and Marty giggle no more, both are pale and goggle-eyed. Moya's brow twitches, a dramatic response for her. Lara's and Joy's eyes remain closed. At least they seem to know what they're doing.

'No Ouija is possible now. The spirits must come directly to me,' says Lara. Then, 'She's here.'

I feel a sudden panic, a lurching in my stomach. Joy is nodding hypnotically beside me. I close my eyes and try to focus. A whiff of something familiar tickles my nostrils: a mix of line-dried cotton and floral perfume.

'It's Mum!' cries Joy. 'It's *my mum*.'

It is her mother's smell, one I haven't breathed in for thirty odd years. Tiny needles prickle my skin. I separate my lashes a fraction. Copious, silent tears are rolling down Joy's ecstatic face; her eyes remain closed and she is breathing heavily.

'She says she never wanted to leave you, Joy,' says Lara.

'I know,' murmurs Joy.

'She says she's proud of you. She says don't worry about Aiden. He's a good lad really and will be okay.'

Positive and encouraging comments about Joy's son and husband and life continue. Everything Lara says – every person and thing she mentions – Joy seems to understand, and so do I, having known her for so long. But, hang on a minute, what about my mum? I thought this was supposed to be her séance.

'The greengage in the back garden, move it to the front,' advises Joy's mum, through Lara. 'It's never going to grow well there, it's too close to next door's eucalyptus.'

It's true that Joy's been having trouble with the fruit tree since she planted it. But surely a spirit should be mentioning more important stuff, like what it's like to be dead, whether God exists, a few pointers on how to live a good life. I want to speak, but know I mustn't; this is Joy's moment.

'The ring, the one you lost, it's behind the sideboard, in the lounge,' says Lara.

Joy nods her acceptance of this fact. Lara falls silent. Joy's breathing becomes less laboured and her tears dry.

Lara's eyes open.

'She has to go now, Joy. She hopes this has been a comfort.'

Joy opens her eyes and smiles.

'Thank you, Mum.'

We all begin to relax, to loosen our grip on one another, to hear sounds filtering in from outside, to swallow and look around the room. Whatever's been happening, we've been going through it together.

'Oh, dear,' cries Lara, 'make the chain, make the chain. Quick!'

We grasp each other's hands again. An energy zaps through the looped string of arms, pulsating with incredible force. Then it moves from travelling through the circle, to trying to pull our fingers apart. We grip tighter.

'That's it,' says Lara, 'don't let go.'

'Be gone,' she orders, flatly and sternly. 'You are not welcome.'

Our hands and arms are jiggling and shaking, as if we're having a collective fit. We keep holding on. Lara repeats the command. The energy, the thing, the whatever it is, leaves as quickly as it appeared and our arms flop down, weak and loose.

'*What* was that?' I ask.

'Relative of mine, I think,' states Moya, unemotional as ever.

'She's still very near the boundary from the other side,' says Lara. 'She wants to come back across. When did she pass over?'

'Twenty years ago.'

'She must be put to rest, but I'll need extra help for that one.'

Moya nods. Phew, we really are in the twilight zone.

'Shit,' says Olly, glancing at Marty. 'I hope none of our dead relis come through. Can you stop them, Lara?'

'I'm trying to concentrate, Oliver,' admonishes Lara.

She remains silent for a few minutes, during which time I

realise I'm desperate for the loo.

'This is rather strange,' Lara finally says. 'I was certain Shirley would make an appearance. Maybe the force of the other spirits has pushed her to one side.'

Typical Mum, never one to draw attention to herself or make demands. Lara says it's time for a break, but we're a good mix today. We should stretch our legs, have some refreshments and see if Shirley will come, once this hoo-hah with the last spirit has blown over.

Hoo-hah; that is a Mum expression if ever there was one. I run for the loo.

We wander about the garden, seeking out shade. It's so hot my eyelids are sweating. Olly looks disorientated and attempts to roll a spliff. Lara reminds him he's not allowed.

'Erm ...' says Olly, racking what's left of his brains for an excuse to escape.

'Left the gas on?' I suggest.

'Yeah! Left the oven on, must get back, must –'

'What were you cooking?' asks Lara.

'Erm ... cat.'

'You were cooking a cat?'

'No. Feed cat.'

'I didn't think you had a –'

'Next door's.'

Lara refuses to let Olly go, telling him his presence is essential, that it has, in fact, been requested. He's cacking himself.

We nibble wholesome homemade biscuits and sip more tea. It's all rather bizarre and incongruous, but then much of life is. Someone you love dies, yet you still have to do the laundry.

Cancer and chemotherapy don't stop you running out of milk or getting a parking ticket. Marty begins to talk to me about the building work. Sitting cross-legged (just about, although his jeans are clearly experiencing some duress) under a tree, with his belly protruding from his shirt and bald pate, he looks a bit like Buddha, or a troll. His comprehensive listing of the advantages of solar power in the domestic energy environment is interrupted by a rustling, cracking, yelling, then a thud. We all turn to see Olly lying on a now-broken fence panel, between Lara's garden and her next-door neighbour's. He's obviously tried to jump over and leg it. Joy calls him a pathetic coward, and even Marty looks shamefaced on his behalf. Olly says sorry, but he was 'freaked out'. I tell him I don't think that's possible, not in the twenty-first century. Lara claps her hands and orders us to regroup in the sacred circle. I tell Lara I'm not feeling too good. She clasps my hands in that way of hers.

'She will come, Georgina,' says Lara. 'She's waited fifteen years for this. It will start the healing.'

I'm tempted to do a runner, too.

We re-seat ourselves in the garden room. The sun has moved and it's even warmer and darker in the wooden box. No jokiness now. We join hands and close our eyes, as before, without being instructed to.

Lara emits a long, deep sigh.

'Shirley's here. She's pleased to see so many familiar faces. She knows everyone, except me.'

My heart is pounding, but I don't feel a presence or smell anything familiar.

'What do you want to ask your mother, Georgina?'

'Why did you fall?' I say, before the words even form in my mind.

Lara frowns for a few moments, then, 'She's saying it was an accident, Gina. She didn't want to go. She wanted to help you, and the family. She knew you were finding life difficult. She feared you got that from your father.'

'He died from a heart attack,' I say, although what relevance that is, I have no idea. Maybe I say it because it's all I've ever known about him: 'Dad died suddenly, from a heart attack, when you were a baby.' Mum never elaborated.

'He was depressive, I think that's what Shirley is trying to say. She always wanted to tell you, but never did. He didn't find life easy.'

Sounds familiar.

'Shirley regrets not being able to talk to you about it,' says Lara. 'She was never sure how to broach such things.'

'It doesn't matter. It's not her fault. I was a bit of a mess. I've always been a bit of a mess. Perhaps I did get it from Dad. I see the link. I didn't know he got depressed. I never knew him. He's just a blank space.'

'Shirley says hold steady, but she has something to tell you.'

'He took his own life, didn't he?' I say, again not knowing where the idea has sprung from.

'Yes,' Lara says, quietly.

Silence while it sinks in.

I shake my head, 'I don't know how I know. I've never even thought such a thing before. Perhaps Milady, when I was younger, perhaps she let something slip.'

'It was during one of his depressions,' says Lara.

'Oh. Poor Mum. I'm sorry.'

'People told her to say he died of something else, so it would be less difficult for her, and you. The stigma.'

'I understand. You tried to protect me. But you were so distant, I couldn't connect, couldn't go to you when I needed help … to make sense of myself.'

'She's sad when she sees how you and Susan get along,' says Lara. 'You must tell her what you're going through.'

'I will, I promise.'

Lara pauses for a moment.

'The house. She needs to talk about the house. She's finding it hard, Georgina. She's becoming confused.'

Lara and I gaze at each other; I'd forgotten there were other people in the room.

'I sense she's trying to say everything she's been waiting to tell you for years and it's becoming jumbled,' says Lara.

'Tell her I'm sorry I wouldn't listen before.'

'It's okay, you're listening now.'

'The house?'

I fear for a moment that Mum's going to pass comment on the new wallpaper in the back bedroom or the colour I've chosen for the front door.

'The fire escape …'

'Yes, what happened, how did you fall, Mum?'

'A cake,' says Lara.

'A cake? I don't understand.'

'She's definitely saying something about a cake, a birthday cake. About eating it when she shouldn't have. I can't quite work it out,' says Lara.

Olly's eyes pop open. I see something shift behind them, move into position, then click into place.

'The cake!' he declares. 'The knockout birthday hash cake Mad Pete made for me, up in the attic flat. Triple strength, home-grown grass. Shirley called round unexpected, to give me a present. She saw the cake, cut up into slices. She'd been on one of her diets, but asked if she could try a bit. I told her no, it was fattening, she wouldn't like it, it didn't taste right, anything to put her off.'

'But she did try it,' says Lara, 'when you left her alone in the kitchen. She had one slice, then another. She began to feel dizzy, went out to get some air … and lost her footing at the top of the fire escape.'

'Oh my God! *That's* why Shirley fell,' says Olly. 'And it's my fault.'

Here, in this room. The layout is the same. With it having remained a poorly maintained, rented flat since Mum died, the kitchen is exactly the same. This is where she laughed shyly and tried not to disapprove of Olly and his spaced-out friends. And ate cake. What a ridiculous, terrible way to go.

I wobble back down the rusty, rickety fire escape. How can this accursed thing still be here and Mum not? Susan and I were away the weekend it happened, and when we returned she was gone. Leon pointed out numerous times in therapy that I hadn't actually accepted that Mum had died, that my constant sense of her presence revealed this.

I pace about the house, trying to get things straight in my head and heart. I briefly question whether the séance was genuine, if it really was Mum, if I should believe any of it. But it feels real. It doesn't even feel extraordinary. And what about Olly and his culpability? I decide to deal with my father first. That I appeared to know that he killed himself, without ever having been told explicitly, seems stranger than communicating with my mother. I ring Milady to check facts.

'He wasn't an easy man, your father,' Milady states, 'though a most charming and attentive individual when "up".' I sense the inverted commas in her speech; I don't know if I want to hear any more. 'But utterly wretched when he was down. And, like most people prone to wretchedness, he made everyone around him wretched, too.'

I end the call quickly, having established that my father did kill himself.

My childhood begins to make more sense. The way my father died explains why there were few photos of him around when I was growing up, why there was a sense of sadness and upset around his memory, but not really of lost love or longing. I assumed it was too painful for Mum to talk about because she loved him and this was also why she never found anyone else. Maybe that's still true, but suicide accounts for the lack of talk about him and 'if only your father could be here to see this' type of comments. Mum secretly nursed the truth about my father's death, which was so difficult for her, but really feels irrelevant to me. He still died when I was a baby and, in all probability, Mum saying it was due to a heart attack protected me – from feeling he didn't love me enough not to do it, from fearing that I might share his mental problems. Because I never knew him, have no memories at all, one fantasy father can only be replaced by another. And there's no point in imagining what I may or may not have inherited from him. It certainly wasn't ovarian cancer, was it? So, for now at least, I must put my 'real' father in a metaphorical box and leave it to one side; I'm too busy trying to stop my own life slipping through my fingers.

I think about Mum, about the past, about our past. I light candles in the attic and talk to her as if she's there. I don't know if she is, I can't sense her presence or anything, but it makes me feel better. I've always spoken to her, since she died. And usually horribly, telling her to go away and leave me alone. Now I tell her she did the right thing in trying to protect me. As I talk, I begin to realise why Mum was so fearful of any 'strange behaviour' on my part; any little oddity she must have perceived with heightened sensitivity, worried I could be showing signs of being like my father, of sharing his mental instability. I understand Mum better now: her distance, rigorous conventionality and reserve were her way of coping with the grimmest of realities. I was surprised to hear Milady refer to Dad as a real live wire when 'up'. It's hard to imagine Mum young and in love, with someone who could be outgoing and sociable. I thank Mum, tell her I love her, that I forgive her the secret and hope she can forgive me, for everything. I blow out the last candle in the attic.

Mum is dead. She is not coming back. Acceptance is a hammer blow to the head, a javelin through the heart. Moya helps me through a seasick night of wailing grief that's taken fifteen years to come.

13

SOMERSAULTS

When Marty arrives on Monday morning, I ask him to start work on the attic. I want the fire escape taken down and a staircase reinstated from the first-floor landing to the top floor as soon as possible. I ask him to rip out the horrid kitchen and tiny shower room and make it into one huge, open space.

'What's it going to be, Gina? A living room, a bedroom, a studio type thing?'

'Just the loveliest space it can be, okay?'

'Okay. And, erm …'

'Oh, alright, put in a couple of sodding solar panels if you must. But no wind turbines.'

Next day, I call in on Lara. The fence panel is still lying broken on her lawn. I select one of Lara's least poisonous-looking herbal teas and we sit at her kitchen table drinking it.

'I think the séance went well,' says Lara. 'How about you?'

I exhale deeply.

'It's all been a bit mind-blowing − talking to Mum, everything that came out about Dad. Not to mention Joy's mum turning up.'

'Shirley's been trying to communicate with you for a very

long time,' says Lara.

I nod, guiltily.

'I hope she'll be able to rest in peace now,' says Lara.

'I hope so, too.'

We both sip our steaming tea.

'Have you heard from Oliver?' Lara asks.

'No,' I say, 'and I don't bloody well want to.' Lara continues to gaze at me. 'Why,' I eventually ask, 'have you heard from him?'

Lara places her mug on the table.

'Yes, I've been seeing and hearing rather a lot of Oliver. He's been hanging round here ever since the séance.'

'But why?' I ask, surprised.

'He's adamant that he must apologise to Shirley,' says Lara. 'But I don't sense her presence any more. And, I don't mean to be uncharitable, but having Oliver droop about the place is becoming rather a nuisance. I had to send him on his way again, just before you arrived. Would you mind having a word?'

'Olly's the last person I want to see. I know he didn't deliberately set out to hurt Mum, but if he wasn't such a dopehead then she would still be here.'

'I know, but I really didn't feel anything negative towards him from Shirley. She just wanted to clear up what had happened and make contact with you. But Oliver's developed some paranoid idea that Shirley is bent on revenge, that she's behind the unpleasant things that have been happening around his house.'

'What things?'

'He was a bit vague – said something about stuff in the garden being vandalised, and graffiti.'

234

'That sounds more like the work of a hoodie than a haunting.'

'I told him that, but he wouldn't listen. Maybe you can get through to him?'

'Oh, okay, I'll have a word – for you.'

'Murderer' is spray-painted in huge, red letters across Olly's garage door; he's standing in front of it with his mouth open.

'Gin!' he shrieks, as I approach. 'Look what she's done.'

'Look what who's done?'

'Shirley,' he whispers, pointing at the garage door.

'You must be losing your marbles – Mum isn't responsible for that.'

'But it's true, isn't it?' he says, distraught. 'It was my birthday cake, I asked Mad Pete to make it. If I hadn't, then she never would have … Oh, Shirley, I am so sorry, please forgive me.'

Olly grabs my hands. I pull them free.

'I had no idea it would happen, Gina. I feel so terrible. Shirley was a wonderful woman, so kind, I never thought –'

'Do you remember when I came home to find Susan playing in the road? You were supposed to be babysitting, but you'd got so stoned you'd fallen asleep in the back garden.'

Olly nods.

'Do you remember when you were driving us to that festival in Yorkshire? You were so out of it, you took a wrong turn into that one-way system and we were nearly obliterated by a lorry.'

Olly nods again.

'What's it going to take for you to realise that you can't spend your whole life stoned out of your brains?' I say, my voice growing louder. 'How many more people are you going to endanger or actually kill before that finally sinks in?'

'I'm never, ever smoking again. I haven't touched it since I found out the truth about Shirley.'

I'm tempted to believe Olly, as I've never seen him so distressed.

'I really am a ... a murderer,' he says, slumping down on the ground, his head in his hands.

Seeing Olly so genuinely upset and remorseful causes my own anger to dissipate. I sit down next to him, feeling weak and resigned.

'It was an accident, a stupid accident,' I say. 'And nothing can bring Mum back or change the past, can it?'

'No,' says Olly, quietly.

I glance up at the garage door.

'Joy did that,' I say.

'Joy?'

'Yes. She loved Shirley, too, didn't she? My mum was like a second mum to her, after hers died. I'll talk to her, try to get her to leave you alone.'

Olly nods, gratefully.

'And you must stop hassling Lara.'

'But I need to make contact with Shirley, to beg her forgiveness. How else can I get through to her? How else can I carry on?'

I sit in the dining room looking at the telephone, thinking about everything that's happened these last few days. I'm sure Leon would tell me the séance was some sort of collective hallucination, but that my final acceptance of Mum's loss is a good thing. I wish I could discuss everything with him, and try to make sense of it. I think of Leon a lot, of all the advice he gave me as a therapist and friend. It's the best I ever had. Even if I didn't take it. I miss him. I should apologise, he's only next door and … maybe I'll phone Joy instead, it'll be easier.

Just as I'm about to pick up the phone, there's a sharp knock on the front door.

'Joy, I was about to call you.'

'Can I come in?'

'Of course.'

We sit at the dining-room table. I study Joy for a moment; she seems agitated and uptight – a boiling pot about to blow its lid.

'What were you going to ring me about?' she asks.

'Olly – I was going to ask you to leave him alone. Assuming I'm right in thinking it's you who sprayed "murderer" across his garage door?'

'You were going to ask *me* to leave *him* alone,' Joy exclaims. 'That's rich. That scumbag deserves to be tormented till his dying day. Which couldn't come too soon, in my opinion.'

Joy opens her handbag and pulls out a chocolate bar. She rips off the wrapper and begins to chomp through it furiously.

'I know how you feel, but Olly didn't –'

Joy slams what remains of the chocolate bar down on the table.

'I can't believe you're making excuses for him.'

'He didn't mean for it to happen. He's mortified.'

'Good,' says Joy, picking up the chocolate and stuffing it into her mouth.

'I'll make coffee,' I say.

When I return from the kitchen, another empty wrapper is lying on the table, as is another untouched chocolate bar.

'Want some?' Joy asks, pushing the chocolate across the table. I set the cups in front of us, then take a seat.

'No, I'm fine.'

'Look, Gina, I'm not saying it was deliberate, it wasn't like he pushed Shirley to her death with his own hands. But cannabis is illegal – for a reason.'

'I know, but he could never have known what was going to happen. You must be able to see that.'

'God, Gina, why aren't you more angry with him?'

'Because it won't change anything, because there's no point in tormenting Olly when he's tormented enough already. I can't allow myself to be eaten up with hate and blame. It's the same with the hospital, Joy, what's done is done.'

Joy suddenly stands, pushing the table and making her cup jump and spill. She begins to pace about the room.

'Am I the only one who thinks people should be responsible for their actions? That they should be *made* to be responsible for their actions. I'm sure the hospital didn't *intend* for you to be misdiagnosed, for the wrong surgeon to operate on you, for your test results to be left to gather dust on a desk while the cancer was spreading, but that's what happened. And someone, somewhere, is responsible. I'm sure Olly didn't *intend* for –'

'Do sit down, Joy, you're making me dizzy.'

Joy plonks herself onto a chair and grabs the remaining chocolate bar.

'And you don't need to keep …' I say, before hesitating.

'Keep what?' says Joy, staring into my eyes as she tears off the chocolate wrapper with her teeth. I return her gaze, willing her to see my empathy, my respect for her.

'You don't need to keep eating, when you're so obviously not enjoying it.'

'I am enjoying it,' she declares.

'Whatever you say.'

I sip my coffee, while Joy devours the chocolate. When it's finished she gathers up the wrappers and puts them in the kitchen bin, before retaking her seat.

'Aren't you going to ask why I've come round?' she says.

'Um, okay, why have you come round?'

'To let you know that if you don't tell Susan about the cancer then I'm going to.'

'What?'

'You heard. Someone has to, if you won't. Even Shirley said she needs to know. You've always had a go at me for being bossy, but I can't sit on the sidelines watching problems get bigger and bigger when I can do something about them. It's the same with your medical treatment. Mistakes have been made and the hospital needs to admit that, otherwise they'll keep on happening. And Olly. Him and his lifestyle were – however inadvertently – responsible for Shirley's death and he needs to face those facts. And Susan –'

'For God's sake, Joy, who appointed you as moral bloody policewoman in charge of my life? I will tell Susan – I promised Mum I would – but I'll do it in my own time. And I'll put a complaint in about the hospital if and when I want to.'

Joy stares at me. I can almost see the steam coming out of her ears. I also remind myself that she's over twenty stone and I'm barely eight. We once had an arm-wrestling contest and Joy had my hand flattened against the table in a nano-second, and my shoulder hurt for weeks afterwards. I wouldn't stand a chance. But, instead of leaning across the table, jamming her hands around my throat and throttling me, Joy drops her head and lowers her gaze. Tears plop onto the table.

'Everything that happened at the séance, it made me realise that Susan's in the same position I was with my mum – not even knowing how seriously ill you are,' she says, softly. 'Don't leave it till it's too late. Susan's your daughter, your only child. She'll want to help, she'll want to make a difference. She should at least be given a chance.' Joy sniffs. 'If I'd have known earlier I could have helped my mum. I could have gone to the doctor's with her, gone to the hospital, made her get a second opinion.'

'Joy, you were fourteen; there was nothing you could have done for your mum. Everyone expects their test results to be correct. No one had an inkling they were wrong.'

'But if Mum had told me sooner, I know I could have done something. She kept it from me – the lump, the biopsy. If we'd been closer, if I'd been a better daughter, she would have confided in me, would have told me what she was going through. Then I could have helped.'

I grasp Joy's hand.

'Look at me, Joy.'

She raises her eyes.

'You and your mum were close. You were a loving daughter. She found a lump in her breast; she had a biopsy, and was told it was clear. No wonder she didn't tell you – she didn't think there was anything to tell. God, I've got Stage III cancer, I'm halfway through treatment and I still haven't told my daughter.'

'That's what I mean,' says Joy. 'Think what a legacy that's going to leave Susan. I know you've always had a difficult relationship, but it's never going to be mended if you don't give yourselves a chance.'

'Do you really believe you could have done something to prevent your mum's death?' I ask Joy. 'Have you really felt guilty all these years?'

'Yes,' she croaks, 'yes, yes, yes.'

Joy has a good cry. She's also sick down the loo. Usually, when she's upset or shocked she becomes hysterical – laughing and shaking and spouting inanities. This time her reactions feel more real and we actually talk about her mum's death. Joy didn't know her mum had cancer until six weeks before she died; she was kept away from the funeral so that it didn't 'upset her' and the auntie who moved in to look after her rarely spoke about her mum. I also remind Joy that I, other kids at school, teachers and parents never mentioned what had happened; there was just an awkward silence and an exchange of embarrassed looks if anyone talked about their own mum in Joy's presence, and a few months later it was as if it had never happened.

'We were all hopeless at dealing with your mum's death. I just didn't know what to say or do, so I ended up not saying or doing anything. I never knew you were blaming yourself.'

'But I was, and always have done. If I'd loved her more, been a better daughter, she wouldn't have died.'

'Oh Joy, that's not true.'

Joy shrugs.

'Even if you don't feel it, tell me you *know* it's not true,' I persist.

Joy hesitates, then nods slowly.

'And even if you feel scared or unsure or whatever it is that's been preventing you from letting Susan know you're ill,' Joy says, 'tell me *you* know she needs to be told, and as soon as possible.'

'I do know, and I will tell her.'

After a restless night I decide to ring Olly first and tell him that Joy has agreed to leave him alone. And that Mum has forgiven him. He asks how I know this. I say that Mum visited me in a dream and told me. He asks why I didn't say so yesterday. I say I only dreamed it last night. He's about to say something else when I advise him to stop asking questions and be grateful. He says he is, and is promptly flooded with tears of relief and gratitude. I'm sure I could make Olly do anything now, if I say it's at Mum's behest, but I ignore the temptation of such megalomaniacal thoughts. Instead, I tell him he can be a responsible and sober grandfather to Chrissy, that I know this would make Mum happy and would prove to her that he really is sorry. He swears he will.

Should I ring Susan now? It's Wednesday, so she'll be at work. I don't really want to ring her there. I'll ring her at home later. But what if Graham answers, or Chrissy? What if I throw Susan off balance in the middle of cooking dinner or something? Should I go round in person? Or should I ask her to meet me somewhere, tell her I have some news? But that seems so melodramatic. I consider texting or emailing, but that seems too impersonal. In the end, I walk into town, choose an arty card and sit in a café to write it.

> *Dear Susan,*
>
> *I'm sorry that things have been fraught between us recently. I have some news I need to tell you, but I've been unsure of the best way to go about it. I didn't want to phone or visit and put you on the spot, so I'm writing instead. I hope this is a good decision, and not just a coward's way out!*

I'm being treated for ovarian cancer. That's why I had the hysterectomy, not because of cysts. I have Stage III cancer (quite advanced, but not without hope), all visible tumours have been removed and I've had three cycles of chemotherapy so far and have three more to go.

I'm sorry I didn't tell you sooner. Better late than never, eh?!

Again, so sorry not to have let you know sooner and to be telling you like this. I'm sure we'll speak soon.

Love,

Mum xx

I reread the card once, ignore a dozen worries about inappropriate tone, flippant use of exclamation marks and brevity, and post it first-class. It's a relief to have done it, at last, although I immediately worry about Susan's reaction. Will she be angry or resentful I didn't tell her sooner, will she be upset and shocked, will she wish I'd let her know in person, or be grateful I didn't? I'll just have to wait till I hear from her.

When I get home, Phyllis calls. She says she's going to be in the area for an animal charity fundraising do on Saturday and will 'look in on me' if she has time. The last thing I need is to have to entertain some seventy-year-old, twin-setted spinster. I may have to claim to be too weak to accept visitors, and, the way these last few emotionally exhausting days have gone, it might not be a lie. Mind you, I am curious to finally meet the woman I've worked with for ten years but never encountered face-to-face.

Despite plans for an early night, I stay up till the small hours researching ovarian cancer on the Internet. Maybe Joy's right, maybe I should put in a complaint about the hospital and shouldn't be so passive. During my Internet trawl, I discover that I could have inherited the 'ovarian cancer gene' from my father's side, although this accounts for only five to ten per cent of cases. I doubt whether this matters, then realise that of course it does: Susan, Chrissy. Suicidal tendencies, a predisposition to depression, mental instability, and now, possibly, ovarian cancer; gee, thanks Dad. And that's not even counting the mousey hair. I also find out that the disease is often diagnosed late because symptoms are vague – stomach pains, feeling full, bloating, needing to wee more often – and can be associated with any number of more minor ailments. That said, nine out of ten women do go to their doctor because of these symptoms. I wonder how long it took other members of the support group to be diagnosed with their various cancers, and if any were misdiagnosed to start with.

'Wendy,' I say to the mum-of-four from the Midlands during Thursday's session (no word from Susan yet), 'how long did it take for your breast cancer to be diagnosed?'

'It was picked up early, due to the screening programme I'm on. What with losing Mum and Auntie Maureen to it, and then my sister having had it a couple of years before, we all knew I was high risk. But I was still really shocked when it happened to me.'

'Did you worry you might be next in line?'

'I'm not sure. Life had been so hectic just coping with everything. Perhaps I thought it couldn't possibly happen to me *as well*, not after everyone else. Practically every year another relative or friend was diagnosed with cancer. But that's what made me have the screening, the regular check-ups, which allowed them to catch it early.'

'What about you, Margaret,' I say, after noticing that she's quieter than usual, 'how did you find out? Did it take long to be diagnosed? Were you shocked?'

'I wasn't really shocked, just thought "bloody typical",' she says, while shredding a tissue into tiny scraps. 'My husband's diabetes had been getting worse. He'd had it since childhood, but it had really affected his eyesight and strength, his ability to work. He was told he shouldn't drive any more. He's an electrician, so he was pretty much done for. My youngest daughter had finally got out of an abusive relationship and come back to live with us, temporarily like. So much for John and I working hard all our lives and looking forward to retirement. Anyway, my youngest, she'd had an abortion, a late abortion, because she didn't want this boyfriend's child. I'm saying all this in confidence, you understand? I know I may sound matter of fact, but it was a terrible time. She asked me to be with her at the clinic. It was awful, because she needed me to be supportive, but I couldn't be. I said I'd look after the baby, but she said no, she'd made her decision and she was going to get it done whether I helped her through it or not. And my oldest had had two miscarriages in six months and she so very much wanted a child. Ironic, I'd call it. Sick. And there's Stacey, giving her life for her baby. Christ, I wish we could smoke in here.'

Margaret rummages in her handbag, finds a fresh tissue, and resumes shredding.

'I felt like I was holding the whole family together, dealing with everyone else's problems. Then my mum was rushed to hospital in Glasgow. I went straight up. I was told on the phone it was a stroke, but it wasn't. She turned out to have had a bad ear infection which made her off balance, she'd fallen and was concussed, not her usual self, for a good few days. But she ended up coming through it good as new. When I was up, I saw my brother. I said in passing I hadn't been feeling too well myself, probably the stress of everything, but that I hadn't told the family down south because of all their problems. He asked what was wrong. I said my tummy was always upset, that I'd been rushing to the loo with diarrhoea. Even, you know, having a bit of blood there sometimes, which was not at all usual for me. The more I told him, said everything out loud, the more it just didn't sound right. And then he, well, he put the wind right up me. Said I had to see a doctor, those were the symptoms a friend's husband had and it turned out to be serious. So I did see someone. And it did turn out to be serious. Can't stop smoking, though.'

Margaret stands abruptly and goes outside for a cigarette. She is a heavy smoker, but I think she wants an excuse to get out of the portacabin. She's back in a few minutes. She admits she doesn't usually like talking about such personal stuff, that she's happier listening to others. We discuss this for a while, whether we feel more comfortable listening or disclosing information about ourselves.

'I don't want to speak out of turn,' says Margaret, 'but I find Nadia very difficult. She doesn't give support or reveal anything about herself. I don't know why she's here.'

Everyone looks at Nadia. As usual, she is staring at the floor and doesn't respond, other than to flush slightly.

Harry holds up a hand.

'One of the rules of the group is that we address each other directly, not in the third person.'

'I think it's up to you if you don't want to speak,' comments soft-spoken Heather, gazing at Nadia, who continues to study her sandals. 'I believe you give to the group by being here every week. It must provide something for you or you wouldn't come. Although I never have a clue what you might be thinking or feeling.'

Nadia remains silent.

'That's what I'm saying,' says Margaret, 'that's what I find difficult about you, Nadia. We all reveal our feelings and secrets, make ourselves really vulnerable, and you just sit there. Maybe if someone says nothing, you fear they're thinking the worst.'

'Such as?' asks Harry.

'Such as I'm a stupid old woman who'd be better off dead. Why should I be surviving cancer, when Stacey's not? I visited her earlier. She's not even going to get home. The baby's fine, but she's dying, and she's got everything to live for. She thinks she's made the right decision, thinks if she'd had a termination she wouldn't have survived anyway, says death's easier to face because she's given life to another. But that's all past for me. My children are grown up. What have I got to live for?'

We fall silent for a minute.

'This isn't really about Nadia, or Stacey, is it?' I say, tentatively. 'It's about your own worst fears for yourself, it's about anxieties that we all have. About the meaning of our lives, aging, mortality. Maybe it's also something to do with what you were saying about you and John, about working all your lives and looking forward to retiring and feeling that's been taken away from you.'

Margaret nods, while sucking in short, harsh breaths. I can't tell if she's trying hard not to cry or trying hard not to lose her temper.

'I'm sick of it!' she shouts.

'Of what?' asks Harry, calmly.

'Of trying to make the best of things and be brave and stay positive. Of waiting to get cancer again. Just waiting and waiting for it to come back. I don't feel bloody positive. I feel bloody angry. I've got a three-month check-up next week and I'm going crazy. All my life I've had to slog my guts out for every little thing and this is my reward. My husband's half the man he used to be, I never see my son, my daughter ended my grandchild's life before it had even begun. What about me? Where's my life? Where's my happiness?'

'Touché,' says a male voice.

We turn and stare. Alfredo is standing in the doorway. He's lost weight and is even more gaunt.

'Touché? Touché! Have you ever made sacrifices, put everyone else before yourself? Have you ever given a damn about another person?' asks Margaret, bitterly.

'You're alone. I'm alone,' states Alfredo, taking a seat. 'Every single one of us is scared, isolated. Nothing matters now or makes any difference. When all's said and done, it comes to nothing. You're on your own. But I didn't need cancer to tell me that. I knew it from the age of five. Father dead, mother couldn't cope, in and out of the care system for years.'

I sense Margaret resisting saying something awful, like, 'I don't blame her for not wanting you.' Her lips twitch and the bottom half of her face contorts as she struggles to keep the words in.

'But we're not alone, are we?' Nadia says, the strength of her clear voice, as well as her clipped English accent, a surprise. 'We are here, together. It's hard, but we do want to know and understand and help each other. At least we're trying.'

When Nadia finishes talking we gawp at each other in disbelief, before breaking into spontaneous applause. We all laugh, including Alfredo, and so does she.

The session has been both draining and exhilarating. It's extraordinary how things can flip so quickly. It's as if people have been turning somersaults, conjuring new selves, changing shape – movements as seamless as they are unexpected – before my eyes, when all we've been doing is sitting, talking. It reminds me of Leon, of when he revealed he was Irish and all about his background, suddenly becoming a whole other person.

When I get home, there's still no phone call or message from Susan. The card should have arrived by now. When I don't hear anything on Friday morning, I email her at work, after realising I don't even have her personal email. An automated response immediately pings back saying she's away on a training course and will be back in the office on Monday morning. At least this explains why she hasn't been in touch. If she doesn't get in contact over the weekend, I'll ring her.

Too early on Saturday morning, a rather nice dream about Ainsley Harriot is infiltrated by the horrible, dry, hissing sound that Marty makes through his teeth, which he calls whistling. I should be glad he's here getting on with the work, but I'm not. And I bet the neighbours aren't either. I finally get out of bed mid-morning. I look out to see Marty talking to a young woman in the back garden. I hope she's not here to complain about the noise (not his whistling, but the concrete-tile cutting or whatever the dreadful row has been for the last while). Poor Leon, I can't believe I shouted at him for drumming.

I go downstairs in my bathrobe to put the kettle on. Marty and the young woman are standing outside the kitchen window, but don't appear to have seen me. Closer up, she looks to be in her thirties and is of average height, with a slim, delicate build. I poke my head out the back door.

'Anything up?'

'Gina!' exclaims the woman, and she rushes forward and shakes my hand with both of hers.

I nearly recognise her voice, but I certainly don't recognise her physically. She is striking, with hair as sleek and black as a Japanese woman's, and pale, fine skin, littered with freckles across her narrow nose, and prominent cheekbones. Her well-defined brows and unusually long, straight eyelashes frame eyes of light brown, almost gold, like a tiger's.

'I'm Phyllis.'

'Um …?'

'From *The Cat Lover's Monthly.*'

It takes Phyllis five minutes to convince me that she is *the* Phyllis, not Phyllis' daughter, granddaughter, maid, niece, or someone who happens to be called Phyllis who also happens to have set up exactly the same publication over ten years ago.

'I don't mean to act so stupidly, but I imagined you to be, well … at least my age, if not a generation older.'

I sit at the patio table sipping tea while Phyllis talks about her passion for animals, and cats in particular. Her love and enthusiasm are touching. I can imagine leaving money to the proverbial cats' home. What has cancer done to me? The purchase of a book on houseplant care, a growing love of country and western music and, now, serious consideration of charitable donation to an animal sanctuary. Or perhaps it's middle age. If I start to fancy Daniel O'Donnell and Alan Titchmarsh over Iggy Pop and David Bowie, then I know I'll have reached the point of no return, and that death is preferable.

As I sit, Marty and Phyllis discuss renewable energy, wind turbine design (Phyllis has had one installed at the sanctuary), homeopathy for animals, compost toilets, carbon emissions, and various other tedious environmental topics. They are both dumbstruck when they discover a mutual love for, and obsession with, obscure seventies folk-rock band The Low-down Mothers. Marty offers Phyllis a rare, bootleg recording of a 1973 gig. I don't tell Phyllis that Marty made it himself and has had a stack of unsold copies knocking about his attic ever since.

This has got to be love at first interaction; I don't think love at first sight of Marty is possible. I see him rendered painfully aware of his body. He glances down at his pot belly, gingerly toys with his stringy, tobacco-stained ponytail, then briefly contemplates his filthy hands and gnawed-down nails. Phyllis is talking about government legislation to improve health and the environment, and remarks that banning smoking in public places is one of the best things it can do. I give Marty a helping hand by removing the roll-up from behind his ear, under the guise of brushing back a strand (and there are only strands left) of hair.

Marty is performing at a local pub tonight, and it doesn't take much to persuade Phyllis to stay over at mine after attending her charity do in the afternoon. She says her fundraising friends will be delighted that she'll be able to join them for Sunday lunch tomorrow, but I sense her real motivation has more to do with Marty.

That evening, when we're in the pub, Olly turns up. Phyllis, to Marty's visible relief, pays no attention to his younger, better-looking, semi-famous brother. Marty and Phyllis both become misty-eyed during Marty's rendition of *The First Time Ever I Saw Your Face*. I am convinced of Phyllis' feelings for Marty when she turns round and requests that the table of noisy lads behind us, 'Please be quiet, please, because I am trying to listen, please,' something so clearly difficult for her to do. Ten minutes later, I yell at them to shut the fuck up or I'll poke their eyes out which, although less subtle, is far more effective.

I wake up smiling on Sunday. I think it's due to Marty and Phyllis and their innocent amazement at each other's existence. I must remain a romantic at heart, despite decades of amorous disappointments. Still, I'm sure nothing will happen, as I can't see Marty being unfaithful to, let alone leaving, Tessa. It's not until I'm driving to the supermarket to stock up for the week that I realise I've felt fairly good all weekend. Unfortunately, the window of reasonable health and energy between chemo sessions seems to be shrinking. Still, session four tomorrow, then only two more to go. At least the windows reassure me that it is possible to feel well again.

I decide to take a quick look around the clothes section before the food shop, and end up buying a floaty summer top. Perhaps normal life will resume, after all, and I'll be able to shop for holidays and parties, rather than hospital stays and post-chemo days.

Phyllis insists I join her and her fund-raising cronies for a long Sunday lunch. I talk about cats for three solid hours. I turn out to be the woman with the most diverse and wide-ranging cat knowledge there: from children's picture book cat heroes, to geriatric cat care, to cats in art and literature. I realise, with horror, that I am accepted as one of their own, that I am, in fact, inspiring awe.

Soon after we get back to my place, Marty arrives with the

bootleg LP. He and Phyllis are worse than a pair of blushing virgins. Marty can't stop staring at Phyllis. Phyllis can barely meet his gaze. I end up making small talk for them in order to break their silence and embarrassment. Once Marty leaves and Phyllis finds out he's in a long-term relationship (I'd call over twenty-five years pretty long-term, but what else could I say when she asked me?), she looks deeply pained and immediately rushes off to catch a train home.

By the time I've finished tidying the house and getting organised for the next day's chemo it's late in the evening. Maybe Susan isn't home yet, or hasn't opened the post. Perhaps she has and doesn't know how to respond. Why didn't I just phone her up and tell her straight out? Waiting for a response is becoming as bad as worrying about how to tell her in the first place. But I feel too tired to think about it properly now. I'll ring her tomorrow, after chemo. I'll sort it all out then.

14

BARREL BOTTOM BLUES

I'll be honest: I am facing death and, in certain ways, its spectre is not a bad one. I know that cancer doesn't equal the end. But. I'm supposed to be battling now, the righteous and moral fight, for life over death, good over evil. The fight of my life, *for* my life, against cancer – this enemy, this alien invader. But is it? My body has generated these deadly, multiplying cells, which will ultimately destroy me if left untreated, causing their own annihilation. It's more palatable to position death beside me, rather than within, to remove it from myself, when my own cells are mutating, are killing me. I've always been in conflict with myself psychologically, pulling one way, then the other, as in a tug-of-war, so it shouldn't surprise me that my body is in conflict with itself, too. Yes, I prefer death waiting to embrace me, as in a Kathy Kollwitz etching, or suspended over my bed, as in a Frida Kahlo painting: an outsider.

Do I feel like fighting, like being brave today, propped up in this hospital chair with a bag of Carboplatin draining into me? No. I feel like letting my weapons – my will to live, my reason, my outrage at this having happened to me – fall and clatter to the ground. I want not only to let these weapons fall away, but also my hard work, my effort, my constant struggle to keep going, to get up, to refuse to surrender to all those head-under-the-duvet mornings, weeks, years. Thank God, part of me thinks. At last. Goodbye. No more wanting, no more caring, no more desire, to remain frustrated or otherwise. What a relief. Let me succumb, and gladly. For nothing in life turns out how you imagine it will. My promise of joy, my wondrous secret unfurling inside, became Susan, a woman who can't stand me. My one true love, light of my life, my man, my husband, my fire, my passion, became, well, the rest is history, and it certainly wasn't what I anticipated when the thunderbolt of love hit, never to strike again. Chrissy, who was to be the perfect child and make Susan's life complete – who would put right all my bad parenting, who would prove to her, and me, what motherhood should be – has been nothing of the kind. And becoming a grandmother, which initially catapulted me into middle age and made me peer over the edge of my grave, has turned out to be a joy. But today, life's meaning is evasive. Perhaps that's why love has always remained such a fixation, promising a daily miracle here on earth. Promising, but never delivering.

Another secret. When things were at their hardest, when every day was a leaden weight breaking my spirit as it bore down on me, I would have welcomed an excuse to give up and not exist. So long everybody and everything, with none of the responsibility for my own death, not like suicide. I have told Leon this, admitted my sometime wish that life would end. He just nodded; it's called the death instinct. Psychotherapists, eh, an answer for everything. Dream you were making love to your mother? Of course, that's only natural. Had a rant at someone who didn't deserve it? A classic case of displacement, don't you know. Irrational fear of choc-ices? That'll be an unconscious projection of an unnameable anxiety. Give them their due: they do tackle what nobody else can or wants to. Nothing shocked Leon, and he didn't just let it flow over him like Olly, but tried to understand. Leon. Who I paid to listen to me. Who refused to listen to me again. Who I still haven't apologised to. Maybe Susan won't get in touch; why should my having cancer make her any more likely to want to see me, or us any more likely to get on? If anything, it's going to add another layer of difficulty and ambiguity to our relationship.

Today is one of those grey, weighty, deathly days. I'm sure if it was blinding sunshine and feasting birds I wouldn't be thinking of the end so easily, so lightly, so warmly. The sky is the lid of a tomb. I don't know what's happened to me since yesterday, since the weekend, when I was feeling pretty good. But of course I do. More chemo, that's what's happened. A horrible dose of a different reality. Dr K assured me I need feel no pain, when I wrested him by the arm earlier and asked what happens if this abominable 'therapy' doesn't work, told him what I'm scared of: pain, deterioration, disability. He said if it's terminal I can have as much pain relief as I need (but not enough to kill me, he added pointedly). But that's being negative, for now I must believe in survival. Forget your womb, your hair, any amount of suffering, wretchedness and fatigue, remaining alive is the aim. Growing up was hard, so is growing older; I never discovered the easy bit in the middle.

Sleep. There is nothing I want but sleep.

A nurse rouses me to plug in another bag of poison. I want to lob it out the window. Treatment is interminable today. There is no escape from what I feel, no future fantasy to which I can yield the present. I'm not reading, puzzling or anything, just reclining in the reclining chair and thinking about being dead. That's the sorry truth. Cancer's the sorry truth. Chemotherapy's the sorry truth. For millions of us.

An hour later, I'm hooked up to another bag of liquid. Where the hell does it all go? I should have inflated like a water balloon by now.

After chemo, I return home in the now-familiar state of complete exhaustion coupled with wired wakefulness.

'Susan's rung a couple of times,' says Moya. 'I told her you'd be home about now. She asked if it would be okay to call round, but I said you usually felt pretty rough after chemo and went to bed.'

'I'll ring her back.'

Perhaps it's the drugs affecting my mind and emotions, but I seem to have lost all anxiety about this interaction with Susan; I seem to have lost all feeling about everything. I dial her number. Graham answers.

'Hello, Gina. So sorry to hear your news – you must let us know if there's anything we can do to help.'

'Thanks, Graham, that's very kind of you.'

'Susan's here, I'll pass you over.'

'Mother?'

'Susan. You got my card?'

'Yes, I opened it today. I've been away all week on a training course. I, I never would have said those things – in the garden – if I'd known what you were going through.'

'And I should have told you earlier, much earlier. I know that now. And apologies for the snail poo. I should have respected your wishes.'

The mention of our latest fall out, and what it was over, must strike us both as ridiculous, and we manage to laugh. The phrase 'life's too short' pops into my head, perhaps into Susan's, too.

'How's the treatment going?' she asks. 'The … chemotherapy?'

I begin to fill Susan in on some of the details of cancer and treatment, wondering why I've been so scared of telling her, why I feared she'd be unsupportive and blaming.

'Is there anything I can do? Can I come over?' she asks.

'Well, Moya's been helping me through the worst post-chemo days. I usually feel dreadful for a week or so after, so perhaps we could meet up next week, when I'm feeling better?'

'Okay. But I'll ring tomorrow, to see how you are.'

I'm spaced out for the following week, depressed really, with treatment hitting me even harder psychologically than it does physically. Even I grow tired of myself moping about saying, 'I feel like death', 'I wish I could just die now and get it over with,' and, 'What's the point?' Anti-depressants have been suggested. But why? Surely this is a logical reaction to what I'm going through. I can't be bothered to get dressed, think about the house, eat, anything. Susan's phoned most days, but I can't think of anything to say other than I'm feeling terrible and we'll meet up when I improve. Lara's given me a special bracelet to keep the sickness and fatigue at bay. I asked her if she had anything for mental sickness. She returned with a bottle of something I'm supposed to sniff four times a day. Really.

Even a full week after chemo, when I usually perk up, I don't feel much better, and continue to stay in bed with the curtains drawn. Life may have seemed a long, slow swing of the pendulum ever forwards, but now it is moving back; preservation is the best to be hoped for. But perhaps a deterioration of spirit is even worse than physical suffering. I don't want to turn into an embittered person, stuffed with disappointment, resentment, vain regret. I don't want cancer to do this to me, to change my personality, despite having spent most of my life wishing I was someone else. Existence has never appeared stranger. It's not time – the past and the future – which is intangible, but the present, the living second. Life is experienced so much in the head, in thought, in remembering back and imagining forwards, that it's the present that is elusive, enigmatic, ghostly. I've been 'thinking too much', as Mum would have said.

Moya interrupts my morbid mental wanderings by handing me the phone, accompanied by a stern look.

'What?' I say.

'I think it's time you used it – to call Susan. She'll be home from work now. She's been ringing every day and it's time you rang her – so it's not so one-sided. And …'

'Yes?'

'It'll do you good to interact with someone, to be distracted by something, to do anything other than spend all day locked away in this room, talking to yourself.'

'I'm just entering my second teenagerhood.'

Moya refuses to smile.

'Oh, hello Mother,' says Susan. 'I'm glad you've rung. I've been looking up information about treatment for your sort of cancer and –'

'That's really kind of you, Susan, but Joy has literally turned into a walking encyclopaedia of ovarian cancer.'

'Oh. And there's a support group at the hospital, apparently, and … do you know about that already?'

'Yes, I've been going to it.'

'Oh. That's good.'

Blimey, why does every interaction with Susan go wrong? She's making a real effort to be helpful and I immediately make it clear I don't need her help.

'It's really thoughtful of you to look out these things for me,' I say. 'I do appreciate it.'

'Well, just let me know if there's anything I can do,' says Susan.

'I will. And, um, is Chrissy okay?' I ask, because I can hear her howling in the background.

'Just another one of her strops,' says Susan, with a sigh. 'Just bear with me a minute – I'll put the phone down while I try to sort it out.'

I hear Susan and Chrissy squabbling, then Chrissy starts howling again. I realise that other people are having problems and worries and crises, as well as me, including members of my own family. Graham comes on the phone.

'Sorry, Gina, Chrissy's having a bit of a turn. Susan says she'll ring back later.'

'What is it? Is everything okay?'

'It is, yes, it is really.'

I don't know what to say, as it so obviously isn't.

'You haven't told her about me, about the cancer?' I ask.

'No, it's not that.'

'Good. I'd like to tell her myself. She knows I've been ill, but I haven't used the word "cancer" yet. I don't know if she'll have heard it before or have any idea what it means.'

'Nor do I, to be honest. Do you want to see her? I know you

haven't for a while, and I know you might not be feeling up to it at the moment, but, when you are ...'

I tell Graham I'd love to see Chrissy, but I am feeling worse than usual post-chemo, so will have to check with Moya that she'll be happy to be around, too.

Moya says she is, so we arrange for Chrissy to come over tomorrow.

Next morning, I open the curtains on another monochrome, drizzly, lifeless day, even though it's mid-summer. Nothing is done with any passion: the rain is light and steady, the cold is an irritation rather than a threat to life, the sky is a medium, dull grey. Hating such weather is unfortunate, living in Britain. I feel detached and subdued, which is unusual for me, as I'm usually feeling something, and intensely.

Susan and Chrissy arrive with Susan running late, looking tense and strained. Chrissy rushes into my arms, and Susan rushes off to work. Chrissy has a small, portable keyboard with her, its volume turned up to 'max'. She seems her normal self, although maybe with a slightly manic edge. We go into the front room.

'What d'you think of this one, Grandma?' she asks again and again, as she runs through the keyboard's pre-recorded tunes. Although the noise is loud and abrasive, I am grateful for it, for the life force that inevitably accompanies Chrissy.

'Chrissy, my darling, I love you,' I say, aware I'm being clingy, desperate, in pain.

'I love you too, Grandma,' she replies, lightly.

Chrissy sits on the floor and unpacks stuffed toys and colouring things from her small rucksack. She soon becomes absorbed in drawing. She chatters away as she works, face pinched in concentration, and with much pencil licking and turning this way and that of the paper; full artistry if I'm not mistaken.

'How's Trudy the Turd?' I ask.

'Not sure,' she replies, distractedly. 'Her last adventure was to Saturn and she liked it so much she hasn't come back.'

'Oh?'

'But there's someone else, a whole lot of someone elses.'

'Who are they?'

'Well, it's early days …' says Chrissy, mysteriously. I'm sure she's just winding me up; she's never normally so reticent. But she is growing older, growing up, so perhaps she's starting to lose her young child's spontaneity and instant enthusiasms.

'Go on – tell me!' I insist.

'Oh, okay,' says Chrissy, and she jumps up on the sofa and begins describing her new creations and showing me her pictures.

The inhabitants of Foxling Village are an unlikely bunch. They live in a series of rustic barns and haystacks, but with lava lamps and TVs and a jukebox that dispenses endless sweets as well as music. Grandpa Foxling has vivid green eyes, just like Olly's.

'What's Grandpa Foxling doing?' I ask.

'He's a post-fox, but it's the olden days so all the letters have to be chiselled into stone and pushed along in a wheelbarrow.'

'And what about the girl fox on roller-skates, who's she?'

'She's called Kissy, and when she grows up she's going to be an artist during the week and a pop star on weekends.'

'Very sensible. And that?' I say, pointing to an angelic-looking fox with a kindly smile and extra-fluffy fur, who I'm rather hoping is me.

'That's Mummy Foxling. She has secret magic powers, which she uses in her spare time, but really she runs the toy shop and is always happy and lets Kissy do *exactly* what she wants.'

We go through the various residents of Foxling Village: there's Daddy Foxling (who does possess an uncanny resemblance to Graham, but is dressed, unaccountably, in top hat and tails); Uncle Barty Foxling (the cowboy boots and ponytail are a dead giveaway); and Milady Foxling (no interpretation necessary), who sometimes provides transport for the others by hooking them up to her mobility scooter, whether they be on skateboard, bike or rollerblades. There's young Bradella Foxling – Chrissy can't decide if it's a boy or girl or, possibly, a bit of both. Even Mrs Hatchet Foxling the schoolteacher, with unibrow, beady eyes and nasty expression, is present. I don't appear to be there.

'What about a grandma? Isn't there a Grandma Foxling in the village?'

'Well, she's there, but you never get to meet her. I mean, you don't see her.'

'Why's that?'

'She *tells* the stories. She lets you know what all the others are doing. She's the …' Chrissy struggles with the word, 'rator.'

'Narrator.'

'That's what I said.'

'In that case, I think Kissy Foxling is going to go on an adventure with Grandpa Foxling and Uncle Barty Foxling to Chocolate Dreamland, with the help of Mummy Foxling, who gets them there by magic.'

'Yes!'

Chrissy and I spend the rest of the day writing, drawing and colouring in our Foxling book, as well as eating various snacks which she prepares 'to keep us going', i.e. cheesy biscuits spread with an inch of butter and Rich Tea with jam on. By the end of the adventure, Grandpa Foxling has eaten so much chocolate at Dreamland that he has to be pulled home in his wheelbarrow by Milady Foxling, and Uncle Barty Foxling gets his ponytail stuck in a nut-flaking machine and ends up in Foxling Hospital, after being heroically rescued by Kissy Foxling, who also wins a lifetime's supply of chocolate drops (or 'droops', according to Chrissy's spelling). Despite the superb quality of the puns placed throughout the adventure (by me), Chrissy collapses in hysterics at her own, 'And they all lived chocolately ever after,' ending. Just as I'm starting to worry that she might wet herself, Susan arrives. Her expression lightens when she sees that Chrissy and I are having fun together. She asks if it's been okay or too much of a strain. I tell her it's been lovely and has done me good.

'Seriously, Mother, how are you feeling today?' asks Susan.

'Another time, eh? Once I've told …'

I glance at Chrissy, who's repacking her rucksack.

'Why don't you drop Chrissy round tomorrow?' I say.

'Will do.'

'I've not been very well, Chrissy,' I say, after lunch the next day.

'I know,' says Chrissy, looking at my scarf-wrapped head. 'You've been having cancer.'

'Yes, that's right. How do you know?'

'A boy at school called Aaron had it. He got it in Year One and was away a lot and his head went bald. But he's back now, and so is his hair.'

'Good. Good for him.'

We smile at each other. Neither of us seem to have anything more to say. That was easier than I thought.

We decide to give Foxling Village a break for the afternoon and go on the computer instead. A pile of junk has been accumulating due to the house renovations and Chrissy is keen to sell it online, especially when I agree to split the profits fifty-fifty. Chrissy is an expert eBayer, advising on which photos to upload and the best way to advertise items. I also make some rather rash purchases of my own, which, when egged on by a seven-year-old, seem like a good idea.

We finish the rainy afternoon (bloody British summer) with me 'resting my eyes' and Chrissy, knowing my hair will grow back differently, adding a variety of ridiculous hairstyles to photos of me, in a software package I have no idea how to use. I hear her giggling at her creations and, by the time Susan picks her up, she has doctored every picture I have.

'Thanks, Mother,' says Susan.

'No problem. It's been a pleasure. Chrissy and I have talked about me having cancer. A boy at school had it and now he's better. Anyway, you all have a great holiday and I'll see you when you get back.'

'Yes, we really must get together properly,' says Susan.

'Definitely,' I say, 'and I should be feeling much better by then.'

Chrissy gives me an extra-squeezy hug goodbye. Susan and I try to do likewise. We're like a couple of wooden statues trying to embrace, but it's a start.

By Thursday afternoon, ten days after the last chemo, I'm feeling better physically, but can't work or concentrate. I decide I must go out. Working from home in front of the computer makes me housebound enough, but I've felt so awful since the last chemo I've not left the building. I think about ringing Joy to see if she wants to meet up, but realise it's one of her market-stall days so she'll be busy. I force, really force, myself to shower, put on a bit of make-up and a headscarf. I also force Moya to agree that she doesn't need to be here so much. I know she's happy to help, but I also know she's in the middle of getting her cottage ready to sell. And I must be such depressing company; I don't want to bring her down with me. What was it Milady said? When my father was feeling wretched he made everyone around him feel wretched. I don't want to do that to my wonderful friend. I need to cope by myself, and she's got her own plans for the future to pursue.

I walk into town and wander around aimlessly. All I can think about is the next chemo session. And mine and Susan's parting hug. I'm so glad we're speaking again, that she knows about the cancer and is happy for me to look after Chrissy, but the awkwardness of our embrace seems a sadder indictment of our relationship than the decades of rowing. I know there's a lifetime of tension between us that needs tackling, but I have no idea how we're to do it.

As I mooch about a posh department store, the displays seem to mock me, with their assumption that healthy, aspirational lives are being led. The swimwear that presumes there is modesty left to preserve, a holiday to look forward to; the high heels and fancy hats that there are occasions to dress up for, events to attend; the greetings cards that imagine life is strewn with occasions other than those requiring a 'get well soon' or 'in sympathy'. The autumn collections are starting to arrive. I wonder if I'll be here to see next spring's. Scarves: no longer items to keep you warm or set off an outfit, but necessary disguises for a bald head that screams cancer.

I try to get a grip. I take the lift to the fourth-floor café and end up with a pot of tea in front of me, looking out at the overcast city. It's late in the day and the place is empty, apart from a pair of well-heeled, well-preserved couples, who are seriously discussing the Conservative Party leadership. Such talk bored me senseless when I was fifteen; it still does at nearly fifty. I'm relieved when a pair of younger women walk in. They look like tourists: a mother in her late thirties with thick dark hair and a rather beautiful but stern face, and a daughter in her mid-teens, a little overweight, with the same jet curls.

'Sit next to me!' I want to shout. 'I'm not really dying.' I pretend to study a menu, so that no one can see my eyes beginning to fill. It's impossible to fight off any longer, I'm sinking, I'm –

'Gina! Gina?'

It's Margaret. She's carrying an espresso and a pastry on a tray. I smile. I try not to cry.

'I don't want to intrude or anything, hen. Are you waiting for someone?'

'No, just, you know, having a break.'

Margaret's come in for the homewares sale, buying new towels, and bed linen she didn't plan on, but it was such a bargain. I enjoy the small talk. Instead of seeming inconsequential, a waste of time, it's a pleasure to discuss the thread count of sheets, the meaning of tog values, the quality of the coffee they serve here.

The pair of older couples get up to leave.

'God, what a bunch,' whispers Margaret. 'I know they're my age, maybe even younger, but what a dreadful collection of old farts. I hope I never get like that.'

I beam at Margaret. I tell her I've been feeling low, that I've been sitting in the café because I don't want to go home and face … what? More of myself, perhaps.

'How many chemos have you done now?' she asks.

'Four. Number five in a week and a half.'

'You're drained, exhausted, depressed.'

'Yes, I think I am depressed.'

'Don't let the cancer do this to you. Don't let it break your spirit. That's why we talk about fighting it. It's not just the physical effects, Gina, dreadful though they are, it's the psychological, too. C'mon.'

'Where to?'

'The support group.'

'No, I really couldn't.'

'Anywhere better to go?'

'No, but –'

'For me?'

I've never seen Margaret so high and happy, shouting hello and waving to a couple of the others across the car park. I follow her into the portacabin and slump into the seat next to her like a sulky zombie.

'I went for my check-up last week and I'm all clear!' Margaret declares, before everyone's even had a chance to sit down. 'I don't need another for six months. Up till now it's been every three. Six months feels really good, like a proper length of time, in which I can do things, apart from worry about the cancer coming back.'

We congratulate her.

'I wasn't sure whether or not to come today. I don't want to rub other people's noses in it, you know, those still going through chemo or waiting for test results. Then I met laughing girl here and thought it would do her good.'

She pokes me in the ribs. Harry says it's great to see someone surviving so well, and with such a difficult cancer.

'Can I, can I just talk?' Margaret asks.

We nod.

'Me and John, we've decided to sell up. We bought our council house when the kids were little. We've done a lot of work to it – put on a double-storey extension, a conservatory and a garage. We had three agents round in one day. It's worth two hundred and fifty thousand pounds, and that's going for the conservative estimate! I nearly died on the spot when they were coming up with figures like that. We've already had two viewings and have got our eye on a new build in town. A 'city-living apartment'. Swanky, eh? It's absolutely beautiful, brand new, secure parking, nice little communal garden, and the kitchen … We'll have about eighty thousand pounds left if we buy it, to do … whatever we bloody well like!'

I feel like clapping and cheering. I do.

'We've been wanting to visit my sister in Australia for ages. And if we get the apartment we can go abroad whenever we want – no gardening to do, no four bedrooms to look after, no maintenance. We can be away for months, can come and go as we please, and I'm due to retire at the end of the year.'

We spend a lot of the session discussing Margaret's plans.

'Do you think having had cancer is affecting the choices you're making now?' asks Harry.

'Definitely. The clear tests are like the lifting of a death sentence. I mean, I know it may come back, but I feel I have time now. It's made us think about what we want in our lives, like not to work ourselves into the grave, to look after ourselves. When we found out how much the house was worth we thought we should give anything left after the move to the kids as – like everyone – they're struggling. But they'll still get their inheritance when we go, and we need to enjoy our lives now, while we still can. You know, John and I, we still have a lot. We still love each other, we still enjoy each other's company, after nearly forty years. And everything we've got, we've worked for, it's not like it's been handed to us on a plate. And … I'm giving up smoking!'

Margaret is in the middle of telling us about the hypnotherapy she's having to help her quit, when time's up and Harry has to end the session. We head to the pub to celebrate. I feel buoyant, refreshed. We don't even mind when Alfredo, who hasn't said a word or made a noise all session, tags along with us. Margaret orders champagne. It's wonderfully uplifting to be with someone so positive, who's been through so much.

'I can't believe I'm clear,' beams Margaret. 'The tumour up my arse was as big as a lemon!'

'My consultant said the one in my left breast was the size of a plum and the one in my right a gooseberry. I felt like a fruit salad,' says Heather.

'What d'you reckon on these?' asks Alfredo, and he pulls his shirt collar down to reveal the hard pink lumps on his neck caused by the lymphoma.

'Cobnuts,' I say.

'What's a frigging cobnut when it's at home?' cries Margaret. 'I'd go for radishes – a horrible vegetable everyone's familiar with.'

'I think they're more like grapes,' says Wendy. 'Black. Seed-less. From Spain.'

The fruit jokes continue. Even after the two hundredth, we're still laughing, although the champagne is no doubt a contributing factor. Alfredo lowers the tone by saying he's got a love lance the size of a cucumber, which he is 'willing to loan out to any of you ladies one last time before I die'.

'I'd even offer to poke Harry, I'm so desperate,' he says.

'For a total tube, you can be a right laugh,' concludes Margaret at the end of the evening, which is as close to affectionate as these two are likely to get.

15

FOR ONE NIGHT ONLY

Next morning, I pad slowly up the hallway to answer a bang on the door, feeling deeply hungover, but not unhappy. The new sofa Chrissy and I ordered on the Internet has arrived. Even as they unload it from the back of the van, still wrapped in thick polythene, I know it's a mistake. It's made of red leather and is in the shape of a huge pair of lips.

As I stand in the doorway, shielding my eyes and vowing never again to shop when on a Skittles sugar high, Dougie pulls up in his taxi, a worse-for-wear, sapphire-blue Mondeo. Last time I was in it he was extolling the virtues of his latest business idea: taxis in which you *have* to smoke, i.e. as soon as you get in, Dougie swivels round from the front seat, hands you a complimentary fag and lights it, this being his idea of the ultimate in hospitality. He was toying with the name of *Smokin' Wheels* for the company; I suggested *Malignant Motors*.

Removing himself from the taxi is a visible and audible effort for Dougie, especially with the sporty, bucket-shaped driver's seat he's installed. Once out, he makes a half-hearted attempt to hike his jogging bottoms up over his arse cheeks, then pulls Brad from the back seat. He shoves his son up Leon's front path, orders him to, 'Ring the bloody bell,' then slams back into the taxi and speeds off. Brad appears unfazed.

'Hello, Chrissy's Grandma,' he lisps cheerfully.

Leon opens his door; my heart leaps. We have been studiously avoiding each other since my meltdown in the garden. But I can't pretend I haven't seen him or scurry back indoors because I'm just about to sign a sheet for the delivery man.

Leon shakes hands with Brad.

'Are your parents here, your mother or father?'

'Daddy dropped me off.'

'Dropped you off? But you're only seven years old, aren't you, Bradley?'

Leon steps onto his front path to scan the street for a parent. We hear a panting and click-clacking advancing along the pavement. Tar soon totters into view and up the path. She places a hand on the wall for support, her breath coming in erratic, painful bursts.

'Sorry Doc ... it's Dougie ... he's having ... trouble ... adjusting ... to Brad's ... condition.'

There's a sudden breeze and Leon's front door slams shut, making us all jump.

'Oh, I seem to be locked out,' says Leon. 'Have you still got that spare key I gave you, Gina?'

'S-sure,' I stutter. 'Why don't you all come in while I try to find it.'

Everyone hangs about in my hallway while I attempt to locate the key.

'Could you contact your husband, Mrs Spokes?' asks Leon. 'It really is advisable that both parents be involved in the assessment process.'

'Certainly, Doc,' Tar replies, and she pulls out her mobile, jabs a few buttons, turns to one side slightly, as if for privacy, then screams in one long breath, 'If you ain't here in two minutes flat you ain't seeing your wife, your kids or your house ever again.'

'He'll be right back,' she chirrups, as she puts her phone away.

I call Leon into the kitchen. I try to discern his emotions, but his face remains blank.

'How are you having anything to do with the Spokes,' I whisper, 'after what happened at the barbecue?'

'Their son has been referred to me for assessment,' Leon replies simply. I find his professionalism admirable, if incomprehensible.

'And about my outburst in the garden –' I begin.

'Let's just forget it,' he interjects.

'Oh, alright.'

While Leon rummages through the old biscuit tin full of spare keys to see if he can identify his, I chat to Tar in the hallway. As Dougie pulls back up in his taxi, I ask Tar what it's all about, certain Leon won't tell me, being a stickler for patient confidentiality.

'Brad needs to be assessed by a 'ead doctor. That's what Dougie's ashamed of, what he's so angry about.'

'It ain't that,' huffs Dougie, as he steps into the house, his big beery face flushed with – Tar's right – shame and anger. 'All me kids have had assessments. Why, Keanu's been done by The Challenging Behaviour Unit, The Antisocial Behaviour Unit, The Keep Our Communities Safe Unit, The Drugs Rehabilitation Unit, The Young Offenders Unit, The Truancy Unit. He's been given the once-over by every facking unit you care to mention and I have stood by that boy all the way. You know that, Tar.'

Dougie has trouble swallowing; he really is choked up.

'But never, never ...' he stumbles on.

Tar folds her arms across her chest, thrusts her weight onto one hip, raises a brow and curls a lip, personifying disdain.

'Never what, Douglas?' she demands.

'Never has a son of mine had to see a shrink because he won't stop wearing his sister's clothes! He's gonna be a pervert.'

Leon walks up the hallway from the kitchen, spare front-door key in hand. He's followed by Brad who, with most unfortunate timing, has decked himself out in the Princess on the Silver Horse net curtain ensemble.

'Take it off,' Dougie hisses. 'Take that off you facking poof or I'll break your facking neck.'

Leon stands in front of Brad protectively. 'Mr Spokes, kindly refrain from talking to your son in that manner. I must request in the strongest possible terms that you control your temper, and your language.'

'I didn't mean to upset you, Daddy,' grizzles Brad.

Moving past Leon, Brad goes to place a hand on his father's arm, as if to comfort him, but Dougie shoves him away, and over. Brad lands with a little 'plumpf' on the floorboards.

Despite his despicable language, I don't think Dougie intended to push Brad over. Dougie is a hard man, with a short fuse and clear enjoyment of violence. He is a man other men avoid eye contact with, a man with a past, a man who has been at Her Majesty's pleasure on a number of occasions, and no doubt should have been a whole lot more. But he's a fizzer, a popper, an exploder. That's not to say an outburst couldn't do serious damage, but his aggression is palpable, visible. Tar, on the other hand, transforms into something altogether more frightening.

As Tar's gaze travels from tearful son to bullying husband,

her eyes become black glass; there is nothing to be seen within or behind, all is locked away.

'Don't you listen to none of that, son,' she says perkily, helping Brad up, before kissing his wet, podgy cheek. 'Now you go on next door with the nice doctor, here, and I'll be with you in a tick.'

Brad snivels gratefully at his mother, wipes his nose from wrist to elbow, then follows Leon out of the house. Tar then turns her attention to Dougie. Staring down into her husband's face from the vantage point of her high heels, Tar pulls off her wedding ring, holds it up in front of him, then lets it drop. It lands with a tinkle and rolls to the skirting board.

'Now, Tar, what d'you go and do that for?' Dougie asks, sweat beading his brow.

Dougie bends over with a strained grunt to retrieve the ring and, as his fingers close around it, Tar deftly lifts a foot and stabs her stiletto heel into the back of his hand, nailing it to the floor. He looks up, smarting. Tar slowly leans towards Dougie, pushing down on her heel. She whispers in his ear, grinding her foot as she does. Dougie's eyes pop hideously; you can almost see the blood vessels bursting.

I don't catch what Tar says but, as she stands tall once more, simultaneously releasing Dougie's hand, she ends with an audible '*my* son'. She then stalks out of the house, leaving the front door gaping.

Tar is a mother who, despite what any anthropologist or social commentator or, indeed, social worker, might say about her child-rearing practices, would not only die, but kill, for her children, even if the target is their own father.

As I say goodbye to a rather upset Dougie, the postwoman

arrives and hands me a bundle of mail. One envelope is addressed by hand, and I recognise the writing. I go into the front room and open it. It's from Susan, with the date and address of the holiday cottage in the Lake District written at the top.

Dear Mother,

Here we are on holiday. It was a long drive, but Graham and I shared it which made it more manageable. The M25 was chock-a-block, as usual, but the M6 was even worse, and we were stuck in a traffic jam for over fifty minutes. The cottage is as charming as ever, although it could do with a fresh coat of paint and some new carpets now. The weather has been mixed so far – sunshine and showers – but at least it's relatively warm. I didn't feel too well this morning so Graham's taken Chrissy out for the day. I didn't plan to write this letter, but here goes.

I was shocked by the news that you have cancer. It is, of course, shocking news. But it also made me realise that you are a person in your own right, not just 'Mother'. I found a lump in my breast a couple of years ago. The GP and consultant were as certain as they could be it was nothing to worry about, and it wasn't (turned out to be a fibroid), but I didn't tell you about it. I told myself at the time it was because I didn't want to worry you. I told myself I'd deal with it better alone, that there was no point causing anxiety for you, or anyone else, if it turned out to be nothing (I told Graham, of course). Luckily, it wasn't serious, but if it had been I'm not sure who I would have told or how.

When I dropped Chrissy round the other day you looked so small and thin. I wondered if I had done that to you, if all the rows and confrontations over the years had made you weak and ill. Just like all the rows with Chrissy make me angry and down. I'd never considered how our arguments made you feel before, just assumed you were impervious.

I don't really know why I'm writing this. I just want to say that I'm sorry you're ill, but I'm glad we're talking again, and I'll see you when we get back.

Take care,

Susan

I decide to reply straight away; Susan wouldn't have included her address if she didn't want me to write back.

Dear Susan,

I'm glad you've written and told me something of what you feel. I don't think we've ever written to each other before, except postcards. When you were little you used to leave me little notes sometimes. Maybe we'll get on better as pen pals than as mother and daughter?!

I'm also glad we're talking again. Telling various people about being ill has been difficult sometimes, but the support group has been, well, very supportive and helpful. I'm sorry to hear you had a health scare, but I'm glad things were okay. I can understand your decision not to tell me, but I would have liked to have known.

Don't worry, you haven't made me small and thin! The chemotherapy has knocked out my appetite. It knocks the stuffing out of you full-stop. Anyway, I'm finally feeling better after the last session. Yes, we really must get together properly once you're back from holiday, and before the next treatment – to go out for a meal or to the cinema or just to meet up for a coffee or something.

Much love,

Mum xx

It feels a little strange to be writing to Susan. I hope we don't end up getting on together perfectly on paper but remaining at odds with each other in the flesh, like a fantasy Internet relationship that turns out to be based on illusion and delusion. But at least we're communicating, and without accusation or recrimination.

After posting my reply to Susan, I mull over the previous couple of weeks. There's nothing I can do about the physical side effects of the treatment, other than look after myself and bear them as best I can. But Margaret and the support group and our night in the pub have shown me that I've been isolating myself when I don't need to, that I am not alone. Although I've brought up the subject of my outburst in the garden with Leon, I don't feel I've apologised properly; now I know how frustrating it is to be cut dead by the person you need to talk to. But it's a relief to be back to being civilised to each other. I resolve not to hide away, to start living again.

I refocus on the various work-related stories, articles and correspondence I need to deal with, and which I've been letting slip. I'm also having to answer a daily barrage of emails from Phyllis, about various things I'm writing for the magazine, when I know she really wants to ask a million billion trillion questions about Marty. Marty's ordered the kitchen units and worktop for the refit, which will be the last major job after the top floor is finished. In the three weeks since the séance, Marty and various mates have removed the fire escape, built the internal staircase to the attic flat and gutted it. Now he's working on replacing the skylights, and will then be installing the solar panels, which, despite Marty's eagerness, I'm still less than enthusiastic about. After that, there'll only be decorating and smaller jobs left to do, although Marty does refer to anything that doesn't require a cement mixer and a labourer as 'cosmetic'.

I've also been racking my brains, unsuccessfully, about what I could buy or do for Moya to say thank you for all her amazing care and support. But what can you get a woman who's completely rejected all feminine trappings and whose main interests are fishing and country and western music, which are hardly my areas of specialist knowledge? I'll have to employ outside help for this one.

As well as reconnecting with practical concerns, I go to see a film with Margaret and a comedy show with Joy. I spend all of one day shopping for and preparing an evening meal for Moya, Joy and Tim, Marty, and Lara and her husband. I also invite Leon, but he says he's already made plans. I really enjoy the meal, enjoy doing something for others, for a change, when they've all done so much for me. It's a long, relaxed evening, marred only by Tessa ringing Marty every twenty minutes to ask when he'll be home (I did invite her, but she's not accompanied him to a social event in years) and Marty having more chest pains.

The morning after the meal, I ring Marty on his mobile, but there's no answer. I'm worried there's something seriously wrong with him. By midday he still hasn't appeared. Apart from last night, I know that chest pains and shortness of breath have sent him up to the hospital more than once recently. I call his home number and, after about thirty rings, Tessa answers. Her voice is distant, yet weighty, as if laden with troubles. She says she doesn't know where Marty is. I ask if he might be at the hospital or doctor's. 'No idea,' is all she replies. As I replace the receiver, Marty arrives in his van. He begins to unload the solar panels and associated paraphernalia. I'm regretting it already.

I can't help thinking, worrying really, about Marty and Tessa. And Phyllis. Marty and Tessa's relationship sank into mutual apathy and resignation decades ago. But now Phyllis is so obviously interested in Marty, I again question why he's stayed with Tessa for so long, and whether he and Phyllis could be happy together. I did tell Marty earlier that Phyllis has hinted she'll be here again in autumn for another fundraiser. He didn't say anything, but I did catch him doing bicep curls with tins of paint during his tea break.

Marty drives me up for a routine appointment at Oncology in the afternoon. I told him I'd prefer to take my car because I don't know how long I'll be, but he insisted, saying he'd pick up some building materials while I'm there. The vehicle sharing is all part of him trying to reduce his carbon cowboy-boot print.

'You've served your time, Marty,' I say, as we approach the hospital.

'What?'

'With Tessa. You have given her twenty-five years.'

'Hmm. Yeah, I was hoping the reclaimed wood might have come in for the –'

'Do you still … you know?'

'Gina!'

'Well, do you?'

'No, not for thirteen years now.'

Wow, I really do wonder how people cope with that. I can imagine being fairly happy celibate if single, but no sex with your long-term partner? How depressing and frustrating. I remind him that his sons are now adults, that it would do them good to stand on their own feet rather than continuing to mope about at home aimlessly, living off him. I tell him he can change his life, that he doesn't need to be miserable forever, that real love comes and pokes its fingers through your ribcage and into your fleshy, beating, longing heart once in a lifetime. If you're lucky. Marty says he gets the message.

Once in Oncoiogy, bloods are taken, then I wait for the results and have a jab in the arm. Walking out of the hospital, I realise I've paid hardly any attention to what the nurse has been saying. I go back in and ask if the chemo session is still set for Monday. It is, although my white blood cell count is relatively low, which, apparently, means I'm more susceptible to infections. I ask if treatment can turn your brain to fluff, too. The nurse tells me that poor concentration, absentmindedness and disorientation are such common side effects they are known informally as 'chemo brain'. She looks me in the eye and says, 'It's a tough treatment, Mrs Jarvis, one of the toughest. You're doing very, very well.'

As Marty drives me home, I wonder if focusing on his life is providing a convenient distraction from my own. I'm suddenly less sure of my opinions. How can I give relationship advice? Maybe Marty has done the right thing all these years, in standing by the woman he fell in love with – despite her mental and physical problems – and their children.

'I'm sorry about what I said earlier. I don't know how you and Tessa are,' I say, when Marty pulls up in front of the house. 'We've never really got on, so that must cloud my perception.'

'It's okay, Gina. You're just being honest. When you lie to yourself for long enough, you start to believe it.'

We don't discuss it further, and I decide not to interfere. But when I get back to work on the computer, there's *another* email from Phyllis. She really is dreadful at lying. She painstakingly recounts how the bootleg LP Marty gave her mistakenly ended up in the rubbish and has now been taken away by the bin men. She asks if I could ask Marty to make a recording of his copy for her, saying how she'll pay for it and reimburse him for postage and his time. She writes her address at the end, as if I haven't known it for the last ten years. Should I forward the email to Marty? I leave for the support session, still unsure.

'I know this might be a bit of a challenge, but can anyone find anything positive in the experience of having cancer?' asks Harry.

There are only four of us today, not including Harry, because Margaret and Nadia are both on holiday. I glance around the circle: there's ashen, emaciated Alfredo, clearly teetering on the borderline between this world and the next; Wendy is extra puffed up and fairly threadbare – which she makes no attempt to hide – due to a particularly strong reaction to steroids and more chemo; my wig keeps slipping and the skin on my face and forearms is up in red blotches, which I'm finding hard not to scratch; slim, trim, well-presented and groomed Heather, with stylishly co-ordinated outfit *and full head of hair!*, qualifies as the only normal-looking one among us.

'Okay, I'll go,' says Alfredo, after a short silence. 'That is the crappiest question you've ever asked, Harry. There is nothing positive about cancer. All that stuff about living a better life is fine if you survive. But what if you don't? Mine's terminal. It's a terrible disease.'

'I do agree,' says Heather, tentatively, 'it is terrible. But it can also force you to really live in the here and now, to –'

'I don't know if that's true,' interrupts Wendy, but with an apologetic smile. 'I'm spending my whole life waiting for test results, to get through operations, to get through treatment, to get from one week to the next. And the worry is never-ending – about my health, the future, how the children are coping, my husband, and the rest of the family. And now, on top of everything else, I'm starting to look like the Marshmallow Man out of *Ghostbusters*. Every day I wish the cancer was gone, that this was over, that I never had it in the first place.'

'I know,' says Heather, sympathetically, 'I know that's how it is. I was only going to say that the cliché about cancer forcing you to make the most of every day *can* be true. But I do admit you need a certain level of physical health for that to be possible.'

'But how can you enjoy life more *with* cancer?' asks Alfredo. 'It's a sick bloody joke.' He folds his arms across his chest and stares out the window.

'I know you're experiencing a hostile reception, Heather, but do elaborate, if you'd like to,' encourages Harry.

Heather smiles.

'Okay. My answer to your question, Alfredo, is, perhaps, a little philosophical, but it is something I've thought about a lot. I think I – I think a lot of us – live for the future. It's actually very hard to make the most of each day. We focus on something, hopefully achieve it, then it's straight on to the next thing. But when your future is in doubt, it can make you live in the here and now. No more crying over the past, no more putting things off. This is it. Cancer has forced me to make the most of what I have. I used to be chronically shy – it was disabling really – but now I can't be. I mean, there's nothing to be shy of, nothing to be scared of. If I can cope with cancer, I can cope with anything.'

'I see what you mean, but can't it work the other way, too,'

I ask, 'make everything seem pointless, make you feel defeated before you've even begun?'

'It didn't for me. Maybe I was a "defeated" type of person before cancer. I used to get terribly anxious, you see, in social situations – parties, meetings, even parents' evening at infant school, for goodness' sake. I used to think, like they tell you to, "What's the worst that can happen?", to try to get things in perspective. But it wouldn't really help. Now, when I feel myself tipping into the old pit of anxiety, I think, "The worst that could happen *has* happened, but I'm still here, living life, meeting people, working and enjoying myself." Cancer made me realise what hidden strength I had, still have.'

'One thing cancer made me realise,' says Alfredo, 'was who my real friends were. My mother, she was devastated when I told her the news, seemed to take it worse than me. Then I knew she did care. And I stopped being Mr Nice Guy, started to say what I really thought and felt, no matter what. So, I suppose it's done me some good, though I'd rather not have it, any day.'

Given what a wind-up Alfredo is, it's unlikely the rest of us share his positive view of the 'honesty' that cancer has bestowed upon him, but he sits nodding in agreement with himself.

I'm about to speak when there's a knock on the door.

'Yes?' calls Harry.

An unshaven, bleary-eyed man peers in.

'Greg!' cries Harry.

'Hello,' says Greg. 'I thought you'd be about to finish?'

'Yes, we are, I was just about to sum up and close the session,' replies Harry. 'What can we do for you?'

Greg steps into the room. He is holding a tiny baby.

'Are you Stacey's husband?' I ask.

Greg nods.

'How is she?' asks Wendy.

'Actually, she's in the hospice. But that's why I'm here, to say thank you – she asked me to. This group meant a lot to her, it really helped.'

'Margaret will be sorry to have missed you,' I say, standing up and looking at the baby. 'Oh, she's beautiful. Life does go on, eh? Sorry, I didn't mean to sound flippant or …'

'You don't sound anything,' says Greg. 'And yes, it does go on. Whether you want it to or not.'

'Take a seat, mate,' says Alfredo. 'I reckon you've got as much need of a cancer support group as the rest of us. Although Harry, here, was just getting us to say how great our lives have been since cancer came into them, like we've won the lottery or something.'

'Alfredo's not convinced there can be any positives,' says Heather. 'And, looking at what your family's going through, Greg, I don't blame him.'

After Harry closes the session, we decide to stay in the portacabin for coffee and a chat because we can't think of anywhere else to go, and no one fancies the hospital canteen, especially Greg. His baby daughter really is perfect, and her life-affirming cries only serve to make us smile and coo all the more. Despite Stacey being in the hospice, Greg's visible exhaustion and strain, and the fact that it's cancer that has brought us all together, we're relaxed and talkative. Greg hands a card to Harry and asks him to read it out. It's a message from Stacey, thanking Harry and the group for their support and telling us to, 'Go out and enjoy life and don't have any regrets – I don't.'

'Stacey made the right decision,' says an emotional Wendy,

'not to have a termination. Everyone can see that's true. I'd have done the same.'

'Thank you,' says Greg. He looks down at his daughter, cradled in his arms. 'Maybe she'll turn out to be the miracle we've all been praying for.'

When I get home, I think about Stacey's words. She told us not to have any regrets. But I do. *Je regrette tout.*

Before making something to eat, I walk to the off-licence and buy the oldest, priciest bottle of single malt they have. I knock on Leon's door. I'm just about to walk away because he doesn't appear to be in, when he opens it a crack.

'Sorry to disturb you, Leon, but I've brought you this.'

He opens the door wider.

'It's an apology,' I say. 'For my meltdown.'

I hand him the bottle in its sturdy presentation box.

'You were right. As usual,' I carry on. 'We should have talked things through and then none of this awfulness would have happened.'

Leon's eyes widen as he looks at the label and vintage.

'I want us to be friends again. Or at least friendly. I miss it.'

A woman walks up the hallway behind Leon and places a hand on his shoulder protectively, or perhaps possessively.

'Oh God, I've done it again,' I say, 'just barged in and blathered on and you haven't said a word. I'll leave you both in peace. Just … sorry, and thank you, and goodbye.'

Bizarrely, I step forward and shake Leon's hand, then step sideways onto my own front path and let myself in the house.

I may have behaved like a gormless prat, but at least I've apologised.

After dinner, Olly phones, and asks if it's alright to come round. This is odd, as he usually just turns up. I tell him that's fine and he's over in five minutes, not his usual hour and a half. When we were married he once popped out for a pint of milk and didn't come back for a fortnight.

'I'd like you to help me with something, Gina, if that's okay,' he says, while standing nervously in the kitchen.

'Well, it depends what it is. If it involves minimal effort and attention, then sure. If it involves anything like the brain power needed to set the timer on the oven, then count me out.'

'I seem to have lost a few years,' says Olly. 'Quite a few years actually.'

'I don't know what you mean.'

'For example, 1984 to 1986. What was I doing then?'

'Being stoned and acting like an idiot I imagine.'

'I'm being serious.'

'So am I.'

'Shall I make some tea, while you try to remember?' Olly suggests.

'Okay.'

Olly fumbles about with cups and storage jars.

'Is it milk first and then water or water first and then milk? And when does the sugar come into it?'

'It doesn't matter, whichever way you choose to do it.'

'But I can't remember how I used to do it, not since ... not since I stopped smoking.'

It soon becomes clear that, since giving up weed, Olly has slowly woken from a dream state, a dream state that started in the mid-seventies and has lasted nearly thirty years, with only occasional variations courtesy of hallucinogens, cocaine and ecstasy.

'Okay, let's be practical about this,' I say. 'I'll get a pen and paper and write down each year and then we'll work out where you were living and what you were doing.'

I fill in a few significant events, such as getting married, moving into the commune, Susan starting secondary school and us getting divorced, but it's based on my knowledge rather than Olly's.

'Where did I go when you finally chucked me out?' he asks.

'Friends' floors, a bender for a while. Then Stella took you on as a client and got you your first commission. Things looked up after that.'

'What did I do with the money?'

'I don't know. You ended up with a house and studio, so Stella must have advised you to do something right with it.'

'Thank God for Stella, eh?'

'And me. I did run our home and lives and marriage for over fifteen years, remember.'

'Yeah, sorry Gina, it's just … I seem to have lost half my life. I can remember my childhood and early teens more than my twenties and thirties.'

'Well, at least you've got another half to go.'

Olly and I spend the rest of the evening writing out a chronology of his life. The best way of provoking memories turns out to be reminding him of sporting events, i.e. 'Where were you when Gazza famously started crying for some reason I can't remember?'

'Oh yeah, 1990 World Cup, was still living with you and watched it here, in the front room.'

Olly leaves at midnight clutching the two-page, mostly for-gotten summary of his life; he cuts a rather pathetic figure.

The following day, I make my way over to Marty's house on the other side of the city, while he's working in the attic. The only way to decide whether to encourage Marty and Phyllis in any way is to see Tessa again, whom I haven't spoken to properly, face-to-face, for years. Early this morning I had Phyllis on the phone – for ages – discussing inconsequential rubbish, before stutteringly asking after Marty, then leaving agonised silences if I mentioned anything about him. And today Marty displayed a hitherto undisclosed interest in re-homing a cat. They are unhappy apart. Could they be happy together? I feel an almost evangelical duty to help, but I need to be sure about Tessa. Also, Marty has confessed that he's been up to the hospital three times in the last few weeks with chest pains and shortness of breath, which remain unexplained, despite heart monitoring and tests. I'm worried that doing all this work on my house could be too much for him. Tessa should know how he really is.

I knock on the scruffy, battered front door. No answer, although I'm sure I can hear the sound of a TV coming from an upstairs window. I knock again. Nothing. I try the door and it opens. I step in.

'Hello. Anyone home?'

From the hallway, I see Tessa lying on the sofa in the front room, looking half asleep.

'Hi, Tessa. Just thought I'd pop in, say hello.'

She peers at me as I enter the room, as if I'm a shadow, a ghost, a visitor from another space–time continuum.

'Oh, hello.'

She heaves herself up. She does look ill. In fact, she looks even worse than me: bloated, grey, blurred somehow, as if seen through a smoky, distorting lens.

'How are you?' I ask earnestly.

'Hmm. You know, emphysema's a hard thing to put up with every day.'

'Has it got worse?'

'Well, it's not exactly got better …'

I spend half an hour listening to her recount how dust mites, carbon monoxide and especially the lack of care from Marty are all contributing to and exacerbating her 'conditions'. No mention of the fact that she has chain-smoked pipe tobacco in filterless roll-ups for the last thirty years, takes no exercise, lives on junk food and rarely opens a window. I'm going to bring my cancer into the conversation. I feel oddly nervous.

'I've got cancer, had cancer. I'm in the middle of treatment. Marty's probably told you. He's been very kind, running me up to the hospital for appointments and stuff.'

Tessa nods. Is she about to empathise?

'I had a scare last year. A funny mole on my cheek. Turned out to be nothing, or so they said. The doctor wanted to remove it all the same, just in case it was bothering me. I said it's not bothering me, I've got much worse to put up with than that, what with …'

And she's off again: her cancer scare, the uselessness of the medical profession, her kids' problems, Marty's lack of understanding. No questions about me, the cancer, my treatment. I wonder if she'll be any more concerned about Marty. I'm very unsubtle. She doesn't seem to notice.

'Marty didn't seem very well the other night, when he came over for dinner. He had chest pains and difficulty catching his breath. He's been having them quite regularly. I'm worried all the work he's doing on the house may be too much for him.'

'He's always thinking there's something wrong with him. Never is. He does it for attention.'

I spend nearly two hours with Tessa; it feels like a weekend. I never want to see her or the house again. The place is a tip: unloved, sparse and grimy, truly depressing. It is an accurate reflection of my mental state on a particularly bad post-chemo day, but with rotten carpets.

Back home, I try to ignore the fact I've just seen Tessa and maintain a reasonable, balanced, non-interventionist approach, but …

'Bloody hell, how can you live with her, how can you live like that?'

Marty's sat at the dining table. I place his tea and biscuits in front of him.

'I just bumped into Tessa,' I lie, before changing my mind. 'No, I didn't, because she never goes out, does she? I've just been over to see Tessa. I've been to your house.'

Marty smiles sheepishly.

'Don't be so pathetic, man!'

'She's ill, Gina.'

I pop my eyes.

'Yes, you're ill too, but –' Marty tries to continue.

'But nothing. She's been "ill" her whole stinking life. Shame it hasn't killed her.'

'Why have you always hated her so much?'

I wasn't expecting that. I take a deep breath.

'She never had anything to complain about and yet that's all she did. That's all she still does. Maybe I was jealous of your devotion to her, especially when compared to Olly. But all she ever did was throw it back at you.'

Marty dunks a biscuit, but says nothing. I try a different tack.

'To be honest, she'd probably get on better without you. You act like such a doormat, she takes no responsibility for herself. If you stop doing everything, she'll have to cope on her own. That would be a good thing. Where's her motivation to do anything while you're there to do it for her?'

'But what if she can't cope on her own? What about the children?'

'And exactly how old are "the children" now?'

'Twenty and twenty-two. Look, Gina, I've felt guilty. Guilty that their mum is … is the way she is. I hoped that if we stayed together, if they at least had me bringing in money, providing a home, taking them out at weekends, being … normal, well, I hoped they'd be alright.'

'And are they?'

'You know how they are. No jobs, up all night playing computer games, sleeping all day.'

'They're just lazy. You shouldn't let them get away with it. Or Tessa.'

'You don't understand. I'm nearly fifty. I've kept on hoping it would get better. If I give up now it's like admitting I made a mistake, that I've kept making the same mistake for twenty-six years in staying with Tessa – that it hasn't helped her, the kids or me.'

'Better to accept that and move on than make it a lifetime's mistake.'

'Come on, Gina,' says Marty, quietly, 'look at you and Olly. He's my brother and I love him. But he's been an absolute shit from day one, and yet you put up with it, still loved him, still went back for more. You're no better than me.'

'I know, Marty, I completely agree. And I had nothing to stay with Olly for – other than his beautiful green eyes. What a fool I've been. I've wasted so many years, and can't afford to waste any more.'

'You'll get through all this, you've decades left. Don't worry,' says Marty.

'Do, do you love Tessa?' I ask.

Marty shakes his head, just perceptibly.

'That's why you never married?'

'I couldn't do it. The vows – how could I say them? She stopped talking about it eventually. And I knew, in my heart of hearts, she didn't really love me, didn't care for me, as a partner should. I don't blame her. She's an unhappy person. I don't think she's capable of it.'

'Oh, Marty, it's easy to waste a life, and realise it too late. All this environmental stuff you do – the recycling, the reclaiming, the reusing – it's time to apply it to your own life, to rescue what's decent and dump the rest. Even you can see – occasionally – when something's beyond salvaging.'

The sound of the front door opening interrupts our conversation.

'Coo-ee, it's only me,' Joy calls, as she walks down the hallway.

She stops short.

'Am I interrupting something?'

'No, it's fine, all fine. Just having a chat,' I say.

'Yeah. Hi, Joy, but must, you know, get on,' says Marty. 'Catch you later.'

'Urg!' cringes Joy, after she's made herself a coffee and directed me into the front room. 'I don't know how you can live with such a hideous thing.'

Joy's referring to my life-sized Iggy, which is back downstairs. Waking in the dead of night to find him grinning at me insanely did become rather disturbing.

Joy sits us on the sofa next to each other. I hope she's not about to go off into another medical rant. Her face is open, shiny and intense; she looks like she's on ecstasy. My anxiety levels reach crisis point.

'What? What is it?'

'You've got to come with me. You have to. It's a once in a lifetime experience. It's gonna be fantastic.'

Oh dear. Joy frequently tries to persuade me to accompany her to various silly and expensive things no one else will agree to: rebirthing weekends, colour analysis, think positive for success seminars; even I drew the line at colonic hydrotherapy.

'You know we don't share the same taste in, well, anything. Why don't you just tell me what it is?'

Joy quivers with anticipation.

'Have a guess,' she says.

I'm regularly transported back to the playground by my interactions with Joy. Guess what I'm getting for my birthday? Guess who I fancy? Guess what I'm getting you for your birthday? Guess who fancies you? She still wants me to guess. I still can't help being curious.

'Give us a clue.'

'I've got three tickets, but Tim won't come with me. Aiden agreed at first, but then said only if I paid him fifty pounds. What kind of a family have I got?'

It must be bad if hubby Tim has refused.

'Just tell me, Joy.'

'Guess, guess, guess.'

'Um … *Cats?*'

Head shake.

'*The Vagina Monologues?*'

'Certainly not.'

Unable to contain herself any longer, Joy lurches forward, grabs my shoulders and nearly rocks my head off my neck.

'It's *David*. He's coming here. For one night only. There was a cancellation at the theatre and he stepped in at the last minute. It's already sold out.'

David. Here. One night only. The recognition that I have no choice but to accompany Joy is absolute. I agree to meet her outside the theatre this evening, seven o'clock sharp.

'The other ticket – is anyone else going?' I ask.

'No, I can't believe it, no one else wants to.'

'Is it okay if I ask Susan? She should be back from holiday today.'

'Yes, that's a great idea. She had a bit of a soft spot for him in her teens, didn't she?'

'Only because you used to pin pictures of him on her bedroom wall without even asking. He was totally uncool in the eighties.'

'David couldn't be uncool if he tried.'

I say goodbye to Joy and text Susan, asking if she'd like to join us. She says yes.

Just as I'm about to have my pre-night out shower, Olly rings.

'What's happened to Marty?' he asks.

'What do you mean?'

'He's … I think he's just moved in with me. I mean, his guitars were already here, but he's come round with a couple of bags of … I thought they were rags, but he says they're his clothes, and a radio.'

'Maybe he's planning to stay for the weekend.'

'He's brought his LPs, too.'

'A long weekend then. A short break.'

'What? No, he says that's it, that's all his stuff.'

'Um … it sounds like he's left Tessa.'

What have I done?

I drive over to collect Susan on the way to the theatre. I park up and beep the horn. I immediately regret it, remembering that horn beeping is something that Susan disapproves of. But she instantly appears in the doorway, smiling.

'Thanks for inviting me, Mother,' she says as she gets in the car. 'It's been ages since I've gone on a night out.'

'No worries, it'll be like the old days when Joy used to force us both to listen to his music.'

'Oh, I don't know, I used to quite like him,' says Susan. 'Is Joy meeting us there?'

'Yep.'

You can't miss her: the twenty-stone black woman dressed in vibrant, Quality Street-coloured silks, boinging up and down with adolescent hysteria at the bottom of the theatre steps. The one with the enormous smile, enormous Tina Turner hair extensions and – sorry to mention it again, but it is unmissable – enormous bust. Both Susan and I can't help but laugh at Joy's excitement at seeing the teenage obsession she never grew out of. We barely have time to say hello before Joy steers us straight into the theatre and into our seats, bypassing any drinks, snacks or visits to the loo to check wig positioning. We are in the front row, slap-bang in the middle. Joy keeps squealing and squeezing my hand. Susan and I exchange looks and grins. If they don't get the curly haired, gold-earringed entertainer on soon, I may suffer broken bones.

'He's *exactly* the same,' cries Joy, when he comes on stage. 'Oh, he's still so dreamy.'

David Essex is not the same as he was in the seventies, although his songs are.

I don't think it can get any worse than *A Winter's Tale*. I can't believe I know the lyrics to *every* one, thanks to thirty years of recordings playing continuously in Joy's home and car. Joy has smuggled in a litre water bottle of gin and tonic to help her cope with her 'nerves', caused by being so close to David. I have a few swigs; even Susan joins in. I begin to enjoy myself and am awash with nostalgia. The memories flood back: Joy, aged thirteen, dressing up to go into town to buy his new single; Joy trying on clothes and asking, 'Do you think David would like it?'; Joy practising signing her name as 'Mrs Essex'; a more mature but still fanatical Joy trying to persuade Susan of the merits of his music, as well as his overall gorgeousness, while I groan in the background. I can't say I blame Joy's husband for not wanting to be in my seat tonight. Things become a bit tricky during his cover of *Let's Spend the Night Together*, when the possibility of a thousand menopausal women storming the stage reaches tipping point. But, I have to admit, it turns into a great night. David has to do three encores and is mauled for over an hour at the stage door; I begin to feel quite sorry for him.

'I could die happy now,' Joy raves, in the car on the way home. She's kissed him. And got him to autograph her top, over her, um, chest area; luckily, he had a big pen. I reckon a nationwide tour could save the NHS thousands, as Mr Essex has worked more magic in one evening than a year of HRT. For the rest of the audience, you understand, not me; I want to make that clear.

I drop Joy home, then Susan.

'Thanks for tonight, Mother, I really enjoyed it,' she says. 'It reminded me of the past – you, me and Joy dancing about together when I was little. Good memories.'

'Yes. There are some of those, aren't there?'

Susan nods, then waves goodbye.

16

EVER FALLEN IN LOVE
(WITH SOMEONE YOU SHOULDN'T HAVE FALLEN IN LOVE WITH)?

Marty arrives on Saturday morning and tries to work on the house, while being plagued by calls and accusations from Tessa and his sons. I keep giving him hugs and telling him it'll be alright. Susan and I exchange a few texts, and Olly and I take Chrissy to a farm-cum-adventure park on Sunday. I tell Susan that Olly's changed his ways; she looks unconvinced, but is at least willing to give him a chance.

It's great to be on friendly terms with Susan, but I can't help feeling it isn't real; it's just too easy. If it had been so simple for us to have got along all these years then why have we done little else but fight and reproach and criticise? But maybe I've got it all wrong, again. I feared Susan would be unsympathetic and blaming when I told her about the cancer, but she's been nothing of the sort. I keep thinking we need to sit down and thrash out the reasons behind a lifetime of conflicts, but maybe we don't. Maybe we just need to see each other regularly, behave civilly and share relaxed, normal things – going out for the evening, chatting on the phone, being part of the same family.

Other things are preoccupying me, too, as well as mine and Susan's relationship. The fifth chemo session is on Monday and, after stumbling down into a depressive dungeon after the last one, I'm dreading it. I've written a page of advice to myself on how to handle it and recognise that the effects are only temporary; it largely consists of staying in bed and calling Margaret.

As soon as I'm through the door of the chemo suite my head is engulfed in a black cloud, crackling with anger and dangerous thoughts. Dr K studies my blood test results carefully. We talk about cell counts, how mine are within an acceptable range, but still low. He's disappointed that last week's injection didn't raise them more. He asks if I want to delay treatment for a week, but I say go ahead. Then there'll only be one more left. I'm last to be hooked up and the nurse puts the drugs through slowly. By four o'clock, everyone else has gone. I'm exhausted and in a foul mood, knowing I'll be here another couple of hours, then returning to a half-life at home. I put the reclining chair back into its horizontal position and will myself to sleep.

I wake with a start, due to the sense of another person in the room. It's not a calm yet busy nursing presence, but an intense and static one. Leon.

'What are you doing here?'

'Well, er,' he mumbles, 'thought I'd pop in, wanted to say thanks for the whiskey.'

'You could have waited till I got home, I'm hardly feeling my best.'

'I called round, but Marty said you were up here, on your own, and ...'

'Oh well, you're here now.'

I press a button on the chair and it slowly moves upright. Leon goes to assist, but I wave him away.

He runs his hands through his dark-orange hair.

'Do you mind if I talk?' he asks.

'Only if you give me fifty quid at the end of it.'

Leon looks blank.

'That was a joke,' I explain.

Leon 'ha-has' unconvincingly, then fetches a chair and sits next to me.

'Your garden's looking nice,' he says, after a short, uncomfortable pause.

'What? It's been flattened by bags of cement and had workmen traipsing all over it. It's never looked worse.' Hold on a minute, didn't I start talking about the roses when I was trying to find a way to tell Susan my cancer news? I wonder what Leon's building up to.

'I'm sure you didn't come up here to talk about my garden,' I say.

'No. I wanted to explain, explain why I couldn't agree to work in analysis with you again. If you're willing to hear me out, that is.'

'Okay, go ahead. I've accepted it now, for real this time. And the cancer support group has been brilliant, has filled the gap. Sorry I wouldn't listen before.'

Leon clears his throat.

'It's true I'm fully booked. But also, I was worried about breaching professional boundaries. I wouldn't be any good for you. I couldn't be your therapist again, for you.'

'Oh, Leon,' I protest, but without anger, 'that's as crap an excuse as a boyfriend dumping you because he's "not good enough for you". I came to you because you know me, because I don't have to explain myself all over again. I hoped that "shit, I've got cancer, please help" would be enough. But you said no – too busy. And now you're talking about professional boundaries. I know we're neighbours, but surely we could have worked round that? Quite frankly, those bloody big fees you charge should pay for you to maintain those professional boundaries, or whatever it is you're supposedly worried about. And that wasn't a joke.'

Leon sighs. I never could stop moaning about the cost of therapy. We sit in silence for a bit. Embarrassment creeps over me.

'Sorry. Again,' I say. I try to smile, conscious I may resemble a macabre, grinning skeleton, as I've removed my wig due to overheating. 'Never could come to terms with those fees, could I? I could blame the cancer for making me act like such a tit but, as you and I both know, that's what I'm always like. Maturing emotionally was always one of my "issues", wasn't it?'

Leon gives me a wry grin. 'I hated what you said in the garden, and it came so out of the blue, seemed so unfair. I also hated it because a lot of it's true, a lot of it hit home.'

He looks at the floor.

'Go on then,' I say, 'confess to being as pathetic a fuck-up as the rest of us.'

'I do live in my books, my theories, through my patients. Work gives me an intensity of emotional and psychic connection, a sense of worth and meaning that are completely missing from my private life. It's like I'm living by proxy. Where have I gone wrong?'

'Blimey, Leon, you're the shrink! If you can't fathom it out, who can?'

A nurse comes in to hook up another bag to my IV pole. Leon asks if he can get me anything to eat or drink.

'I'd love something cold – ice cream or an ice lolly or milkshake.'

'The hospital shop's still closed for refurbishment, I'm afraid,' says the nurse. 'The best we can do is tea, coffee or soup from the machine.'

I tell Leon not to bother because even the thought of those makes me queasy. Leon says he needs to buy another parking ticket because his will run out soon, but he'll come back after, if that's okay.

I nod.

It's been good to be with Leon again, to feel his honesty and patience. I think of all the people who have been marvellous to me: Moya, Joy, Marty, Lara. Even Dougie popped in to see me at River Street a couple of days ago. Okay, so he did use the opportunity to eat two rounds of sandwiches, drink a gallon of sugary coffee, smoke half a packet of fags, and offload all his problems since Tar's chucked him out – after he pushed Brad over in my hallway – and he's been forced to live alone in a rented flat, but still …

I look at the drip and then at the clock. Surely I can't have long to go.

Leon returns. He hands me a chilled, bottled milkshake which he must have gone out of the hospital grounds to find. Just what I need.

'You're a lovely person, Leon,' I say, while slurping through the straw. 'You're kind and generous. And clever, of course. And even-tempered. Look, you're blushing. And you assessed Brad, despite Dougie threatening to break your legs if you told him he was gay.'

'Yes,' says Leon, uncertainly.

'I've thought over what you said about why therapy ended. And you're dead right. I did finish it as soon as you suggested I cut off from Olly completely. It's only since you pointed it out that I've realised.'

'I felt bereft, Gina, when you left.'

'Really? I suppose therapists become attached to their patients, as well as vice versa. I thought you'd be glad to see the back of me. All that effort, and I was so resistant to change.'

Leon rubs his forehead, as if in great pain. I lean forward and take his hand, pat it and squeeze it. He looks at me. It's wonderful to be able to give comfort, as well as receive it.

Leon stands.

'Gina, I've come to say that I want to be here with you as a friend. But not just a friend. I mean, as a person who knows you and cares about you and ...'

Leon drops to the floor, as if his strings have been cut. He's kneeling next to me, holding my hands. It's so melodramatic, I begin to giggle.

'Gina, I love you. I have always loved you. That's why I couldn't be your therapist again.'

'No, you can't do! It's supposed to be the other way round – patients falling for their therapists.'

'Well, not in my case. I was devastated when you finished. I kept telling myself it was because we didn't wind down properly, because I'd let you down professionally. But really, I missed you, terribly.'

'But haven't you worked all those feelings out, discovered they're projections or something?'

'I have tried, have examined and re-examined transference

and counter-transference in all its many and varied forms.' Leon pauses. 'But I still love you.'

What magical words. What a riot of emotions.

'But all that stuff you know about me. The deepest, the darkest, certainly the most embarrassing …'

Leon shrugs, 'And what about all the good stuff? Your humour, the stories you tell, the love you feel and give. Not to mention the fact you're a dead ringer for Debbie Harry.'

'And there's me thinking you were incapable of being superficial. Hold on, what about moving in next door, did you have an ulterior motive?'

'No. I'd made an offer on the place before I even realised you lived next door. But I didn't want you to find it weird. That's why I checked before going ahead. Of course, I hoped we'd get on as neighbours and friends. I also hoped you'd start to see me as a person, rather than your ex-therapist. And I would never have dared say anything, but after everything that's happened …'

'When's your birthday, Leon?'

'October twenty-third.'

Ooh, Scorpio: passionate, intense, great in bed.

I look at Leon. I have just noticed, he has green eyes. Not the startling emerald of Olly's, but a soft, earthy moss-green, speckled with golden flecks, like tiny flames.

During the week following chemo, when I'm incapable of doing pretty much anything, I mull over Leon's declarations, but it's all a bit unreal. For a start, how can he possibly be attracted to me? I know good bone structure never goes, but hair, a healthy body weight and half my insides have. And what about me – could I really have feelings for Leon? Maybe I'm just desperate. But I don't feel desperate. I mean, I do feel desperate about being ill, this treatment, if I'll get better. But I don't feel a desperate need for a love affair. I couldn't have thought less about it in the last thirty years. But maybe I'm desperate for support. I don't know if I'm even capable of being in love at the moment. I certainly don't feel the delirious rushes, the lurching stomach, the eye-popping highs coupled with the heaven-blackening lows. No, I feel content and relaxed in Leon's presence, my emotions on an even keel. I don't feel scared, I don't feel insecure and I'm not lost in a world of fantasy and imaginings that bear no relationship to reality. My feet are on the ground, my head is fixed to my shoulders, my heart is calm and subtle. I couldn't possibly be falling for him, could I?

'You need time to fall in love, to know a person,' says Joy, over lunch at her kitchen table. 'It might not sound all hearts and flowers, or fireworks and obsession in your case, but that's the way it is.'

'But if I was in love with Leon, or there was even a possibility I could fall for him, wouldn't I have known before now?'

'Bloody Olly's always got in the way. I know you've had a few half-arsed relationships, but you only ever really wanted Olly. Have you seen Leon much, since what he said at the hospital?'

'He's been calling in most days, just for half an hour or so because I've been feeling so rough. We've chatted about pretty much everything, but not what he said. I don't know what's going on – if he's just playing it slow or is half-regretting his words or if he's waiting for me to say something.'

'You're ill, Gina, and he's a considerate guy, so he'll be taking his time, being cautious.'

'Yes, he is considerate.'

'And he has no idea what you feel for him. Try to see it from his point of view. Unless you told him you love him?'

'No, of course I didn't. I mean, maybe I could, but it came so out of the blue. And I've never looked at Leon that way. I often marvelled that I *didn't* feel anything for him, despite the intimacy of therapy. Leon was always receptive, patient, caring. I could talk to him about anything. But I put that down to him being good at his job.'

'Does it bother you, the fact he used to be your therapist?'

'Not really. It finished over six years ago, and a lot has happened since then.'

I scoop up a spoonful of frozen raspberries and ice cream, while Joy pops the end of her baguette into her mouth and pushes her empty plate to one side.

'Do you want my baguette, Joy? I'm sorry, but I can't eat it. You know what my appetite's been like since chemo.'

'No, I'm full.'

'Really?'

'Yes. Why can't I be full after one baguette?'

'Well, usually you …'

'Act like a human hoover and snaffle up everything in sight while pretending I hardly eat a thing?'

'Um, yes.'

'I don't want to any more. The over-eating started when Mum died – with me trying to fill the huge space she left with food. It's been my comfort, my punishment, my crutch, my everything. But, since the séance, things have started to change. I feel closer to her, somehow, like she's still around, looking out for me, but I've lost that desperate craving to have her back again, permanently. I no longer need her like I did when I was a kid.

And admitting that I've always felt guilty about her death was a big step. Now I can finally see that it wasn't my fault, that I couldn't have done anything to prevent it. I've forgiven myself.'

'I'm so pleased for you, Joy,' I say, squeezing her hand across the table.

'Yeah, it does feel good.'

'And,' I say, as another change in Joy dawns on me, 'after I told you about Leon confessing his love, you didn't even smirk. I was anticipating a five-minute laughing fit, at least.'

'That's changed, too. I'm no longer stuck at fourteen years old, trying to deal with Mum's death, trying to squash my feelings down only for them to leak out in bizarre ways.' Joy smiles. 'And, talking of mothers and daughters, how are you and Susan? You were getting on fine when we went to see David.'

'Yeah, we're good. We've been texting and phoning. And, since Olly's stopped smoking, she's been letting him pick Chrissy up after school on a Friday if I'm not up to it. It's just … we're both trying so hard to be polite and friendly and respectful, it feels like we're walking on egg shells, that we're not being honest.'

'Just give it time. The more contact you have, the more you'll relax and be comfortable with one another.'

'But that's what I'm scared of – that as soon as we're not on our best behaviour we'll start rowing again.'

'Not necessarily. You could be building a genuinely better relationship, based on how you both are now, rather than going over all that old stuff from the past. I think it's positive.'

'Well, fingers crossed.'

'So, what are you going to do about Leon?'

'I really don't know. Wait and see, I suppose.'

After lunch with Joy, I drive over to Moya's cottage. Although she's already done a lot of fixing up outside and work in the garden, in preparation for putting it on the market, she thinks my 'female advice' on presentation will help her to sell it, and she needs all the money she can get to make her Cornwall dreams a reality. I did remind Moya that she is also female, but she just said, 'Oh, you know what I mean.'

I'm familiar with Moya's cottage, but she's asked me to imagine I'm viewing it for the first time, as a potential buyer, so that I can give her objective feedback. First impressions are positive. The cottage is one of a pair of small semis close to the sea, and borders the swankiest area of town. It has a small front garden and decent-sized back with a lovely, slightly overgrown, typical cottagey feel. I know Moya's spent a lot of time raking out gutters, fixing downpipes, repointing and painting, so no one should be able to find fault with the outside. The garage is at the bottom of the garden, but Moya has turned this into a well-equipped workshop. So far so good.

When I walk back round the side of the house and in through the front door things are, um, not quite so impressive. Letters and newspapers have piled up in the small hallway, and stuff seems to have been dumped anywhere: fishing tackle and books in the kitchen; motorcycle helmets, driftwood and huge rusty bolts and bits of metal – that Moya must have picked up from the beach – litter the sitting room; and the dining table can't be seen for maps, billy cans, fishing magazines, a high-vis jacket and a large torch. I trip over a tool box at the bottom of the stairs.

Upstairs is a different story, with the two bedrooms and bathroom being rather sparse and utilitarian, but orderly and clean. It's as if the clutter just didn't have the energy to climb the stairs.

'Well,' I say, as Moya puts a coffee percolator on the stove, 'the outside looks spot on, the garden's lovely and upstairs is fine. But downstairs needs a major sort out.'

Moya sighs, 'I thought you might say that.'

'And maybe even a fresh coat of paint,' I suggest. 'I mean, what made you choose this pale, yellowy-brown colour for the whole of downstairs?'

'Hides tobacco stains better.'

'Hmm, Laurence Llewelyn-Bowen would not approve.'

Moya and I go to the local DIY store and choose paints for downstairs. She looks a bit glum at the prospect of all the work she still has to do, but I reassure her that it should only take two or three weeks and then the house will be ready. By the time I leave her cottage later that afternoon, Moya is togged out in painting overalls, tanked up on espresso and whistling to the radio; I drive away feeling grateful that I've managed to help her out, even if only in a very small way.

When I get back to River Street, I'm surprised to find Leon on my doorstep.

'Georgina, Gina, Gin,' he stumbles.

'Leon, Leon, Leon,' I reply, equally stupidly.

We smile and laugh.

'Glad to see you've been out. I just thought I'd, I'd …'

'Do you want to come in?'

'No, it's alright,' says Leon, turning a large, thick envelope over and over in his hands. 'I just want to ask you something.'

He pauses, then starts talking incredibly rapidly.

'I was wondering if you'd be alright to travel. I arranged this holiday with a friend of mine, from university, but he's ill and has had to pull out at the last minute. And I've got two tickets and it's only for a week, on a Greek island. I think you'll like it, it's supposed to be beautiful. It's a twin room, but I could make it into separate if that's a problem. And it's free, all paid for, and if you don't come I'm on my own. The flight's this Saturday, so if you can think about it, quickly, and let me know, then that would be …'

At last, Leon meets my eye.

'Okay, I'll think. I'll let you know.'

He places the envelope in my hand.

I let myself into the house and open the envelope. It contains details of the island, apartment and flight times.

I think, but no decisions are forthcoming. I'm not going to know if I should say yes or no until I've gone, am I? I have a suspicion that Leon's only just booked it. I wonder if I can go, if I should go, from a medical point of view. I'm up at the hospital tomorrow for checks, so I'll ask then. I'll let Leon know after that. I know I've been physically sick, but I'm sick of other things, too. I'm sick of worry, sick of pain, sick of nausea, sick of exhaustion, sick of fear, sick of pills, sick of needles, sick of being brave, sick of telling people, sick of soldiering on. I'm sick, sick, sick of sickening cancer. More life, that's what I want, more life.

Although the thought of a holiday has lifted my spirits, Dr K makes it clear he'd prefer me not to go. He recommends I complete the sixth and final chemo cycle, then wait a month, at least. But, with all the checks and extra jabs and with me tolerating chemo fairly well, he thinks I'm probably fit enough to travel, and I'll be back the weekend before the last treatment is due. He says that if I do go, I must rest, not overexert myself, not sunbathe, be careful to eat hygienically, and all the rest of it, i.e. I might as well stay at home in bed in a darkened room.

When Leon phones later, I still haven't made a decision. It would be silly to jeopardise my treatment so far, but I can't seem to say 'no' either. I search the Internet for information on the foolishness or otherwise of going on holiday while undergoing chemo, but can't find any definitive answers or come to any conclusions. I do learn that travel insurance will be sky-high and I'm also reminded that I'm being treated for a disease that frequently recurs. It could be great to spend time getting to know Leon properly, but it could also turn out to be a disastrous mistake. Despite all the misgivings, I am tempted to go, to have a break from these last few months. But I'll be taking my ill health with me. The phone rings. I expect it to be Leon again, but I'm greeted by a familiar Glaswegian drawl instead.

'Hello, Margaret! How was the holiday?' I ask.

'It was great, fine, wonderful. You know.'

'Are you alright? Is something wrong?'

'I can't believe how upset I am. It's Alfredo. He died. Harry told me. I thought I'd let you know. The funeral's tomorrow.'

'But, but he was at the support session a couple – less than a couple – of weeks ago. He seemed, I mean, he didn't look great, but –'

'It can happen like that. Up and about one week and gone the next. Or weeks, months, of being bedridden, of appearing to be at the end, but still clinging on. I'm going to phone his ma. When I've calmed down. Sorry, this has been such a tactless way to break the news.'

'No, it's alright. I'm just shocked. Ring me later, okay?'

'Will do.'

I sit, stupefied. I say a prayer for Alfredo, like I used to do as a kid. Hands pressed together, fingers pointing skywards, eyes closed. Dear God …

I write a poem for him.

I phone Leon. I say I'd love to come on holiday.

I read the poem at Alfredo's funeral the following day. Harry, Margaret and Heather also attend. The only other people there are his mother and her friend. His mother is a small, stout, black-clothed figure, a cliché of an Italian mama. In her broken English, she says how he used to talk about us, that we made it easier to bear; he was in a lot of pain and knew he was dying.

'You enjoy life,' she says, emphatically, when we go back to her small flat for tea and sandwiches after. 'You enjoy life when you young, when you can. Alfredo, he never happy, even when small boy. So … prickled. Such shame.'

It's odd to be referred to as young, but then I suppose I am to a seventy-year-old.

I feel sadness, but also otherworldliness. Perhaps because I'm still able to walk this earth, rather than having been consigned to it. The coffin, the box, the body contained therein. All gone, no return. Absolute, final.

In the face of death, Alfredo's mother, like Stacey, talked only of the comfort of others and enjoying life while you're able to. I shall take their advice.

Heading into town the next morning, I can't seem to avoid the Spokes, although, with seven children, there certainly are enough of them. Dougie pulls over in his taxi to tell me about his failed efforts to persuade Tar to take him back. Then I bump into Tar and Brad coming out of McDonalds. And I spot Keanu riding a

BMX up and down the high street (and with him being so lanky and the bike so tiny he looks like he's escaped from the circus). I even run into Donna in Debenhams' 'Summer Shop'. From burials to bikinis. The gap between the profound and mundane has narrowed to imperceptible.

Donna is make-up free and her bling has gone. She looks even more beautiful.

'Hello mate, how are ya?' she greets me, voice unchanged.

'I'm, I'm having treatment for cancer, but I'm going on holiday, so I'm sort of bad and sort of good.'

'Dad said.' Donna squeezes my arm sympathetically.

'You off on holiday, too?' I ask.

'Yeah. Mauritius. Photo shoot for a calendar. Topless, but tasteful. Ain't allowed to wear much slap, gotta look natural and that. Mum's coming, too, and Brad, for the week. The agency is well looking after me. I ain't allowed to go down the Jordan route or nothing, I gotta be sophisticated. It's a new look what is called *natural glamour*.'

'Oh. What does that mean?'

'No fake tits, surgery or Botox. As much sunbathing as you like, mind, but no spray tans, cos you can tell the difference in the photos, apparently.'

'Is that true?'

'Nah, it's bollocks. But it's a free week of lying on a beach for me. Gotta have me hair dyed as well. Not allowed to be blonde no more. Too many of us.'

Donna grasps a tress of her naturally fair hair and stares at it.

'What colour's it going to be?' I ask.

'T-shun.'

'What?'

'I dunno. Me agent kept saying t-shun or something. I didn't know what she was on about, but I didn't wanna let on.'

'Oh! Titian.'

'Yeah, that's it. What's that when it's at home?'

'A beautiful, rich auburn. A lovely, coppery red.'

Donna's jaw drops.

'They's dyeing me ginger? I'm gonna ring that poxy agency right now.'

Donna explodes down her mobile, repeating the word 't-shun' more times than she should, before cutting the call off.

'They is saying I have to have it done. I can't believe it.'

'Donna,' I say, 'what are you?'

'Eh?'

'I mean, are you a Westerner? A European? A Brit?'

'I'm British, aren't I? English, British.'

'Well, the redhead gene is found almost exclusively in Britain. Okay, mostly further north, and in Ireland too, but it's *very*, *very* British. You will be the epitome of the natural glamour *British* beauty. Red, ginger, titian – call it what you will – is even more British.'

Donna's eyes narrow. I can almost hear the cogs turnin'. Sorry, turning.

'I dunno …'

'Maybe the agency's right, there are too many blondes, natural and dyed. But few redheads. Lots of Scandinavians are blonde. And Germans.'

I think that's done it.

'Hmm. Well, if you put it like that. I'm supposed to be getting it done up London tomorrow. What's the colour called again?'

'Titian. Rhymes with mission.'

'Okay. I'll call them back and say it's alright. I can always dye it back again, can't I? Anyway, where you off to, anywhere nice?'

'A Greek island.'

'Ooh, lovely. Not going with shithead are you?'

'No, Leon's taking me.'

'Oh, him. Is he your boyfriend, then? I wouldn't have smashed his face in at the barby if I'd known. I feel well bad about it, now he's helped Brad out.'

'No, he's not my boyfriend, not yet, I mean, we, I …'

Donna leans forward and whispers in my ear, 'I reckon he's got a big one. I can usually tell a mile off. Never been wrong yet.' She winks, then goes to the counter to pay for her spangly thong bikini bottom.

Spangled thongs; not at my age, not in my lifetime, ever. I settle for a well-cut, beautifully patterned one-piece with matching sarong and beach sandals. I smile all the way home.

17

THE GREAT ESCAPE

The last time I went on holiday was with Joy, two years ago.
We did a mid-week city break – as befitting two middle-aged
women – and visited Florence and Rome, where we saw sights,
photographed each other in front of them, and ordered bitter,
iced drinks in many, many bars. It was all very civilised, but
you can't beat lazily sipping cocktails and smoking cigarettes
on a sunlounger, interspersed with floating about on a lilo and
guessing which females have had breast implants. Unfortunately,
due to the chemo, I can't smoke or sunbathe, and have gone off
drinking. And, because this one's with Leon, I'm worried I might
have to go to museums or the opera. I suspect I'd have more fun
holidaying with Donna.

Just after I've heaved the suitcase from the top of the
wardrobe, Susan phones.

'Mother, I was wondering if you'd like to come over? Chrissy
would be pleased to see you and –'

'Thanks, Susan, that's really nice of you, but I'm just about to
start packing.'

'Packing?'

'Yes. I'm going on holiday tomorrow, to a Greek island, with
my neighbour. I was going to ring later and let you know.'

'What neighbour?'

'Um, Leon. The psychotherapist.'

Susan snorts.

'What's that supposed to mean?' I ask.

'What?'

'The snort.'

'I did not snort.'

I sigh, 'Okay, you did not snort.'

'This is very short notice, isn't it? And who is this Leon? And how long's it for? Should you really be going on holiday in the middle of chemotherapy?'

'Yes, it is short notice, but I've known Leon for years. He used to be my therapist, actually.'

'Isn't that illegal? Couldn't he be struck off?'

'No, it's not illegal. And, anyway, we're just going as friends. His travelling companion let him down at the last minute so I'm filling in instead.' I know I'm fibbing a bit, but I can't seem to stop sliding headlong into the old pattern of trying to placate a disapproving Susan. 'And my consultant says it'll be fine,' I add, 'that it should actually do me good.'

'Really? Oh, okay then. Well, I hope you have a nice time. See you when you get back.'

'Yes, see you then.'

I pack medications for every complaint imaginable, both cancer- and non-cancer-related, as well as herbal remedies from Lara. When the taxi arrives at 7 a.m. on Saturday to take us to the airport, I'm unsure how to behave with Leon. Are we holidaying as friends? Does he expect us to become lovers? Do I expect it? Do I want it? Am I even capable of it? Leon's declared love, but we haven't kissed or anything.

Leon's company is a pleasure; he's intelligent, witty, thoughtful, deep. And Donna reckons he has a big one. There's excitement, meaning to be read into a word, a glance, an accidental touch. But the journey is gruelling: taxi to airport, long wait at airport, four-hour flight, more waiting at Athens airport, then a bus to the harbour. I feel so wretched by the end of the three-hour boat trip to the small island, I wouldn't care if I was being accompanied by Chewbacca or Marilyn Manson, and I'm desperate for sleep. We disembark at one in the morning and transfer to our accommodation is by horse-drawn carriage because no vehicles are allowed on the island. This could be romantic, but isn't, as we're so shattered. We fall into separate beds.

Chill. Firm, unfamiliar mattress. Hospital? Too quiet. Open an eye. Dark, a faint light blurring the edges of the windows. Holiday – hoorah! Leon? Not here. I look at my watch. Bugger. I spend five minutes locating my flattering reading glasses and look at my watch again. It's midday. The room is almost nippy. I hope it's not bloody cold and raining here. Perhaps it's the air-conditioning. I push open a pair of slatted wooden doors and step onto a balcony.

Brilliant light. Enveloping heat. The clearest, bluest sky. I look out over the whitewashed, orange-roofed houses until I find the shimmer of the sea. I hear a low insect hum and snatches of unfamiliar chatter. The balcony overlooks a pool, which is surrounded by gardens of palms, twisted vines and spiky, subtropical plants, dotted with flamboyant, brightly coloured flowers.

Leon returns with breakfast. We eat, unpack and then explore the small holiday complex and village. Our accommodation is in the old villa, but there is a clutch of modern, low-rise apartments gathered around the shady pool, as well as a bar and restaurant. The owners speak little English, but Leon is fluent in Greek, as well as German and French, and is also passable in Arabic and Japanese, apparently. Have I ever been out with an intelligent man? I mean properly intelligent, not just quick-witted or with the gift of the gab? No. Leon is learned, analytical and playful. He's excited by ideas and fascinated by humans. He has a brilliant mind, but this has its drawbacks. I feel a bit thick, as he enthuses about obscure French philosophers, semiotics, linguistics, psychoanalysis (of course), a new theory he's working on. I try to get my head around notions of the textual eroticism of language and, although I do enjoy a little mental masturbation, end up finding it all a bit tiring and pointless.

'But you're a writer!' Leon declares.

'But have you read what I write?' I reply.

Talking of work, I've brought the laptop and am hoping for some inspiration for the next issue of *Eurotica*.

I don't know what to do about swimming, which I love. Can I swim in a wig? What if it comes off, revealing my bone head? And chemo makes you sun-sensitive, so I can't even sunbathe properly. Leon catches me moping and gently insists I tell him what's wrong. He says not to worry, we can hire a car and will be sure to find a secluded beach if I want to go wig-less, or what about one of those bandana things – it completely covers the head and everyone's wearing them anyway. The most important thing about the holiday is to relax, eat well and enjoy it, he assures me.

This is changeover day and the rest of the apartments – there are only eight – will be empty until tonight. I venture down wig-less into the shaded pool. I haven't swum since the first operation, way back in March, and I do so enjoy it. I shouldn't let what I look like stop me. When I get out of the water, I put on a new, dark, shoulder-length wig with a heavy fringe. I now have four and, typical of me, I'm not very good at 'normal' (or is it subtle?), the others being a Cher and a Marilyn Monroe, as well as the original highlighted one Joy gave me. I don't know how long I'll be able to stand it for because it's boiling. Leon keeps shaking his head, as if he can't quite get used to it.

'It's not a bit Mystic Meg, is it?'

'It's fine.'

'I want to take drugs, Leon. I want to drink. I want to smoke. I want to get off my head.'

'Why?'

'The island's too beautiful – the light, the colours, the heat. Cancer and chemo are too awful.'

I'm stretched out on a sunlounger with Leon next to me, holding hands.

'You're not alone, Gina. Or you don't have to be, unless you want to be. I love you. Whether you love me or not. I'll be here for you, with you. I *want* to be, anyway. I've fought it for years, and I'm not going to fight it any more. I've gone through every possible scenario in my mind.'

'What do you mean?'

'What if you don't love me? What if you never love me? What if you still love you-know-who? What if this is just counter-transference? What is love anyway? What if, what if … you know?'

I nod.

'But here we are, on holiday, together. Holding hands. That's good enough for me.'

Leon looks at me with such humility and openness. I see the love and passion in his eyes, mysterious and unfathomable. My heart expands with the truth of his heart, his honesty, his goodness. And it frees me somehow, to be myself, to trust myself, and to want to return such a wonderful gift.

'I know you may continue to be ill,' Leon goes on. 'I know that you –'

I put my finger to Leon's lips, then lead him back upstairs to our apartment.

Leon – the bastard – I hate him, for what he has done to me. I hate his moss-green eyes that encircle, that know me, for now he surely knows the entirety. I hate his tight, hard thighs that pinned me down. I swear he nearly broke my spine, as he turned me over, wrestled me round, smashing my reserve, splintering my will, smacking through me. He's had me in pieces.

Leon – the bastard – I love him, for what he has done to me. Cleaved me apart, twisted me, raw and squirming, onto the cold tiled floor, plundered good and proper till I was no more. Heaving, shuddering, sighing, every last bit of inside, out. He had me every way, everywhere. He knows me joyful through my centre, my essence, my being, the whole of me.

Leon – the bastard – I hate him, for what he has done to me. Stripped me, dissolved me, thrown me high in the sky till I disappeared, till I became the air, pulled me down through the earth, till I became the earth. Inside me, between me, an intruder in my skin. His fingers, his mouth, his cock, his tongue, his teeth, his knees, his accursed thighs, the endless him. His skull, his elbows, his razoring hips, his weight, his taste, the all of it.

Leon – the bastard – I love him. He took me down through the grave and back up into heaven, the long eye of the thick iron bar scrambling, mashing from within, bringing me to come, again and again. From ecstasy to oblivion, and back again; death and rebirth made one and the same.

Leon, without question, is the most wonderful lover I have ever had. He has a big heart, a big brain and, well, let's just say that Donna was right. What more could a woman ask for?

'Tra, la-la-la-la. Tra, la-la! Laa!'

'Gina?'

'Yes siree, that's me.'

'Are you feeling … alright?'

'Never better.'

'What are you writing?'

'A story. It's short. Won't take long. Not like a novel or anything.'

I continue to tap away on the laptop while sitting on the balcony.

'Okay, if that's what you want to do. But I thought we could go for a boat trip to another island, if you're feeling up to it, or maybe do one of the tours?'

I pack Leon off to do some sightseeing, the morning after *the* night before, promising to do the midnight cruise around the island later.

What does he mean: *what* am I writing? I am inspired! I'm penning (well, keyboarding) a historical-fantasy, erotic short story. I may have invented a new genre! It's set in the time of the Arthurian legends. Its hero is flame-haired knight Gawain who, myth has it, is at his most potent and active before midday (you're telling me!) and who magically transforms a hideous old hag into a beautiful maiden (you're telling me again!) with his intense lovemaking (artistic license). I email the first draft to Richard. He agrees it's inspired, but requests I refrain from using metaphors such as 'bush of fiery gorse' to describe Gawain's pubes, and excessive exclamation marks. He says I have established Gawain's exact hair colour at least half a dozen times. My reply insists that this is essential to the narrative as there are many, many shades of ginger, from almost blond to bright orange to dark red, and that I intend to cover them all in a series of stories. I'm considering Boris Becker as the template for my next protagonist. I've even got Shane MacGowan lined up (after substantial dentistry work and a new liver).

Despite the ecstasy of last night, I managed not to blurt out 'I love you' to Leon, which I always tend to do when in the throes of passion. I'm still not sure if I'm capable of falling in love and don't want to mislead him. Still, we're certainly sexually compatible – and I'm in perfect working order – which is a pretty good start.

Glancing down from the balcony, I spot a fine figure of a ginger man arranging himself on a sunlounger by the pool. The new intake must have arrived. He's huge, must be six foot four, and obviously into body-building. He's mid-ginger, with small features in an angular face, and wreathes of blue tattoos winding about his arms. When you're pregnant, you suddenly notice babies and adverts for nappies everywhere. Now I've fallen for a ginger, I'm noticing them. Poolside man is trying his best to sunbathe but, with skin a natural shade of very pale blue and a tendency to blister rather than tan, it's a tall order. How could I not have considered ginger to be the absolute epitome of attractiveness before? Is there a secret club for those who know how passionate they are? Or perhaps it's just Leon? I pinch myself. There are now four men of varying gingerness lined up on sunbeds below me. I wonder if I have a touch of heatstroke and am hallucinating but, no, I'm sure they're real. I must tell the Big Norsemen (I sense another historical-fantasy, erotic short story coming on) to apply more sunblock.

I have a lovely time by the pool chatting to Sean (that's the biggest one's name) and drinking slushy cocktails. He's here with his twin brother, Gordon (non-identical, but still huge and more of a sandy-ginger) and various other Scottish friends, which explains why the place is awash with pale skin, freckles and red hair. To begin with, they think I'm taking the mickey, but when I reassure them that I am genuine in my appreciation of their colouring, they open up. Both twins began body-building from an early age to enhance self-acceptance and esteem and, as far as Gordon's concerned, so he could beat anyone he fancied to a pulp: 'Being ginger's turned out to be a right advantage. You're a sitting target for any tube who wants a fight. It's fucking great.' They admit to being innately attracted to dark women, not blondes, 'to balance things out' says Sean. And here I am in my Mystic Meg wig! I could tell them I used to be secretly mousy, and am now secretly bald, but don't think that would enhance my appeal. Their 'women folk' have gone on a shopping and sightseeing trip, leaving the men to 'chill'. They are all over for a wedding, to be held tomorrow, and are making a holiday of it. Gordon takes pictures of the blue sky, palm trees and sunbathing women (i.e. me) on his mobile to send to friends back home in Dumfries, where it's ten degrees, raining and windy. When they get bored, the twins gather weights from the gym and work on their pecs. It could be the beginning of a gay porn shoot.

I can't recall exactly what I spend the next few hours doing, but I know I enjoy it. Leon arrives back late in the afternoon with tales of huge coach queues on the nearby island, forgotten sunblock and heat exhaustion. He is the reddest I have ever seen another human being. As he tells me about his day, he begins to look around him, then his words peter out. I do appear to be the only woman present, surrounded by half a dozen men in their twenties and thirties pumping iron and sunbathing, and there are rather a lot of empty glasses and bottles lying about. Leon goes up to the apartment to shower. I follow.

Though it's more than slightly ridiculous to play out a jealous scene with a woman heading to fifty, in the middle of treatment for cancer, while she's brushing out her wig, Leon does his best. I love him for it.

After we've made up, we go down to eat, and meet Sean, Gordon and friends, and their girlfriends and wives, who, as the evening draws on, proceed to demonstrate the Scots' affection for, and affiliation with, the Irish. Nearly every one of them claims to have come from Ireland 'way back'. Leon's accent reappears and thickens with the drink. He starts to sing rebel songs, but I refuse to let him attempt a Michael Flatley-style dance routine (he thanks me the following day). We all embark on a riotous midnight cruise around the island, finally getting to sleep about three in the morning. Next day, the bride and groom insist we attend the wedding. After the dozenth ouzo toast to the happy couple, followed by an attempt to organise a *ceilidh* under the palm trees in forty-degree heat, everything becomes rather hazy.

Unsurprisingly, it takes a while to recover from the wedding celebrations. We then spend the rest of the week really relaxing: getting up late, floating about in the pool, reading, having siestas, loving, eating out, talking.

The morning before we're due to return home, I lay in the sun with white, waxy, factor 50 total protection smeared over every exposed inch of body. I look ready for a mid-winter attempt to swim the Channel. Leon frowns.

'I know I'm not going to get a great tan,' I say, 'but I still love the feel of the sun on my skin.'

Leon sits under a huge parasol, smothered in the same sunblock and wearing long shorts, white shirt, broad-brimmed hat and sunglasses: the works. Even then, he looks painfully overheated. Leon's confessed that his ideal holiday destination would be one of rugged isolation, with a temperate climate and lots of walking opportunities. He's also confessed that he booked this one with me in mind – thank God – the morning he asked me to go with him.

Leon bravely attempts to stretch out on the sunlounger next to mine. He holds my hand.

'It's the coldness of death I fear, more than anything,' I say, 'not the blackness, the nothingness. Blackness converts. You can imagine a world around you, just like making up worlds on a blank page. It's the cold that renders you inanimate, lifeless. Maybe that's why I still want to lie in the sun, why I want to be baked through to my very core. So I can hold some of the heat within me, forever.'

By midday, we're forced to retreat into the air-conditioned apartment because it's become insanely hot, well into the forties. Leon reads and I play about with my stories on the laptop. Richard emails to say he's decided to run a special issue on redheads, explaining why this is justifiable. Having run issues on rubber fetishism, feet and water sports, I'd say any *Eurotica* 'special' is past justification, but we have to keep up some semblance of art, the pornography market being at saturation point. If I'm up to it, I have the option to write four of the six stories. I agree. I've already written one, have the bones of another two, and a couple of other ideas pinging about my head.

Tomorrow, I shall return home with a wonderful new partner, lots of work, and – never one to ignore the superficial and transient – a surprisingly good tan.

18

BACK TO LIFE, BACK TO REALITY

Leon and I hold hands in the taxi home, arriving back late on Saturday night. Leon asks if I want to stay at his house, but I say I'd better get unpacked and off to bed. We kiss goodbye; it takes an hour.

On Sunday morning, I wake happier than I've been for ages, and I'm also excited about work. I can't resist phoning Richard to tell him the news: Donna has agreed to be photographed for the cover of the *Eurotica* redhead special. We bumped into her at the airport, coming back from Mauritius. In fact, there was a bit of a scene. Dougie had arrived to take Tar, Donna and Brad home in his taxi, but Tar refused to get in. She is clearly determined to stick to – some might say actively relish – her decisions to chuck him out and refuse to have him back. A tearful Dougie ended up driving me and Leon instead. Donna came with us so as not to upset her dad, and during the journey she agreed. Donna is being launched as 'the next big thing' and the 'natural glamour' phrase abounds with her name attached to it. Donna herself remains ambivalent about her new t-shun hair, which she is prohibited from revealing is dyed, but, as she has just signed two highly lucrative modelling contracts, she's not complaining too loudly.

I spend Sunday rushing round getting the holiday washing

done, food for the week in and generally preparing for the last chemo session tomorrow. Just as I finish unloading the shopping from the car, there's a knock on the door.

'Gina,' says Olly.

'Yes?'

'I, er, erm ...' he mumbles.

I study Olly for a moment. Okay, so he's given up smoking, but I can't say he seems much more with it. Maybe I've mistaken a lifetime of being stupid for a lifetime of being stoned.

'What is it, Olly?'

'I was hoping to have a word.'

'I'm a bit busy at the moment – unpacking, shopping, chemo tomorrow, you know.'

'Could I just come in for a minute? It's important.'

'Oh, okay, as long as it's quick.'

Olly sits at the dining table while I empty the shopping bags.

'How's the sculpture going?' I ask.

'Nearly finished. Mainly smoothing off and polishing left to do – the easy bits.'

'Have you seen much of Chrissy?'

'Yeah, and Susan. She's been letting me take Chrissy out more – to the zoo and stuff. She's a great kid. And Susan's definitely mellowed.'

'That's good.'

'Do you mind sitting down, Gina? I can't really talk while you're buzzing about the kitchen. And what's with all the ice creams and lollies and stuff – are you starting up an ice-cream van or something?'

'No, you idiot, it's all I want to eat after chemo.'

'Oh.'

I squeeze the last pack of ice-poles into the freezer, then sit opposite Olly.

'Well, what is it?' I ask.

'I've made a lot of mistakes,' Olly declares.

'That's not something I need reminding of,' I joke.

Olly doesn't smile, just sits mutely for a while, picking at his nails.

'It was a mistake for us to get divorced,' he says, 'a mistake for me to be unfaithful.'

I shake my head.

'Where's all this coming from?'

'I've been thinking – now I *can* think straight – about the past, about all the crap decisions I've made and the crap things I've done. And I'm sorry, Gina, I really am.'

'Okay. Apology accepted.'

Olly looks up at me expectantly.

I sigh, 'Look Olly, all this may be news to you, but it's ancient history to me.'

'But it doesn't have to be – not me being crap, but our relationship. We could start again. I've changed, you know I've changed. I want you back.'

I stare into Olly's beautiful green eyes, dumbfounded.

'Well?' he asks, quietly.

'No. God, Olly, the number of years I wanted you to say such things, and actually mean them. But it's too late. It's *decades* too late.'

'But it doesn't have to be.'

'It does. It is. Anyway, I'm with Leon now. We've just come back from holiday.'

'Leon? Susan said you were away, but with a friend.'

'He was a friend, and now he's my lover, my boyfriend, if I'm still allowed to call him that at my age. Life's changed, Olly, it can never go back to what it was, and I can never go back to how I used to feel – about lots of things, including you.'

They say the only cure for an old love is a new one; shame about the twenty-six-year wait.

Leon wants to accompany me to the last chemo session, but I'm not sure. I've not felt comfortable having anyone with me before. The holiday was one thing – all sunshine, heat, relaxation and, well, sex. But, even though we've only been back a couple of days, it feels far away. What could be a more brutal reality check than sitting with your new girlfriend while she has chemotherapy?

In the end, Leon assumes we'll go up to the hospital together and I don't say no. I try to be cheery and upbeat. But, once I'm hooked up to the IV pole and the nurse has left us, I can no longer contain my real emotions, which, as usual, move with the force and subtlety of a landslide. Leon pulls the curtain around us so we have some privacy.

'Why have we had to get together now, Leon, when I'm being treated for this disease? Why did I give up therapy when I could have stuck with it and got over Olly years ago? Why have I wasted so much time?'

'I know what you mean, Gina. If I'm honest, I fell in love with you the day you walked into the consulting room. No, the day you made that first appointment with Mandy at reception.'

'You have got to be kidding!'

'Not at all. Why?'

'Blimey,' I say, remembering the morning I dragged myself through the therapy centre's front door, 'I was an absolute mess – literally falling to bits after the marriage break-up. I had a dreadful sore throat. And I'd been crying most of the night. Okay, so my voice may have sounded husky, but that was due to inflammation of the pharynx, not barely repressed sexual passion. Even Mandy gave me a funny look, and she was used to dealing with the depressed and deranged.'

'Well, maybe you did have a touch of the Mariella Frostrups, but I remember being intrigued by all of you. As you were leaving, you looked around. Our eyes met and you smiled. It was clear you were going through a tough time, yet you were still open, human, friendly. Even your name – Gina Jarvis – seemed to speak to me.'

'Leon, that's as mad and irrational as me falling for Olly due to the colour of his eyes.'

'No it's not. Olly turned out to be an eejit, and you turned out to be … perfect.'

'What about that woman,' I ask, 'the one who came to the door when I brought the whiskey round?'

'Oh, Ruth. I thought I'd make an effort – after what you said in the garden – to get a life, as they say. Ruth's a fine, intelligent, handsome woman – similar interests, fellow psychotherapist, few years younger than me, wants to start a family –'

'Alright, alright, no need to rub it in.'

'What I mean is, I think – I know – she wanted us to get together. But I don't love her and never will. She's not you.'

I don't say anything.

'What is it?' Leon nudges.

'The L-word,' I say. 'I know we're getting on really well, but

I don't know if I'm capable of being in love at the moment, of loving you as you seem to love me.'

'Not seem to, but do.'

'But what's in it for you, Leon? Look around you – look at the circumstances of my life.'

'I love you, Gina, and I always have. I want to be with you. I don't know what else to say to convince you.'

I'm woken up by a nurse changing the drip, attaching the final bag to flush through and end this last session. Leon's not here, but his jacket hangs on the back of a chair. I'm sure I drifted off during one of his dramatic, heartfelt monologues on the human condition. This is becoming a feature of our life. Our life. It's been a long, long time since I thought like that. No matter what my emotions and thoughts, I can share them with Leon. It makes me feel better, and brings us closer, even if it doesn't change anything. Leon returns, stays till the end of the session, goes with me to pick up drugs from the pharmacy, chats to Dr K, with whom I have a follow-up in ten days' time, then drives us home. He's chilled champagne to celebrate the end of chemo, but I can't do more than wet my lips with it. Leon strokes me to sleep. He spends the first night in my bed.

The usual, awful, post-chemo effects last well over a week, lifting just in time for my check-up with Dr K, during which he declares that treatment, and my response to it, has gone 'very well indeed'. Another follow-up is booked with an oncology nurse for a month's time, to check bloods and general health, but I'm not due a thorough check-up, with scans, for three months.

That evening, while preparing dinner, I manage to smash a

wine glass, drop a saucepan and burn a finger. Leon takes me by the hand and makes me sit down in the front room.

'What is it, Gina? Tell me what's wrong.'

'I thought I'd feel relieved now that the chemo's over, that this first check-up is out of the way. But I just feel angry. Angry that I've been so ill, angry we've got this hanging over us. I can't … plan, you know? Our future, any future.'

'That's understandable, when you've only been getting by from one week to the next. But things will get back to normal.'

'Normal? Life's changed forever. There's no normal to go back to.'

'Let's just try and enjoy the here and now then – getting to know each other, going out together, sharing stuff. And try not to worry. I know that's easier said than done, but try not to let it ruin the good times.'

'I know you're right, Leon; it's just turning out to be harder than I thought.'

It's true, I am in a funny state. Chemotherapy has finished, but the cancer hasn't, or at least the threat and fear of it hasn't. I'm glad treatment's over, but there's deflation, too, an anti-climax. Getting through chemo, surviving, was the aim, and I've not thought past that. I'm confused about what I'm left with; 'left with' because there is loss – of my familiar body, of health, of a life without cancer. I could go back to the support group – Margaret keeps encouraging me to – but I'm desperate for a break from thinking, talking, living cancer.

The rest of life is good. I feel so close to and happy with Leon, even if I can't whisper back, 'I love you, too.' Friends have been unbelievably brilliant, work's inspiring for once, and the house is looking fantastic and is nearly finished. I'm getting on with Susan, and I'm looking forward to resuming the old routine of picking Chrissy up after school every week. But, sometimes, I can't separate and fold the contradictions, the positives and the negatives, neatly into separate boxes and stack them away. Sometimes, it's all a bloody great jumble lying on the floor in front of me, and I don't know how to order it. Part of me is thrilled when I wake up and feel okay and know treatment has gone well and is over. But another part wants to scream, 'It hasn't ended and it never will!' especially when people make 'you can put it all behind you now' comments. Because I can't put it behind me – cancer and chemotherapy still feel more real than any imagined future with Leon. I can't seem to break the habit of counting backwards and forwards from significant dates: this many weeks since chemo finished, this many months since the hysterectomy, this many weeks till the next check-up.

In an attempt to draw a line under chemo, I decide to sort through absolutely everything, from ancient paint pots in the shed to boxes of correspondence left untouched for years. It's time-consuming, and I'm easily waylaid into reading old letters or trying to remember where and when photographs were taken, but it feels positive to sweep away the rubbish from the past and take the good stuff with me into the future. During the purge I find a cardigan of Chrissy's, which she must have left here weeks ago, and a couple of school books. And I still have some presents from Greece that I haven't got around to dropping off. I drive over to Susan's after dinner on Thursday, unannounced.

Graham answers the door.

'Is it okay to come in?' I ask.

'Of course, but Susan's out at the moment.'

Chrissy rushes up and hugs me. She's obviously not long out of the bath, as her hair is wet and she's in her pyjamas. I give her the gold necklace I bought for her in Greece; it has a seahorse pendant, a creature Chrissy's fascinated by. She asks me a dozen times if it's *real* gold, and gasps or squeaks every time I reply that it is. Then she asks me to read her a bedtime story. After the fifth one, and having spent more time with Ant and Bee than I ever wish to again, I firmly insist that it's time to turn the light out.

'Okay, Grandma,' she says, 'but I'm not going to sleep. I stay awake the whole night. I never sleep and I never get tired.'

'Well, just pretend you're tired and pretend to go to sleep,' I say.

'Alright.'

I go back downstairs to Graham, who's in the front room watching TV.

'Do you know when Susan's due back?' I ask.

'She texted earlier to say she'd be late, but didn't say what time. It's not like her, but …'

We're distracted by scratching noises at the front door; it sounds as if someone is trying to put a key in the lock. Graham gets up and opens it to Susan.

'I'm not drunk,' she says, staggering in.

I have never, ever seen Susan intoxicated.

'Hello, Mother,' she says, 'just the person I need to see.'

She lumbers down the hallway, into the kitchen-dining room, and plonks herself onto a chair. Graham and I follow.

'Mother and I need to be alone,' Susan declares. 'We have things to discuss.'

'Erm, are you sure that's a good idea?' Graham asks, nervously.

'Of course I am!' Susan shouts.

'Okay,' Graham concedes. 'Just call if you need me,' he adds, glancing in my direction, before shutting the door behind him.

'Shall I make you a coffee?' I ask Susan.

Her head wibbles about in a vaguely up-and-down, rather than side-to-side, fashion, so I take it as a yes. I make a large, strong, sweet one and place it on the table in front of her.

'How's it going with this Leon person?' Susan asks.

'Good, great. I mean, it's early days yet, but …'

'Olly told me. Came over in tears actually. Then apologised for telling me that gravity is controlled by NASA when I was a teenager. I only got a C in my end-of-year physics test thanks to that.' Susan's brow furrows. 'I don't know what's worse – Olly out of his brains on drugs or Olly apologising incessantly and asking me to call him Daddy.'

'Hmm, not much of a choice.'

'Seriously, how is it going with Leon? Can I meet him? Will I like him? At least he's got a professional job.'

'Olly's got a job.'

'Making giant eggs is not really a job, is it? Not like being a doctor or a postman or an accountant like Graham.'

'I suppose not,' I say.

Susan's bleary eyes drift about the room, before coming into sharp focus when they spot the bottle of ouzo on the kitchen worktop – a present from Greece.

'Drink!' she declares. 'Pour me a drink!'

'No, Susan, you've had enough.'

'I'll get it myself then.'

Despite being able to talk coherently, when she tries to stand, Susan slithers to the floor. I heave her back up and into the chair.

'Just have the coffee and then get to bed. You've got work tomorrow.'

'I don't care!' she shouts. 'Everything's gone mad.'

'What do you mean?'

'*I* have started therapy,' Susan announces. '*Me.*'

'That's good. I mean, that's one of the best things you can do in life – be brave enough to get help when you need it.'

'It's not for me, but Christine. Well, all of us. Family therapy.'

I put the mug of coffee into Susan's hands, but she immediately puts it back down on the table.

'I'm not criticising, Mother, I'm not, but my childhood was so silly and disorganised. What with Olly and his smoking and the arguments and the weird art stuff all over the house and the wacky people and your embarrassing stories and the yogic flying in the commune. That was real, wasn't it? I didn't just dream it?'

'It was real.'

'I think that's what's made me go the other way. Safe, straight, sensible. But it's gone too far. At least, that's what Dr Curtis said. I'm so strict – "prohibitive" was the word she used – that Christine is already rebelling.'

Susan's never opened up like this. Well, she's certainly told me what she thinks before, but never got as far as self-reflection. I decide not to interrupt, to just listen.

'I did a terrible thing. With the best intentions. But it was wrong. I realise that now.' Susan shudders. 'I was so cross after you gave Christine that snail poo – before I knew what you'd been going through – that I told her she couldn't see you any more. Or Olly.'

'But, but we're her –'

'I know, I know. Do you know what she did? She wrote me

a letter of complaint. They'd been doing them at school. A list of everything she thinks is unfair about how I am as a mother, and how she wants things to change. We're working through them in family therapy. There were about fifty points. I used to do that about you, Mother, make lists in my head of everything that was wrong or stupid or rubbish and then imagine how it should be. But I don't think even I got past more than a dozen. Christine reminded me of me. The same measure of unhappiness, only for different reasons.'

Susan picks up the mug of coffee, sniffs it suspiciously, then takes a sip.

'Of course, some of Christine's requests were ridiculous. You know, so-and-so gets twenty pounds pocket money a week so I should, too. But some of them hit home. "Stop saying no to everything before you even know what it is." "It would be good if you wanted to play with me sometimes, instead of telling me to tidy up or to be quiet." "Try to laugh at things that are funny." That last one seemed the worst somehow – instructing me to have a sense of humour.'

'And did you end up writing a letter to Chrissy?'

'Yes, yes I did. How did you know that?'

'Just seems a therapy type of thing to do. And?'

'I was pleased with it at first. It helped to get everything clear in my mind. But, when we all sat down together and went through it with Dr Curtis, I sounded like a tyrant. It was just a list of dos and don'ts. There was nothing about trying new things or not worrying about getting stuff wrong. There was nothing about loving her. Just do this and don't do that. So controlling, and about things that don't even matter.'

Susan stares into her coffee as if deeply puzzled.

'What a mess,' she says, looking up. 'I've been as hopeless a mother to Christine as you were to me. Sorry! There I go again. Sorry, and I do mean it, Mother. I'm sorry, too, for what you've been going through. It's taken this to make me see you as a separate person, not just as my mother.'

'I know, Susan, I didn't begin to try to understand my mum until years after she'd died. Growing up, I always felt she was too safe, straight, sensible. All those things you pride yourself in being I found oppressive, suffocating. But I've come to learn she had her own reasons for being like that, that she acted from the best of intentions.'

'How can I make it better? Better with Christine, better with you? Is everything just going to repeat itself? Will Christine accuse me of being cold and negative and unloving when she's older? Will she hate me, like I've hated you?'

As Susan talks I notice the kitchen door opening a crack. I initially assume it's Graham, checking up on us, but I soon spot an eye at door-handle height and a puff of golden hair.

'God, I really do need a drink!' Susan declares, and she tries to get up again, but instead wobbles over in slow motion.

Chrissy pushes the kitchen door wide open.

'Mummy's on the floor!' she cries. 'Look at her scrabbling around – she's just like next door's dog when his claws need cutting. Why can't she get up?'

'I think Mummy's had a little too much to drink,' murmurs Graham, as he appears behind Chrissy in the doorway.

'Mummy's drunk,' says Chrissy. 'Mummy's drunk!'

Susan doesn't go into work the following day because she feels so wretched. I call on her in the afternoon.

'God knows what I said yesterday,' she croaks, her hand shielding her eyes as she lies in bed, 'but, whatever it was, I apologise.'

'It's fine, Susan. You were just being honest. We've had a difficult relationship, you and Chrissy have a difficult relationship at the moment. It's better to talk about these things rather than shout and accuse or pretend they don't exist.'

'I can't believe I let Christine see me drunk. She'll never trust me again.'

'It wasn't that bad. Graham was here and so was I, and Chrissy should have been in bed. She was just amazed to see you in such a state and couldn't stop giggling.'

'But it's not funny,' insists Susan. 'It's … dreadful.'

'Honestly, it's not that big a deal.'

Susan struggles to sit up. She looks pale and ill, in pain.

'How are you feeling, Mother?' she asks.

'Ten times better than you look,' I reply.

'Seriously – has the chemotherapy been successful?'

'As far as they know, yes. I mean, the hospital have always done blood tests, but mine have remained the same – negative – throughout. So I'll only know if the cancer's returned if something shows up on a scan or if I get symptoms again.'

'What sort of symptoms?'

'Bloating, pain, weight gain. But anything, everything, can be a symptom, depending on how paranoid I'm feeling. And, let's face it, my body isn't the same as it was six months ago. No womb, no ovaries, no oestrogen, no hair. But, hopefully, no cancer either.'

'Mother,' says Susan, earnestly, 'I'm really sorry about everything you're having to go through. And about how I've been – always going on about the past, being resentful and unappreciative. You had me when you were sixteen, to a man who never wanted to see you again, or me. You brought me up on your own and tried your best. And all I've ever done is moan about not knowing my biological father, about having Olly as a stepfather, about you not being the mother I wanted. I'm married – to a man who's always loved and supported me – I'm thirty-three, I've got a good job and a decent house and even I'm having trouble coping.'

Susan starts to cry, something I haven't seen her do since childhood. Tears slowly spill from her blinking eyes, but she doesn't make a noise or screw her face up, just looks bleak and hopeless. I sit on the bed and put my hand on her arm; she doesn't pull away.

'Don't be so hard on yourself, Susan. And just having stuff – a house or job or whatever – doesn't make you feel great. You're going through a lot right now – helping Chrissy through her problems, coping with me being ill, starting family therapy.'

'But aren't you disgusted to see me like this? Disgusted by the things I said?'

'No. You know me – I'm a live and let live sort of person. You said you hated me. I knew that anyway. And, sometimes, I've hated you.'

'Oh God,' Susan moans, as she lies back on the bed. 'I feel totally out of control, like everything's falling to bits.'

'But it's not. And even if it feels like it is, I'll help you through, if you'll let me.'

'And I want to help you, too. But how can we help each other if we hate each other?'

'We don't hate each other *all* the time. Although we must

admit that the love–hate ratio could do with being balanced a little more evenly.'

Susan manages a weak smile.

'I know a good place to start,' I say. 'Tell me one thing I can do, or stop doing, that would help us to get on better.'

Susan doesn't hesitate.

'Act like you're pleased when I come round or phone up – not like you dread it.'

'It's only because I'm scared we're going to start fighting again. But, yes, a fair point.'

'And you, Mother – what's one thing I can do, or not do, to help make things better between us?'

'Um … call me Mum, Gina, Ma – anything but Mother.'

'It's a deal.'

That evening, I sit on Leon's sofa, staring at the pile of brochures he's left on the coffee table for me to look through. He's keen for us to plan another holiday together, but I can't seem to build up any enthusiasm, especially when the brochures are for grand tours of far-flung places. Sometimes, I think he's too good to be true – his selfless love, devotion and positivity. And sometimes, I find his desire to have such an intense relationship a little overwhelming.

Leon comes in and sits next to me.

'Oh, you've not looked through them. Are you too tired?'

'I am tired, but it's not that.'

'Was it the big discussion with Susan earlier – are you still thinking about that?'

I shake my head. Leon doesn't say anything, just gazes at me.

'Everything's moving so fast,' I say, 'it feels *too* fast sometimes.

I know we've already been away together, but that was more like an escape. A fantastic escape. But this is all happening so quickly.'

'It took me ten years to tell you what I feel. And, to my amazement, you didn't reject me. Now I want to start living our life together. Why should we wait any longer?'

'Because I'm exhausted, because I'm run down. Every morning I wake up and wonder if it's going to be a good day or a bad day. I know I'm slowly recovering from chemo, but I just don't trust anything any more – my health, my life, the future. And for me it hasn't been years, it's been weeks. Wonderful weeks though they've been.'

'I understand,' Leon nods. 'The last thing I want is to put pressure on you. We can take it as fast or as slow as you like.'

'Thank you.'

With the pressure off from Leon to make big plans, I enjoy making small, achievable ones, instead. I continue to sort through the house and garden. I buy some vegetarian cookbooks and try out new recipes. One weekend Chrissy stays over and we train up to London with Leon and go to the science museum. I invite Joy and Tim, Susan, Graham and Chrissy, and Moya round for dinner, to introduce them to Leon properly. I feel proud to be with Leon, and he's such good company. Both Moya and Joy send texts the next day. Moya's says she found Leon to be 'an extremely pleasant young man' and Joy's reads, 'at last you've found someone decent – never let him go!' It's great to be with someone who gets on with my friends and family, and who won't try to sleep with them.

I meet Susan in town during her lunch break the following day.

'What did you think of Leon?' I ask, as we're finishing our soup.

'He's … intelligent, charming, and obviously totally in love with you.'

'But?'

'There aren't any buts – he seems really lovely.'

'Then what is it? You seem … preoccupied.'

Susan sighs, 'I don't want to bother you with my silly problems.'

'Please?'

Susan closes her eyes and rubs her forehead.

'I might be laid off. I found out a few weeks ago.'

'Oh, that's terrible.'

'Streamlining it's called, restructuring.'

'But you've been there ages, and they're forever sending you on training courses. Surely they'll keep you on?'

'The higher up you are, the more expensive you are. And they keep sending me on training courses to try to improve my "people skills". There have been problems, you see. I clash with my immediate boss, a colleague's made a complaint against me, and … I'm not well liked in the office. They'd be glad to see the back of me. Hitler in a Skirt, they call me.'

'Oh, Susan.'

'Why don't they like me? Why? I'm good at my job, I'm conscientious, I always go the extra mile. I'm first in the office every morning and last to leave every evening. And I make sure all the right boxes are ticked, forms filled, deadlines met and targets hit. We're one of the top-ranked Council Tax departments in the country. I even go over colleagues' work and correct their mistakes for them. Okay, so I let them know they've made errors, but surely they can't hold that against me? I'd want to be made aware of any flaws in my work, rather than carrying on in ignorance.'

I wince; poor Susan, she just can't see the world from someone else's perspective.

'You know,' she continues, 'I thought hard work and getting on and being responsible were the right way to go. Firm but fair is how I see myself – in my career, as a mother, in my marriage. But I don't have any friends.' Susan looks deeply perplexed, rather than upset. 'I've been a good person, but no one seems to like me.'

'Graham loves you, Chrissy loves you, I love you, Olly loves you, so does Joy.'

'Thanks, Mum. I hope you're right. Things just seem difficult at the moment. I know it's nothing compared to what you've been going through, but I'm so scared of losing my job.'

'Is there anything I can do to help?'

Susan shakes her head, then looks at her watch.

'Must be getting back.'

I watch Susan as she walks out of the café and up the street towards the council offices. Susan's always worked hard, done what she thinks is right, and tried her best for her family. All things I should have respected more.

When Leon finishes work early on Friday afternoon, we walk over to the school to collect Chrissy. It's unusually sunny and warm for late September, like a summer's day. We remember the last time we were at the school together, when Chrissy had made half the class ill with her 'science experiment' and Mrs Hatcher blew her top about the poo obsession. This seems to have receded, although the Trudy the Turd cartoon character is still very much in existence, and popular with the boys in her new junior school class. We're picking up Brad, too, and they're both excited about having a sleepover together at my house. I did check with Leon that it's okay for him to see Brad socially, and Leon reassured me that it is. His one-off assessment found Brad to be perfectly normal and in need of no further evaluation or intervention. However, Leon's convinced that, with a little more delving, half a dozen different 'disorders' could be pinned on Dougie; no surprise there. Although I have to admit to feeling a little sorry for Dougie at the moment, as he is clearly getting absolutely nowhere in his quest to be reunited with Tar. He keeps phoning me up and asking for advice on romantic gestures that might win her back, but I'm running out of ideas, a situation not helped by the fact that the words 'romance' and 'Dougie Spokes' hardly seem to go hand in hand.

Once we're home, the children busily photograph and list more items on eBay. Chrissy and I have made an incredible four hundred pounds so far, and I've thankfully got shot of the hideous red lips sofa, at only a fifty-pound loss. Even Chrissy said, 'That was a mistake, wasn't it, Grandma?' when she saw it. Mind you, it's only the dregs that are left for eBaying now, such as a dark, ugly painting, which I think is of Don Quixote, but only because standing behind the central, indistinct figure on horseback is a stunted, disproportionately small windmill. I've already tried to sell it but, even with a starting bid of 99p, there were no takers. I tell Chrissy and Brad that if they can shift it, they're welcome to split the profits between them. Having correctly assessed that the painting is unlikely to sell on its artistic merits, the children decide to say it's haunted, and they concoct a ridiculous account of the dreadful things that have happened since it was discovered in our imaginary cellar. I warn them their sales tactics won't work – who would buy something that might bring them bad luck? But, by the next morning, the painting has five bidders and is at over twenty pounds. Even Leon is unable to come up with a theory to explain their motivations. Despite the children's protestations, I refuse to let them try to sell anything else by claiming it's cursed or came alive one night and killed the cat, as I am now being inundated by messages from nutters. By the time Chrissy and Brad are due to go home after their sleepover, they're even more overexcited than when they arrived, their imaginations going into overdrive as to what the painting will finally go for and then what they'll spend the money on. I promise them they can both come back after school next week for the end of the auction.

Early on Sunday, Leon catches a train to the airport; he's going to a conference in Austria and won't be back until late on Thursday. I thought I might enjoy some time to myself, but I mope about, wistfully imagining all the things I could be doing with him – simple things, like chatting, going for a walk, cooking dinner. I think of my life before cancer, of the day the hospital called and left a message with Moya, asking me to get in contact. It was a manic day – full of people and interruptions. Today the house is silent and empty and, despite everything I've been through, my heart is fuller and happier.

By Monday morning the bidding for the hideous painting stands at seventy-eight pounds. I know this because Chrissy rang at 5.50 a.m. to ask me to check. Monday mornings; will I now forever associate them with chemotherapy? I think of all the poor sods up at the hospital, arriving for their IVs, and say a prayer for them, wishing them strength. For me, Marty starting on the kitchen is going to dominate my Monday. I'll be without a sink and cooker for a few days, but it'll be worth it.

While Marty begins stripping out the old kitchen, I crack on with my mission to sweep up after the past and generally sort out the present, too. I phone my solicitor, Alan, and make an appointment for this afternoon to update my will.

The visit is remarkably pain free and it's oddly comforting to know that all my financial and legal affairs will soon be up to date. Alan's an old friend from my and Olly's commune days. He used to have curly, golden hair, live-in tie-dye kaftans and play the mandolin. Now he's bald and suited and drives a Merc.

That evening, I wait for Leon to phone, as he did last night, but the call doesn't come. I try to ring his mobile, but it's off. Worries rush in like hungry mice, nibbling away at my peace of mind. I spend a restless night wondering if he's done it deliberately, if he's had time to think while he's been away and has decided to finish it, if he's met some amazing woman at the conference.

Leon phones early the next morning, and tells me all about how the keynote speech he gave yesterday evening went, and the conference dinner after. Now I remember him saying that he wouldn't be able to phone; I feel such a fool and don't tell him what I've been fretting over. After the call, I lie in bed and think. Of Leon's face, his smile, his hands and embrace. My body tingles and stretches, as if it's been submerged in a warm, relaxing pool of water. I imagine Leon earnestly talking to colleagues, listening intently to papers, writing notes. He really is a remarkable person, and the burden of other people that he takes on in his professional life is also remarkable. He won't discuss *any* of his patients with me; he's such a stickler for confidentiality. I respect him for it. And trust him. I realise I spent so long either unhappily and mistrustfully married to Olly, or on my own, that sharing with Leon has scared me, made me fear I'll become reliant, weak, vulnerable. But the reality is I'm stronger. I even start to wonder, now life is no longer being punctuated by chemo and recovery weeks, where our relationship might be heading, what plans we might make together.

After breakfast, I take my laptop into the attic to get away from the noise of the building work. Up here, I can see right over the city, from where it rises up and out from its slight basin to meet the surrounding countryside. Various landmarks pierce the horizon: the cathedral, the west tower of the city wall, the nearly completed museum and art gallery, in front of which Olly's sculpture will soon sit. An ever-changing skyscape encircles the room. Today, frothy layers of cloud, their underbellies a darker blue-grey, stretch across the limitless expanse of the heavens, making me feel I'm in an enormous painting.

While Leon's away, I make plans for his birthday, which is in a few weeks' time. I practise making an obscure (to me, anyway) Irish fruit bread called barmbrack that he's got a thing about and which he loved as a child. While the first couple of loaves turn out more brick than brack, attempt number three is perfect. I also spend a pointless day wandering about the shops, searching for a present, but nothing seems right. Although I do splash out on some gorgeous silk underwear and equally gorgeous perfume, which is so expensive I don't usually buy it. Cancer, surgery and chemo may have taken my body confidence to new lows, but

Leon's loving is certainly helping to raise it back up again. And I'm not even forcing myself to 'make an effort', but genuinely wanting to, humming away to myself as I slip dresses over my head in changing rooms, spritz fragrances at beauty counters, and examine my high-heeled feet in shoe shop mirrors.

Leon returns from his conference late on Thursday night. We stay awake till the early hours, talking. Leon tells me about the papers he gave, the symposium he chaired and the book he's planning to write with a colleague. I tell him about living in a building site, writing a new will and, um, how the eBay sales are going. I seem to be living the wrong life.

'Have you ever lived with anyone, apart from Olly?' Leon asks, as we lie in bed the next morning, neither of us wanting to get up.

'Only with Susan, of course. Various friends have come and gone, and lodgers, when money was tight. But not a partner. What about you?'

'Mainly as a student, shared houses and stuff. Then with a girlfriend, straight after university, but it only lasted six months.' Leon pauses. 'Would you ever consider living with anyone again?'

'Maybe,' I smile, recognising that I'm happily drifting into the previously uncharted territory of 'making plans'. 'I suppose we could live together, but it seems a bit unnecessary. I mean, my house will soon be totally refurbished, yours is all set up for your psychotherapy and we're literally two steps away from each other.'

'I guess you're right,' says Leon. 'We could always knock a doorway through to each other's places.'

'Yeah, like that actress and filmmaker who live in connected houses.'

Leon draws me closer.

'Have you ever … would you, do you … ever think about getting married again?'

I hold my breath for a second before replying.

'It could be good, it could be wonderful, in the right circumstances, after all this cancer stuff feels further away, further behind us.'

Leon nods.

'What's the date?' I ask.

'September thirtieth.'

'Let's discuss it in a year, eh?'

'Six months?' says Leon.

'Okay,' I smile.

When I go over to the school to pick up Chrissy and Brad later that day, I walk along in a daze. Every time I dare to dream what plans Leon and I might make I feel a little fizz in my heart, and stumble off the pavement. I suggest taking them to the park, but the children are desperate to go on the computer and watch the end of the eBay auction.

The hideous painting sells for £203, and Chrissy and Brad spend the rest of the afternoon compiling shopping lists.

As Leon and I are finishing our take-away dinner, the children having gulped theirs down so they could rush back to their lists, there's a frantic knocking on the front door.

'I'll get it,' says Leon.

I hear Leon open the door and some muffled voices, then there's a bang and some scuffling.

'I gotta speak to Gina, I gotta speak to Gina,' echoes down the hallway.

Two seconds later, Dougie appears in the dining room, unshaven and dishevelled.

'For God's sake, man, I told you to leave her alone,' says a red-faced Leon in hot pursuit.

'What is it, Dougie?' I ask, worried. 'Is it one of the children?'

Dougie slumps onto his knees and clings to my leg.

'It's Tar – I've lost hope. She's never gonna have me back. I've tried *everything*. I'm gonna chuck meself off the flyover onto the motorway.'

I glance up at Leon. His hands are on his hips and, I have to admit, he's wearing a less than sympathetic expression. I look at Dougie. He's a man in torment.

'Don't worry, Dougie,' I find myself blurting out, 'I'll think of something.'

Well, what else could I say?

19

SECOND TIME AROUND

The following morning, while I'm huffing and puffing at the computer, unable to concentrate on work or think of any bright ideas for reuniting the Spokes, Marty comes up to the attic to ask the dozenth spurious question of the hour, when he should be finishing off the tiling in the kitchen.

'What on earth is it?' I ask, snapping the laptop shut and turning to face him.

He hands me a thick, gilt-embossed card.

Phyllis has invited him to be her plus-one at a family wedding, and it's clearly going to be a posh affair.

'What's the matter? This is great news. Isn't it? Don't you want to go?'

'Yeah, I do. It's just …' Marty trails off as he looks down at his paint-splattered T-shirt, 'the clothes … smart ones.'

'Yep, it certainly calls for a suit.' Marty flinches at the word. 'And those cowboy boots have got to go!'

'Will you help me … choose things.'

'Of course. Don't worry about it. Just as soon as the kitchen's finished, we'll go shopping.'

'All done,' Marty announces, late afternoon.

'Really?'

'Yeah. I've just put on the plinths and loaded the last rubbish into the skip. It's completely finished, from top to bottom. So, when can we sort out the, er, wedding threads?'

'Anytime you want –'

'Tomorrow?'

'If you insist, which it appears that you do.'

Although Marty seems incredibly keen on clothes shopping, I know it's because he wants to get it over with. He looks scared, especially after I insist that it's impossible to buy several new outfits for him without him being present, despite his offer to 'let me off the last bit of money for the house' if I agree to do it by myself. Honestly, I owe him two grand.

I forget about Dougie, and how I'm going to endure shopping with a shopaphobic, as I float around my totally revamped house. It's beautiful, perfect, and seems to signify a timely fresh start, a new beginning. Maybe I can look at a few clothes, too, when I'm shopping with Marty, now that life is feeling a little more normal day by day, as a future begins to reappear. Casual tailoring, here I come. And wedding threads. Just for Marty, of course.

That evening, Susan phones.

'How are you?' I ask. 'Any news about the job?'

'No, just the usual rumours, but no real news due till next month at the earliest,' she replies, wearily. 'Can I talk to you … about Chrissy?'

'Of course.'

'I don't know what to do for the best. She's been fighting at school. I've been called in twice this week. She's always been a feisty child, but she seems unable to control her temper at the moment. I don't know why. It's just the usual silly teasing or name calling that seems to spark it off. But Chrissy's been going ballistic. The school's threatening to suspend her if she keeps attacking other children. I can't seem to discuss it rationally with her teachers, I just find myself getting crosser and crosser. I don't know what to *do*. I don't know what's right or wrong any more.'

'Well, it's wrong for her to lash out, but it's wrong for other children to tease her or whatever they've been doing. You've got to try to work with the school. Maybe get Graham involved, so you're not shouldering all the responsibility.'

'Yes, I can't seem to think straight about it,' says Susan. 'But it's good to share it.'

'Chrissy mentioned having an extra day off school next week – a staff development day or something. Do you want to drop her round here?'

'Are you sure? I really don't want to impose.'

'You know I'd love to have her.'

'Thanks, Mum.'

Marty arrives at six-thirty the next morning, prepared to visit a huge, indoor retail development an hour's drive away. It must be love.

'Marty, I don't mean to put the dampeners on things, but it's very *very* early. By "first thing" I was meaning more like nine o'clock. And the shops do stay open till late in these big centres, you know. Still, you're here now, so we might as well make a plan of action.'

As with television makeover gurus, I provide Marty with an extensive list of personal style no-nos, although these should surely be no-nos for anyone, or at least anyone over twenty-two, or not in a band. They are: cowboy boots, leather waistcoats, T-shirts with slogans, biker jackets, reflective sunglasses, very thin ties, unintentionally worn, ripped or holey jeans, camouflage-print anything, any item resembling a 'neckerchief', and any belt with a buckle big enough to incorporate a scene in relief. After much discussion, the entire category of 'headwear' is also added.

'But that's *everything* I usually wear.'

'Exactly. Now, as well as the suit, you'll need casual stuff, too. For the wedding it does have to be a suit. You know that, don't you?'

Marty closes his eyes as he nods, a condemned man resigned to his fate.

'She's asked you to a wedding, Marty, a *family* wedding. That's a big deal. You're staying over with her at a select, country hotel. That could be an even bigger deal. I know what you mean, you sort of won't look like you any more, won't stand out, just another middle-aged man, but –'

'Maybe she likes my, my look.'

I shake my head, 'If it is a "look", then it's one of a man who never knew how to dress and has now lost the will to care. Not a good basis for an image.'

'No. But she really might like –'

'I've asked her. She doesn't.'

'What did she –'

'Roadie for The Grateful Dead.'

Marty grins.

'It wasn't a compliment.'

When I phoned Phyllis last night for some clarification about the latest *Cat Lover's Monthly* article I'm writing, I also quizzed her about her past with men. She appears to have been nearly mortally wounded when her first love rejected her at the age of nineteen, which led to her retreat into looking after animals. She's basically been single ever since, apart from a few unsatisfactory dates or very short-term relationships. She's clearly hypersensitive and a little overly serious. But she obviously really likes Marty.

The shopping trip is a success and we choose a suit for the wedding and two smart, but casual, outfits. Honestly, I could have selected lederhosen and a turban and Marty would have agreed, just to escape from *Suits You* menswear specialists. We decide to go the whole hog and buy some aftershave and a watch. I find my eyes drifting to the wedding bands in the jewellery shop. I tell myself I'm being ridiculous. I wonder what a fifty-year-old bride (almost a contradiction in terms) should wear. Certainly not a lizard-green velvet effort with long, fluted sleeves. I begin to make guest lists in my mind. Sometimes, cancer feels a million miles away.

The next day, Moya rides over to see the house, now it's all done. I've missed her since she moved back to the cottage. She's already had a couple of offers on it, but neither have been high enough for her to accept.

Moya arrives with what looks like a large, rectangular picture, wrapped in brown parcel paper, sitting awkwardly in the sidecar. As usual, she is wearing what she calls her 'piss pot' visor-free bike helmet and giant, old-fashioned motorcycle goggles. I wave to her as she dismounts. She removes the whatever-it-is from the sidecar and strides up the front path.

'Hi, Moya, come on in and see the finished article.'

Moya places the parcel on the dining table, then I give her a tour of the house. I know her idea of interior design is a tad more rustic than mine, but she ooohs and ahhhs in all the right places. When we return to the dining room, she begins untying the string from around the parcel.

'Just wanted to show you *my* finished article,' says Moya, as she removes the paper from the portrait of me that she was working on the day my whole 'cancer journey', as they say, began.

Moya holds it up in front of her and I step back.

Oh dear, much as I adore Moya, I'm afraid her painting does little for me. Thick oils have been heavily applied, mainly in dark, dull browns, with a few murky greys and black to add, um, contrast. I keep trying to see a figure in it, but she is eluding me, unless half her face has fallen off and landed in her lap.

Moya lowers the painting and grins at me.

'Are you pleased with it?' I say brightly, before she can ask me what I think of it.

She nods.

'But not as pleased as I am with the twelve-and-a-half grand a buyer is paying me for it.'

'Wow, that's brilliant, congratulations! And this couldn't come at a better time, what with you planning to move and everything.'

I take the painting from Moya, place it carefully against the wall and give her a big hug.

'Thanks for being my model,' she says, as we pull apart.

'It was nothing. Oh, I have something for you,' I announce.

Now it's Moya's turn to look worried.

From the cupboard under the stairs I take out a package that looks remarkably similar to the one Moya arrived with, but which is wrapped neatly in pristine, white paper. It's a painting I commissioned for her. A risk, I know. The young artist is very good, but unable to paint from anything other than photos, which is why he mainly ends up doing commissions of people's kids and pets. I know that doesn't make him sound like he's a good artist, but he really is the most fantastic draftsperson. I asked him to be a little more inventive with this one.

I present it to Moya.

She takes it, gingerly.

'You shouldn't have, Gina. You *really* shouldn't have.'

'Too late now.'

Moya places the painting on the dining table and slowly, methodically, begins undoing the wrapping. Then she lifts up the painting and stares at it.

There's dear Jacques Cousteau, in his famous red hat, smoking his famous black pipe, sitting in a boat up a Cornish creek. And behind him, partly turned away from the viewer, is someone who looks a lot like Moya, in her famous donkey jacket, smoking a famous cheroot. The sun is shining, the boat is bobbing and the fish are jumping – literally – out of the water. Okay, so it might not look particularly tasteful to an art connoisseur, but my first idea was to have Jacques painted as a merman, so Moya's got off lightly.

Moya turns to me and smiles – a giant, tooth-revealing, eye-crinkling smile. She looks at the painting again and chuckles, then she looks back at me and begins to laugh.

'It's so you, Gina. And it's so me. It's mad.'

When she leaves with the two paintings, she's still guffawing and wiping her eyes.

Well, that wasn't quite the response I was expecting, but it's a good sign. I think.

Since updating my will and legal stuff, I've asked Graham, who does my tax returns, to look through all my old writing contracts and papers to ensure they're in good order. The only vaguely interesting thing he's uncovered is that the small publisher which commissioned me to write the Ruffles the Cat books, more than twenty-five years ago, has now sold the rights to a 'branding, media and intellectual property company'. Graham forwards an email from one of their people, asking me to call. I do.

'Yes, Mrs Jarvis, I believe Ruffles the Cat to be a valuable and historic intellectual property,' says the man on the other end of the phone.

'You're kidding?'

'Absolutely not. The character and series are ripe for a relaunch – with a bit of brand refinement, of course – for a fresh assault on the children's literary and media markets. The good things, just as in fashion, keep on coming round again, but with a fresh gloss.'

'Gloss? Ruffles?'

'Yes, we're working on a significant development plan for Ruffles, to include a new book series, combined with a multi-platform media presence and associated merchandise. And it's so timely that we've been introduced. I know the series was commissioned by the publisher and that all rights and profits remained with them but, now we own the brand, we'd be thrilled if you – Ruffles' original creator – would consider contributing your talents to the visioning of the development project. For a competitive professional fee, of course.

I drop the cordless phone in the bath.

When I call Graham later he convinces me that the media man is both genuine and of sound mind. Apparently, original, out-of-print books are swapping hands for hundreds of pounds. Today's parents, who would have read them as children, hold a cultish nostalgia for Ruffles, and are keen to inflict him on their own offspring – I mean, delight their own offspring with him. There's also a Ruffles fan club. I can hardly believe it. Even Leon, who's relentlessly positive about my writing efforts, can't hide his amazement.

I reread the series (it takes twenty-seven minutes), and have to agree that the books do possess a certain laid-back, if wacky, charm. Can I really be considered so ancient that my work has become a 'historic intellectual property' evoking nostalgia?

Yes, is the answer. This is brought home a few days later, when Media Man calls again, to discuss in more detail the kind of 'creative scaffolding' between the classic and new-generation Ruffles I might contribute to, such as writing a further book series. They're talking about offering me an ongoing creative input role in the overall project, which means I'd be paid regularly for catching a train to London and talking about the cat I imagined over two-and-a-half decades ago. Truth is stranger.

I'm not popping open the champagne till I've signed a contract, but they seem genuinely keen on employing me, and for a competitive professional fee! (I was paid £35 per book back in the seventies.) With Donna's natural glamour media machine in full force and the redhead issue of *Eurotica*, the cover of which she will … um … grace, due out by the end of the year, subscriptions are up dramatically. Financially and work-wise, things have never looked so good for me. Unfortunately, the same can't be said for Dougie.

Despite my increased efforts over the past couple of weeks, it's not proving easy to persuade Tar to take him back. I have done my best, telling Tar that Dougie is pining for her, that they're made for each other. He has sent love letters (heavily spell checked and edited for obscenity and insanity by me), flowers, and has even acted on my suggestion of a 'personalised' gift. Dougie called me this morning, after the large canvas he'd had made of their wedding photo was returned, slashed, divorce papers sellotaped over what remained of the groom's head. I've promised to go round and sympathise later today. But, first, there's my check-up.

'What time's the appointment?' asks Leon, coming up to the attic, where I've taken to working on the laptop.

'Two-fifteen.'

'I'll take you up.'

'I'm perfectly capable of driving myself. I'm not an invalid.'

'You know what the parking's like up there. You'll go round and round, not find a space, then miss your check-up.'

'Okay, you're right. I just hope it doesn't take too long, I've got to go and see … see Dougie.'

Leon frowns.

'I know he's a nutter, but he's also an old friend. I've never seen him so upset and, well …'

Leon opens his arms, inviting me into their circumference. I allow myself to be enfolded.

'Forget other people for a minute,' he murmurs, 'and let me take care of you.'

I hug Leon to me.

The prospect of today's six-week, post-chemo check-up, which I've refused to even think about, has been secretly knotting me up inside, tighter and tighter, as it draws closer and closer.

As predicted, there are no empty spaces in the hospital car parks and Leon has to drop me off and then find a side street to park in. A wave of nausea breaks over me when I enter the building. A nurse takes bloods and examines me. No, no new symptoms since chemo finished. It only takes twenty minutes, and I meet Leon coming in as I walk out.

'How was it?'

'Okay. But not very reassuring, somehow. Just brings back all those feelings. It was only a once-over and bloods, when mine never showed anything anyway. I suppose I'm dreading the three-month check, when they'll redo the scans. Then they'll really be able to see how things are.'

Leon drives me over to Dougie's. He parks, but I don't get out.

'Do you want to talk about it, Gina?'

'I just want to forget this disease, but I can't. I remember Margaret going half-crazy waiting for her three-month check. But when she got the all-clear she felt fabulous. Then she and her husband could really start making plans. You're so understanding, but sometimes I feel even worse about the cancer now – more anxious and scared – because I've got more to lose.'

'What do you mean?'

'You. You are what I have to lose now. Us being together makes it so much easier to bear, and yet so much worse in other ways.'

'Have you thought about going back to the support group?

It's like you said before – just because chemo's over doesn't mean the cancer is. At least, not psychologically.'

'I suppose I've just wanted to avoid anything to do with cancer, but maybe I should go back, maybe I am ready to face it again. Anyway, I'd better go.'

'Do you want me to come in with you? You know what a maniac Dougie is.'

'Is that your professional assessment then – maniac?'

'Pretty much. I know you want to help him, but I don't want you to get over-involved in stuff that doesn't even concern you.'

'It'll be fine. Don't worry. I'll see you later – dinner at mine?'

Leon nods and we kiss goodbye.

Dougie lets me into his tiny, grotty flat. He's nosedived even further since I last saw him. He's already half drunk and tearful, and has phoned in sick to work. My sympathetic shoulder having worn thin, I try a new tack.

'It's time to move on, Dougie. Your children are still your children, that can't be taken away from you. What about trying to find someone new?'

'Where would I find another woman like Tar?'

'Do you like caravan park holidays?'

'You don't understand. I can't live without her. Just look at the state of this place. I can't cook. I've got no one to have sex with. I don't know what I'm doing without her telling me what I'm doing.'

'Look, all you're saying is that you want someone to clean, cook and organise your life for you.'

'And the sex.'

'Yes, and the sex. I don't hear you saying anything about how you love Tar for herself, as a woman, her … personality, her, um, sense of humour.'

Dougie stares at me; he can't have died suddenly because he is still upright.

'Dougie?'

'I know! I know how to get her back.'

'Oh. How?'

'Jealousy, competition. That's how we got together in the first place. I pursued that woman, but she kept giving me the brush off, kept saying how she didn't wanna get involved with someone at work. That was when we was both at the packing factory, before it got closed down. I almost gave up hope. But there was this girl, see. Kelly, her name was. Well, she was keen on me and let me know it. I took her to the pictures, but only cos she asked. Wasn't bothered really. I was too stuck on Tar. Tar found out about the date with Kelly. We was married by the end of the year.'

'Perhaps making her jealous will work again then,' I say.

'Yeah. That's it. I know it is. If that don't work, nothing will.'

'Wonderful. Problem solved.'

'When you gonna do it then?'

'What?'

'Make Tar jealous.'

I slap my forehead.

'Dougie, I want to help, I really do. But I'm stressed and tired and, well, recovering from cancer. Also, I have a boyfriend. And I don't want to do myself a disservice, but I'm nearly fifty, and I'm not much better than bald.'

'You, Georgina, are still one very attractive lady. And I think a little thinning on top adds a certain mature sophistication to a person,' says Dougie, rubbing a hand over his threadbare pate. 'Look at Sean Connery and Ross Kemp and …'

I frown, wondering if it's worth remarking that I don't think the concept of 'baldness as an attractive sign of maturity' applies to women, but then I faint.

I come round to find myself lying on Dougie's greasy sofa, which adds to my resolution to get up fast. Dougie offers to drive me home. I remind him he's been drinking. He says he doesn't care, that nothing matters any more. I decide that, judging from the things he misses most about Tar, it's best to treat Dougie as a small boy in need of organisation and discipline.

'How could you even think of drinking and driving,' I scold. 'That's all you need, isn't it – a lost licence, a lost livelihood and upping the likelihood of losing Tar forever.'

'Sorry,' he replies, meekly; 'Yes, Miss,' wouldn't have sounded out of place.

'Now, sober up, clean this place up and I'll think of a way to make Tar jealous. But perhaps not using myself as the bait.'

Before leaving, I ask one question.

'What happened to Kelly, the girl who made Tar jealous?'

'Er, can't really remember. Hold on … joined the army, I think. Yeah, that's what Tar said. Never saw her again, mind, after our night out at the pictures. Strange that.'

Who am I going to find to make Tar jealous? And how's it to be done? She's not the sharpest tool in the shed, but would surely guess a set-up. And who can be bribed to get flirty with Dougie in front of Tar? And what's the likelihood of Tar attacking and/ or killing the woman in revenge? Or just for the fun of it? I saw her after Dougie pushed Brad over in my hallway and she was terrifying. And why did I faint? I felt fine earlier and feel fine now. Was it the smoky atmosphere, the stress of the check-up, worrying about Susan, and Chrissy's problems at school? I must get home, calm down and think.

It must be so terribly burdensome for Leon: all day listening to patients, all night listening to me. Today's check-up has brought everything back again; no matter how much I want to forget cancer, it's still part of my life, of our life together. I almost had a heart attack earlier. I looked down and there was a black mark on my arm, which I immediately saw as a cancerous growth. It turned out to be a smudge of something unidentifiable that rubbed off in an instant. But that sudden panic, the frightening free fall, made me realise that fear of the cancer returning is simmering under the surface. Maybe, if I start attending the support group again, I'll be more like Heather: a survivor, rather than a sufferer. I decide to go to tomorrow's session. I curl up in bed with Leon, feeling both resigned and relieved.

Next morning, Media Man calls to say he'd like to see four new Ruffles story outlines, to check I'm 'still up to the job'. I tell you, a seven-year-old could write them. In fact, she does, after Graham drops her off at my house when her school is closed for its staff development day.

Although she's never particularly liked Ruffles, Chrissy's happy to work on the outlines with me. I try to encourage a higher opinion of him.

'They want to reprint the old Ruffles books, Chrissy.'

'Hmm.'

'I started to write them when your mummy was seven – the

same age you are now – and, all this time later, children still want to read them.'

'Hmm.'

'They might even make Ruffles games and toys and bed covers. Why do you think children love him so much?'

Chrissy shrugs, 'Little kids like any old rubbish, especially if it's got a fluffy cat in it with great big eyes.'

That's me told.

Chrissy warms to Ruffles after she manages to sneak a Foxling Village inhabitant into the stories, who soon becomes Ruffles' enemy, as she thinks up increasingly far-fetched plans to evict him from his rooftop home. Despite, or rather due to, Ruffles' innocent brainlessness, the plans inevitably fail. By the middle of the afternoon, we've come up with four paragraph-long story outlines, which I email to Media Man. Chrissie also suggested introducing Trudy the Turd into the stories, although only as a joke, I hope.

'Have you, um, grown out of talking about poo all the time now, Chrissy?'

She huffs as she puts her felt-tip down.

'I don't know why everyone's always going on about it. Mummy kept on about it, and Mrs Hatcher, and now Dr Curtis, as if I'm weird or something. The boys in my class never stop talking about poo and farts and wee and bogies.'

'Dr Curtis?'

'Yes, we go to see her every week. Me and Mummy and Daddy. She started to ask about poo, but I told her I didn't want to talk about that any more, not like the boys in my class. It's *so* immature.'

'What did she say to that?'

'She asked if I wanted to talk about anything else. I, I talked about you for a bit, Grandma, although I didn't mean to.'

'Really?'

'Yes, when Dr Curtis asks me questions I start saying things I don't even know I'm feeling. Like that I was upset that you'd been having cancer, but that I knew you'd be alright because Aaron in my year had it and he's better now.'

'Oh, yes, I remember you telling me about him.'

'I said how mean it was when kids made fun of his bald head and kept pulling his hat off. It made me want to beat them up. But I didn't. But if they dare say anything about *you*, then I'll punch them as hard as I can. That'll make them stop.'

Chrissy's face contorts with anger and her hands scrunch into tiny fists.

'What did Dr Curtis say to that?' I ask, reaching out and stroking her hair.

'She didn't say anything. She never says anything's bad or wrong, she just nods all the time. I like her. After I've talked about lots of things she always asks if I want to talk about anything else. Sometimes I say no. Then Mummy talks. Sometimes Mummy gets sad. And sometimes she gets angry. Sometimes she just sits there and doesn't say anything for ages, even though she's been asked a question. If she did that in my school she'd be sent to the headmistress.'

'It is helpful, though – the talking?' I ask. 'Have you learned things about yourself, and other people?'

'Yes,' Chrissy replies, as she picks up her felt-tip again. 'Everyone's bonkers.'

When Susan arrives to collect Chrissy, I ask her how it's going with the school.

'Better – well, Graham's been dealing with it mostly. And Dr Curtis is working on "anger management strategies" with Chrissy, with all of us as a family.'

'That's good; it sounds like you're getting somewhere. I was chatting to Chrissy earlier. She seems angry that I've had cancer, not that she's really aware that's how it's making her feel. Maybe that could be contributing to her behaviour at school.'

Susan nods, 'Could be. When she talks about it with Dr Curtis she certainly sounds angry.'

'Have you got time for a drink?' I ask. 'I've got the cancer support group later, but it doesn't start till –'

'Cancer support group?' Susan shrieks. 'Has it come back again, have you –'

'No, no, it's not come back. It's a support group for people who've had cancer, as well as those going through it.'

'Good God,' says Susan, 'you scared the hell out of me.'

'Sit in the front and I'll bring you a coffee.'

Susan looks less than enthusiastic.

'A glass of wine?'

No response.

'A gin and tonic?'

Susan nods, vigorously.

'The house looks great, Mum,' Susan says, when I bring in her G & T. 'I can't believe I used to storm in here like I owned the place and tell you what to do. Or what not to do. I'm so embarrassed.'

I shrug.

'I've wanted to help,' she says, 'help you through the cancer and treatment and everything, but everyone else had taken those roles – Moya, Joy, Leon, even Marty. It's made me realise how I've been as a daughter.'

'Well, I wasn't there for you when you had your health scare.'

'But that's all mine was – a scare. You've had the real deal.'

'It's okay, Susan. We've both had a wake-up call. And you're helping me now – by being honest about what's going on in your life, and Chrissy's, by letting me in.'

'It's helping me, too,' says Susan.

'Any news about work, about possible redundancies?'

'We've all been sent a letter, saying we can apply for voluntary redundancy or to go part-time. There's some hope this might avoid enforced redundancy.' Susan shakes her head. 'But I can't take redundancy – what if I don't find another job? There's nothing locally. And part-time wages won't be enough. I've been looking at jobs farther afield, though. There's a couple in London I could apply for, but it would mean commuting every day.'

'I don't suppose you'd fancy that?'

'Not really, but when needs must.'

My phone beeps; it's Margaret, texting to remind me the support group starts in half an hour.

As I say goodbye to Chrissy and Susan, then watch them walk down my front path, I notice they're holding hands. They both turn and wave to me at the same time, and smile. Despite what they're going through, individually and together, they seem closer.

I sigh as I start up the car to drive over to the hospital. It's hard to accept that I still need the cancer support group, but I do.

I've just got through the main gates when my mobile rings. I pull over and answer it.

'Can I speak to Mrs Jarvis, please,' asks a young, male voice.

'Speaking,' I reply, hoping it's another media company executive with a big cheque book.

'This is PC Blunt, calling from the station.'

'What, what is it?'

'No need to panic, madam. I'm phoning with regards to an incident involving a Mr Douglas Spokes.'

'Oh, God, what's he done?'

'We have apprehended Mr Spokes joyriding. Over private property, causing extensive damage. He's requested that you come to the station to pick him up.'

Here we go again. I thought my days of picking intoxicated idiots up from police stations had ended since Olly gave up smoking, but apparently not. I drive back out through the hospital gates and over to the police station.

Dougie, having got tanked up in the local golf clubhouse, 'borrowed' a sit-on lawn mower and then tore over the course. PC Blunt lists the catalogue of damage and asks what his excuse is, even though he's easily young enough to be Dougie's son. Dougie replies, 'I was drunk,' as if this is an explanation, rather than a statement of fact. Then he begins to blub about his break-up with Tar. ('More precious than any diamond, mate, the love of a good woman.') I want to paint Dougie's portrait and title it *Potato, weeping*. But then, quite unexpectedly, I join in, collapsing into a plastic chair and saying I was on my way to a cancer support group and this is all too much. PC Blunt looks unconvinced, until I pull off my wig and use it as a hanky. He can barely disguise his disgust as he surveys us both, and his sudden gratitude too, perhaps, for having sensible parents who don't get pissed, steal things, joyride, cry in front of strangers or remove their wigs in public.

After the whole mess is dredged through again, and someone from the golf club appears, Dougie is let off with a caution, on the understanding he pays damages to the club, which is keen to keep the incident out of court and the news. This is extremely lucky, given Dougie's job of taxi driving. I return him to his grotty flat in silence, feeling like the parent of a stupid teenage boy caught shoplifting deodorant or smoking weed in a telephone box.

By the time I get home, it's nearly ten o'clock, and the support session is long over. As I'm thinking about turning in for the night, I hear a gentle tapping on the front-room window. I let Leon in and he asks how the group went. I'm quiet for a moment, embarrassed at having to recount the absurdity of my evening, but then I go ahead anyway. The more I describe, the more ridiculous it sounds, and I find myself playing up the farcical aspects to turn it into an entertaining story. It's a relief to laugh about it with Leon and, more importantly, to share the details of my life – however mundane or ludicrous – with someone who cares and doesn't openly yawn. I invite him to stay over.

'Happy birthday, Leon,' I say, when I bring him a cup of tea in bed the next morning, and hand him an envelope.

I've booked the west turret of a castle (yes, really), which stands on a remote Scottish island, for a week; next May, mind, when the weather shouldn't be too bad and before the midges really begin biting. Leon opens the envelope, which contains all the details.

'This is fantastic,' he exclaims.

'Apparently, the scenery is particularly rugged and there are, um, lots of walking opportunities,' I say. 'And the weather in May will be as temperate as it gets in Scotland.'

'That's great, but … you are coming with me, aren't you?'

'Yes. I have already purchased a pair of waterproof trousers.'

'Thanks, Gina. I know it's not your idea of holiday heaven.'

'Come on, you booked Greece for me, and endured forty-degree heat and swimming every day when you can't even swim. I'm sure I can cope with a week up a misty mountain.'

Leon smiles.

'What's that smell?' he asks, as the spicy fragrance of the baking fruit bread drifts up the stairs and tickles our noses. 'It's not barmbrack, is it?'

I nod.

'God, I love you,' Leon declares, and he pulls me back under the covers.

By the time we emerge, the barmbrack's a little burnt, but still edible.

That afternoon, Media Man emails to say he likes the story outlines, especially the inclusion of the new character, as it ups merchandising potential. He's keen for at least two more to be added, and would like the environment reworked so that it's more 'product friendly'. Ruffles' rooftop and Kissy Foxling's dustbin are not considered 'to adequately exploit the series' retail potential'; it's a cynical world. After an intense day of to-ing and fro-ing, my rate for writing the new stories has not been finalised, but the establishment of my creative input role for the overall project is pretty much in the bag.

The fact that Ruffles is to be resurrected, and is going to

provide me with another income stream (Media Man's business-speak is rubbing off on me) is something to celebrate. I trot down to the offie to buy a couple of extra-special bottles for Leon and I to have with his birthday dinner tonight.

Turning into the parade of local shops, I bump straight into Tar.

Maybe this is fate. Maybe this is my chance to sort out Dougie's problems, right now, before the whole situation, and him as a human being, become unsalvageable. Even if it means becoming an enemy of Tar. Yes, this is it. Deep breath. Here goes. It's in God's hands now.

Luckily, Tar immediately mentions Dougie. I'm sure she still loves him, otherwise she wouldn't constantly talk about him, even if it is to slag him off.

'I hear Dougie's been making a right twat of himself again,' she says.

'Yes. I know.'

'He called Donna from the cop shop yesterday, he did, asked her to come and get him. Didn't know I was listening in, did he? I made her say no. He's probably still in there. And serve him right.'

'He's not, actually. Someone did help out,' I say.

'What? How do you know that?'

'Just heard, on the grapevine. You don't need to worry about Dougie any more. That was the final straw, his lowest point since you two split, he's hit rock bottom and now the only way is up.'

'Oh. That's not what I been told. I heard he's been given a warning at work. One more sickie and he's fired. Behind with the rent, as well, and run up a huge tab at The Boar and Badger what he can't pay. And, I am *not* worried about him. He can stew in it.'

'No, I know you're not, Tar. Anyway, all that stuff is just a smokescreen.'

'Smokescreen? How d'you mean?'

'I know I can be honest because I know you aren't interested in Dougie any more. He thought you'd be jealous, but I know you really, genuinely, won't care.'

Tar's eyes burn into me.

'Won't care about what?'

'The fact he's seeing someone new. She's the one who picked him up from the police station. Must dash.'

I advance a few paces along the road before I hear Tar's quick and anxious tap-tapping stilettos coming up behind me. Suddenly, she's in front. And very close.

'Who is it? Who is she?'

I pull a I'd-really-like-to-let-you-know-but-can't face: a toothless smirk coupled with an insincere frown.

'Tell me!'

'Tar,' I say, placing my hand on her shoulder, 'that's why Dougie got his smokescreen going, so you wouldn't feel jealous, to protect his new partner.'

'Partner!'

'Soon to be fiancée. You did send him those divorce papers, didn't you?'

Tar nods, eyes struggling between popping in amazement and narrowing in seething hatred and jealousy.

'He tried everything, didn't he? The kids talking to you, me having a go, the love letters, flowers, presents, suicide threats.'

'He tried everything, yeah,' agrees Tar, suddenly crestfallen, eyes to the pavement in dull recognition.

'He even tried to understand homosexuality, bought that Pet

Shop Boys CD for Brad, which you, um …'

'Threw at his head.'

'Exactly. I think it's time for you to move on, too.'

I give Tar's shoulder a quick squeeze then start to walk on. Two seconds later, she's in front of me again.

'Who is it, Gina, tell me. I promise – I swear on me kids' lives – I won't smash her skull in with a hammer or wait outside her house and run her down in the four-by-four or tie her up and torture her or –'

'It's me.'

'You? It can't be! I thought you was with the Doc?'

'Didn't last. And I've always carried a torch for Dougie, ever since school. He asked me out when we were thirteen, but I turned him down. I thought he was too good for me.'

Much to my horror, Tar nods.

'I know I'll always be second-best to Dougie,' I carry on, choking on the pride I am desperately trying to swallow, 'and I didn't want to mess up any chance of you two getting back together again. That's why I went to see you for myself, presented every reason why you should remain husband and wife – the kids, the house, the shared love of art. And you convinced me – and I mean *really* convinced me – that you hated his guts and would never have him back.'

Silence.

'No hard feelings, eh?' I chirp.

I walk away as nonchalantly as I can, all physical and mental effort being directed into not running for my life or ducking into the nearest doorway in case Tar attacks me from behind. I don't even turn to see what she's doing. It's a good ten minutes before my heart stops pounding and I slow down. I can't remember where I was going or why. I decide to head back to the safety of home, ringing Dougie on the way. There's no answer, so I leave a message telling him I've told Tar about 'our relationship' and that if I end up dead in a ditch it'll be his fault.

I've not long locked the doors and windows, pulled the curtains and checked my mobile's fully charged in case of emergencies, when Dougie calls. He fills me in on developments: Tar belted round to his place and threatened to kill him, then me ('when she's fully better', her knowledge of my recent cancer preventing her from doing me over in the street there and then); Dougie trembled with joy at this display of jealousy; Tar was reminded of how they first got together; they fell into each other's arms, instead of at each other's throats; and then, well, I order Dougie to spare me the intimate details. 'No hard feelings,' I hear Tar yell in the background. They're planning to renew their marriage vows, i.e. Tar's not letting Dougie back into the house and marital bed until she has a new dress, new ring and second honeymoon. I'm genuinely pleased for them.

I ring Leon and tell him to hurry up and come over and to bring a bottle of wine. No, make that champagne. It's time to celebrate. No, it's time to do more than celebrate; it's time to make plans.

20

THREE LITTLE WORDS

But I spend the next day in the operating theatre. And the following week in hospital, recovering. Excruciating abdominal pains began just as Leon arrived. I thought it was the stress of dealing with Tar but, after five minutes, I could do nothing but crunch down on the floor in agony. Leon called an ambulance.

My bowel had become obstructed and I've had keyhole surgery to unblock it. I seem to be taking it in my stride this time. Hi, yes, me again, third operation in six months, isn't it? I might as well move in; ha, ha. Good – or not so good – to see you again. Oh, so it's not that uncommon an occurrence in cancer patients? Silly me, I was hoping I wasn't one of those any more. Yes, morphine's just dandy for the initial post-op days, but then the nausea and mood swings rather get me down. Sure, I'll get out of bed and wobble up and down the ward for you. No, that's fine: go ahead and check my wounds. Need to siphon off more blood? Just say the word.

At least I know the post-operative routine by now, which painkillers work best for me, and have the faithful, elasticated-waist romper suit immediately mobilised for action. While I'm in hospital, I write a lot of lists. I list all possible symptoms of ovarian cancer from when I first remember experiencing them;

I can't trace them back any further than twelve months. I list the best times of my life. I list the worst. I list my priorities. And I write the same three words, over and over again.

Treatment. Resistant. Cancer. So concluded Dr Kimura after more tumours were discovered during the bowel surgery.

Imagine a pair of old-fashioned weighing scales. On one side are decades of medical investigations and advancements, clinical trials and new therapies, generations of doctors, nurses, researchers and scientists, spanning the globe; there are libraries heaving with knowledge, hospitals with clinical evidence, computers with data. On the other side of the scales are those three words: treatment-resistant cancer. And, in the balance of my life, their weight is greater; it has dragged their side of the scales to the ground and everything on the other side is as light as bubbles, floating away to nothingness, rainbow-tinted hopes that perish in an instant.

Lists, lists, lists. I keep writing and rewriting them, ordering and reordering priorities. But it's not like deciding France or Italy this year, starter or dessert. No. Should I try more treatment with different chemotherapy drugs (I have an appointment with Dr K in a week to discuss options) or investigate alternatives? I may have rejected them before, but chemo hasn't worked. How's Susan going to cope with all this when she has enough troubles of her own? Chrissy – how am I going to tell her that I'm not like Aaron in her year at school, that the cancer hasn't gone away? Leon. I don't want to put him through what I'm having to go through. Why should he endure all the crap, when he's not had any of the good stuff? My head is such a jumble, such an endless swirl of thoughts and worries, I feel permanently seasick. All that treatment for nothing. All that surgery, pain, poison and sickness. All that anxiety, all that getting through a day at a time. Coping. But, when I remember chemotherapy, I also remember Moya looking after me, reading to me, my dream in which she appeared as a huge, immoveable wardrobe. I remember the David Essex concert with Joy and Susan, writing Foxlings books with Chrissy, the friends I made at the support group. I remember Leon confessing his love for me in the chemo suite, our holiday, our lovemaking and conversations, our fragile plans.

For the first time ever, I don't look forward to bonfire night. Usually, a big group of us go to a nearby village, famed for the exuberance of its festivities, and get into the whole thing: the rowdy pagan parade; the pulse of the drumming; the stand-well-back heat of the towering bonfire; the rushing crackle of its burning, toasting the air; the procession of high-pitched arcs soaring into the sky, the second's wait, followed by the explosions of release; the celebration – of brightness and warmth in a season of darkness and cold.

This year, I decide to go to bed early. I've been home from hospital for about a week, since the bowel surgery two weeks ago. I'm up to going out physically, but don't even bother to look out of the window. This year fireworks are silly; not only silly, but irritating and pointless. And noisy: they sound like long, squeaky farts. They are artificial, preposterous. A handful of sparkles thrown into the night sky – a spray of childish, gaudy glitter – serving only to illuminate the dark, insurmountable lump of life, real life.

Leon comes in.

'Depression is often the dreadful bedfellow of illness, of being scared,' he says.

'Don't say words like "bedfellow"!' I shriek. 'They make you sound like a … like a pompous git. And I am not depressed.'

'Oh. Good. Then you'll enjoy these.'

Leon hands me a paper bag; a sheet of card is poking from the top. I pull it out. It's dotted with odd things: what look like tiny, round purple and pink pills, little silver cones, brown pellets resembling rabbit droppings. They are indoor fireworks, an impossibly contradictory concept. I used to buy them for Susan in the seventies. Then they were banned, I can only imagine for the most obvious reasons. Years ago, I told Leon how much we used to enjoy them. Susan never liked fireworks much – too noisy and unpredictable – but she adored the indoor ones, and so did I, even though they stunk the place out for days. The memories of us lighting them on the dining-room table, in this very house, are good ones.

'Come on,' says Leon, 'let's go downstairs.'

'Do them here.'

'But the smell, and the smoke, it might –'

'Oh, Leon, what does it matter?'

The Chinese Dragon has a phenomenal capacity to keep on producing more of itself from the tiniest cone. By the end, 'the dragon' resembles a long, twisted, deformed snake or the blackened intestine of a small animal. Others sparkle, fizz and glow, just like real fireworks, but reaching a maximum height of three inches, while threatening to set the card on fire. Buddha's Mountain is along the Chinese Dragon line, in that a large amount of muck is produced from a microdot. But I find them charming, I really do.

If you are of the opinion that joss-sticks are deeply

unpleasant, creating headache-inducing odours, suffocating smoke and an intolerable amount of dusty mess, then let me tell you that indoor fireworks are ten times worse. After they're finished, my bedroom is filled with such a thick fog of acrid smoke, which then disperses throughout the first floor, that we have to escape to the sofa bed in the attic.

We pull it out and cuddle up.

'I'm sorry, Leon, for being so tetchy, and miserable, and for calling you a –'

'Gina, it's alright.'

'But what about our plans – you know, to be discussed in six months from September thirtieth? How can we do anything, enjoy anything, after this? It's not going to go away. You don't have to go through this, you don't have to stay with me. In fact, I'd rather you didn't.'

Leon sighs.

'I'm just going to stick the kettle on and make coffee,' he says, 'because it looks like I'm in for the long haul tonight. I know you need to talk everything out and, speaking as a psychotherapist, I'd have to say that's a good thing. But, there's one condition.'

'What?'

'If we wake up in the same bed together tomorrow morning, we don't have to go through the you-should-leave-me because-I'm-ill discussion *ever* again. No matter what.'

I nod.

As predicted, I spend half the night listing the numerous reasons we should split up: it's not fair on him; it's not fair on me because I feel so guilty about it not being fair on him; Chrissy and Susan are also priorities, which again isn't fair on him; there's something I need to do and it's going to take up a lot of my time; look, I'm just going on and on about myself which shows just how unfair I am, the situation is, this whole relationship is. In the end Leon tells me it's not fair to give him a migraine by making him listen to hour after hour of me annihilating myself and our relationship, that this is worse than trips to the hospital and coping with any physical stuff I have to go through. We can either be miserable – apart and alone – or we can be happy together and better able to deal with whatever happens.

I wake the following morning to find Leon looking at me. Before I have time to draw breath, he puts his finger to my lips.

'No more discussions, you promised,' he says, softly.

As the day of my appointment with Dr Kimura approaches – to discuss 'treatment options', now I've had a chance to recover from the bowel surgery – I feel more zen. Leon, Susan and Joy all want to accompany me, but I'm unsure. I need to think straight and know I'll be worrying about how they're handling everything if any one of them is present. In the end, due to Leon having a meeting in London on the day of the appointment, Susan being at work, and much lip-trembling from my oldest, bestest friend (as she keeps reminding me), it's agreed that Joy will come with me.

I don't know what I was expecting, but it's a long and complicated discussion, during which Joy scribbles notes but, thankfully, doesn't interrupt too much. More chemotherapy with different drugs is an option. But chemo didn't work before and there's no guarantee it'll be any more effective this time. Most women have at least a few months, if not years, clear of cancer before a reoccurrence, and a fair percentage are cured, whereas mine has spread during treatment. More surgery could become an option, but I've already had three abdominal operations in six months and, due to the new tumours being on and around the bowel (which contributed to its obstruction), it could do more harm than good. And, before any more treatment can be decided upon, I'd need another battery of tests to establish the extent of the disease. Do I really want to know if it's now in my kidneys, my liver, my brain? Such information would be useful to the medics if I start having other symptoms, but, Christ, if I'm destined to peg out soon, there are other things I want to do apart from being fried in scan machines and agonising over test results. I don't want to play the 'what if' game either: what if I'd recognised symptoms earlier; what if Dr Kimura had performed the initial surgery; what if I'd had no treatment and let the disease take its course – would I be better or worse off now? Dr K assures me worse, that treatment should prolong life – slowing the growth of the tumours – even if it can't, ultimately, save it.

Joy can contain herself no longer.

'That's not true though, is it? That stupid gynaecologist may have spread the cancer cells because he thought he was removing a cyst. He may have made it worse.'

'The initial treatment, before we were aware of the cancer, was not optimal, no,' concedes Dr K, his enormous moustache twitching uncomfortably. He then turns to me. 'I know there is a lot to take in, Mrs Jarvis, but do you have any thoughts on how you would like to proceed?'

'I know the cancer is, essentially, incurable. I know that for it not to respond to chemo, to have more so soon, to have had the bowel obstruction, are hardly positive signs. But, at the moment, I don't feel too unwell. I know this could change, like it did with the obstruction, and I could need further treatment at any time.'

Dr K hasn't contradicted anything I've said and clearly isn't about to. Gulp.

'Aren't there new tests,' asks Joy 'that can predict which chemo drugs will be most effective at fighting different cancers?'

'This is true, partly, but growing cancer cells in a laboratory is not easy and has a high failure rate. And tests can only predict which drugs are less effective, not more.'

'I don't want to be up the hospital all the time,' I say, 'having non-stop investigations, going through treatments that aren't working. If my time is limited, I don't want to spend it recovering from surgery, feeling sick and ill from chemo, living on the promise of a longer life, rather than living the life I have left.'

'You are correct, Mrs Jarvis, that we will be hoping to prolong life with more treatments, rather than cure the disease. And, second-line chemotherapy is most effective for patients who have been disease free for some time, which, unfortunately, has not been the case for you. But, there may be clinical trials that you –'

'Look, I've seen *Wit* with Emma Thompson. I'm not noble, I'm not brave and I don't want to sacrifice the end of my life to anyone but myself. I've got something I want to do and I have to be mentally and emotionally with it to do it. I need to remain as *compos mentis* as possible. That's *my* treatment priority.'

'Quality of life, then, is more important than extending life, at this moment?' asks Dr K.

'Yes.'

'Okay. There is still plenty we can do to manage symptoms, even if you want no more tests or treatment for now. We'll see how we go. But you must let me know if you change your mind.'

We all stand up and I shake hands with Dr K. He opens the door.

'Before I go, can I …' I say.

'Yes?' says Dr K.

'Well, you know you've become intimately acquainted with my body. My womb, my ovaries. My omentum, no doubt, my bowels, my blood, my platelets, my cells, my everything.'

'Yes.'

'Can I touch your moustache?'

Silky, luxuriant; it doesn't disappoint.

'I can't believe you did that!' hisses Joy, as we get in the car.

'You can't grow something that size on your face and not want people to notice it.'

'Notice, yes, but not stroke, for five minutes.'

We drive to a pub. Hopefully, being somewhere public will ensure we keep our emotions under control.

As soon as we're seated, I sense Joy's floodgates about to burst, so I beat her to it.

'If you want to gather all the research and guidelines together, along with my medical notes, and present it to the hospital, to force them to apologise, then do. If you want to use me as an example to campaign for awareness, for best practice, for better diagnosis and treatment, then do. If you want to make something positive come out of this, then please, please carry on with everything you've been doing. I know that's what you want.'

Joy nods.

'You're a mind-reader,' she says, quietly.

'But, you have to leave me in peace to make the most of what's left. I can't afford to torment myself and others with what could or should or might have been. I only have time to live with what is.'

Joy nods again, slowly.

I study her beautiful face. We've known each other for over forty years, have accompanied each other through the tribulations of growing up, raising families, becoming middle-aged. Joy's changed recently, for the better – conquering the hysterical reactions and compulsive over-eating. I've changed, too, finally experiencing what it is to love and be loved equally. I'm glad neither of us left it too late. We gaze into each other's eyes and smile. Joy takes a deep breath.

'Right,' she says, 'are you going to tell me what this all-important thing is that you're planning to do?'

'Now it's your turn to guess,' I reply.

Joy frowns as she thinks. I watch the realisation slowly dawn.

'Oh no, you've always threatened to do it and now you are.'

I nod.

'Am I gonna be in it?' she asks.

'You sure are.'

Where is death? Is there a grinning skeleton behind me, bent double with silent laughter, clutching its non-existent stomach, pointing my way? Is there an airborne hooded figure with scythe, circling, biding, knowing the wait will soon be over? Is there an angel at the foot of my bed, a halo of white light? Mother? It's all far less dramatic than that.

Death appears to me that night, in a dream, slow and ordinary, in the form of an old British Rail train. Sometimes gathering speed, usually trundling, a bit grubby and faded, well used. Death's harbinger is not a skeleton, hooded figure or angel. It is Dr K in white coat and ridiculous moustache, patting hands and dishing out pills as he slowly makes his way down the aisle, clipping our tickets and returning them, for a while. All are to be gathered in at journey's end, even his. There are a few other solitary passengers in this carriage: an old man I'd forgotten, with a stick, asleep in his long white beard; a middle-aged Italian, sallow and sad, whose mother loved him more than any other woman would; a too-young mother, her breasts still milky. She and I exchange half-nods of recognition, but prefer to look out of the window. The view of the Kent countryside is a good and familiar one. It is sunny, but cold. I wonder if they have a drinks trolley, something hot and sweet to warm me up.

'I love you,' whispers Leon, as I wake.

'I love you, too.'

21

GINATHERAPY

'Why don't you want to try more chemo, Mum?' asks Susan. We're in the dining room; Susan has one elbow on the table, her head resting in her hand. Her eyes are pink and puffy. 'I just don't understand.'

'I don't believe it'll work. I'll lose as much time preparing for, enduring and recovering from more treatment, as I'll gain by having it. I've been through it already, and it's not worked.'

'I think you should see the consultant again, to double-check you're doing the right thing. I knew I should have gone to that meeting with you.'

'Okay, I will. What about work, have you had any news?'

'I don't care about work. I've applied to go part-time.'

'But how will you manage financially?'

'We can live on less. Work doesn't matter any more. I want to be here for my family, for you and Chrissy. I want to come with you when you see the consultant. Why don't you ring him now? Please.'

I call Dr Kimura's secretary, explain the situation and she says Dr K will see me later today, after he's finished with the rest of his patients.

'Do you think that fighting the cancer should still take priority? Do you think I've made the wrong decision?' I ask Dr K, with Susan sitting beside me.

'Given the ineffectiveness of treatment so far, and the resilience and aggressiveness of the cancer, your decision is understandable.'

'"Understandable" is hardly "right". I'm asking you to be honest with me.'

'These decisions are for the individual patient. We doctors want to offer hope, more therapies, to be able to extend life. We can feel we are failing patients when not actively treating them. But we must also respect patients' understanding of their own bodies, their own lives.'

'But what would you do, in Mum's situation?' asks Susan.

'I cannot say, because I am not in her situation.' Dr K pauses. 'Mrs Jarvis, as you seem to understand and accept that your life will be ending sooner rather than later, and have clear ideas about how you want to spend your time, I think your decision is the right one.'

'What does "sooner" mean?' I ask.

'It is difficult to predict without more tests, but …' Dr K looks from me to my daughter, and then back to me again, 'months, rather than years.'

Susan gasps, putting her hand over her mouth.

'I am so sorry,' says Dr K.

I've never been more certain about how to spend my time. It's not even a choice, but an instinct, a compulsion. I always felt that life was flinging me between two landscapes. There was reality, a wasteland of rough grass and gritty stone paths stumbling over each other and all leading nowhere, overhung by infinite expanses of time, as grey, dull and empty as the leaden sky. Then there was fantasy, a huge and vibrant world, looming to one side, but menacing as a tidal wave, as it threatened to crash dramatically, but meaninglessly, to reveal itself for what it was: illusion. Like many of my kind, the ability to make sense, rework and reinvent with creative endeavours became my leverage, my bridge between the two. Never was I happier than when rewriting life: sending Ruffles on another adventure, composing sacrificial poems to Olly, laughing and blushing at what my fingers had just typed, discussing the next episode of The Foxlings with Chrissy. True to form, I'm doing it again, by writing this book, my own memorial perhaps. Writing has always been my solace, my catharsis, my blessed escape. Now I need it more than ever. Like Dennis Potter, I fear dying four pages too soon, so am averaging a manic three thousand words a day. In nearly five weeks, I've hardly left the house, but have written a good one hundred thousand words.

For all the pains and mistakes, it has been a good life. I have borne a child, I have worked hard and earned a living doing what I was best able to do. I have fallen in love and been loved, although the two only matched up very recently. But that has made it all the sweeter. And these people who have been part of my life are all that seem to matter now, for we are all in this together. In a hundred years, not one of us will still be here. But for now, and now is all I have, it's comforting to think of them living on, after I am gone. For all the hopes and fantasies, this is how my life turned out to be, and these people are important to me. I tried to get things right, and often didn't. And the joys came almost by surprise and, naturally, not quite so often.

I felt every sorrow, every delight, every disappointment, every hope and they made up me. Many things are irresolvable, and the best you can hope to do is live with them. The greatest mystery, perhaps, is this line of females from which I sprang raw and bloody and from which another, raw and bloody, sprang from me. I am dropping out of this chain before my time, just like my mother. I'm glad I've made peace with my daughter, as I never really did with Mum, not during her lifetime. But perhaps peace is the wrong word; I'm glad we've come to understand each other, to accept.

I would love to watch Chrissy grow up. I will miss the playing, the talking, the sharing, the helping, seeing her life unfolding, even as I know mine is diminishing. What will she do? Who will she fall in love with? Will she have children, too? I will never know. I'm fairly certain she is destined to be a creative type. In fact, I'm handing over the writing of the new Ruffles books to her. Well, Media Man has agreed to Susan, as my daughter, being the official writer (she did take a little persuading), but Susan and I both know it's Chrissy who'll really write them. I can hardly believe that Ruffles has turned into the family heirloom, being handed down the generations. I have an idea of where Chrissy might live, when she's grown, for I am leaving her this house, in trust. Perhaps one day, when I am in the faded, black-and-white past, she will read this book, remember, and laugh. I have written it for her, as a raised glass to the future, as much as to make sense of my own passing.

Leon wrestles the laptop from me.

'Don't overdo it. You need to rest, for tomorrow.'

We are gathered outside the recently built museum and art

gallery, in the heart of the city, waiting for the unveiling of Olly's sculpture, which is standing in pride of place on the new forecourt. On its plinth, it's about fifteen feet tall and is draped in a large cloth, which is soon to be ceremonially removed. Standing on one side of Olly is the mayor, in full bling, and on the other is the local MP.

Marty is here, with Phyllis; their weekend away together was a success. He is desperately trying not to moon about all over her because one of his sons has turned up and isn't yelling and swearing at him, for which Marty appears grateful; they are attempting to 'move on'. Wedding bells will chime for Marty, if not for me.

I look at Leon and squeeze his hand. Chrissy is holding my other one, best friend Brad being attached to Chrissy on her other side. Milady (one hundred years old next Tuesday) is here with Uncle Edward, Mum's brother. I told them they could stay with me, but they've booked into a swanky hotel in the city centre. Milady is in a wheelchair, which she uses for longer distances, and, being at child height, is having many animated conversations with Chrissy and Brad, although, as she is also rather deaf, much shouting is involved. She is clawing at Brad's free hand in an attempt to draw him closer. We form a – I have to admit, slightly bizarre-looking – human chain.

'You-hoo!' someone shouts.

I look around and spot Tar. She waves as she weaves her way over. Even she is holding hands, with Dougie.

'I never really thanked you proper for getting me and the old man back together again.'

'Don't mention it.'

'And …'

She pauses expectantly, while rubbing her belly, as if miming that she is very, very hungry.

I have no idea what she is trying to communicate.

'Mum's having a baby,' says Donna, suddenly towering above me in skyscraper heels.

Dougie beams.

'Number eight?' I gulp; can I really be in any way responsible for bringing another Spokes into the world?

'Yeah. It's a blessing on our love,' says Tar.

'We've already decided what we're gonna call it,' says Dougie.

'Georgie if it's a girl,' says Tar.

'And Georgie if it's a boy,' says Dougie.

They are both grinning at me.

'Well, Georgie it is then,' I say.

'They's naming it after you, Georgina, you divvy moo,' Donna kindly explains.

'Oh! Thank you. That's very touching.'

A reverberating screech and throb of electric guitar silences the crowd, as Marty begins the musical introduction to the unveiling, *à la* Brian May at the Queen's golden jubilee; only rather than on Buckingham Palace roof, Marty is planted on top of a less salubrious tower scaffold to the front of the museum. He strokes and coaxes and thrashes his guitar through a wild medley, giving people just enough time to say, 'Hey, isn't that Deep Purple's –' or 'Oh my God, it's Beethoven's –' before moving swiftly into something else. He plays a lengthy version of *Trolls at Twilight*, which I know is his and Phyllis' 'special song' from the bootleg LP. He's quite brilliant, but it does go on rather. After fifteen minutes, various officials attempt to get his attention, but he's so into his groove that he remains impervious. He's certainly drawing quite a Saturday lunchtime, pre-Christmas crowd: kids with parents, sprawling groups of teens, many women with many bags, and bored males of all ages thankful for an excuse to stand and stare at something other than rows of merchandise. I spot Margaret and her husband and beckon them over, then Joy and Tim join us. Eventually, Marty comes back to reality and gives a quick, but furious, guitar hero finish. The crowd emits a mighty cheer.

The mayor takes centre stage.

'It is with great pleasure that I stand before you in order to unveil this marvellous new sculpture, which has been commissioned to celebrate the redevelopment of our art gallery and museum, and crafted by one of our very own sons.'

Olly, smartly dressed and not looking quite so dopey, now he's genuinely pot free, grins and nods.

'This sculpture – an irregular organic form – represents a new direction in the creative output of Mr Oliver Jarvis, a significant move away, so he informs me, from the eggs for which he is renowned. I know we have all been eagerly awaiting this moment, so, without further ado, I shall reveal this important new work of art for our city.'

The mayor cuts the ribbon. The drape slithers to the ground in a respectful hush. People stare.

'Trudy!' exclaims Chrissy, pointing at the sculpture.

I take it in. Yes, it is an irregular organic form, rather than a symmetrical egg. But what kind of organic form? It is carved beautifully from the pale, subtly sparkling Caen stone. However, the way the smooth, wide column extends upwards, bulging slightly in places, tapering at the top …

Chrissy is yanking my hand and whispering furiously, 'It's Trudy the Turd, it *is*.'

I hate to say it, but it does look like a – albeit artistically crafted – giant poo. Leon and Graham exchange looks, as do Susan and I. Chrissy and Brad crumple onto their knees in fits of laughter. Olly smiles radiantly; people start clapping.

We head to our old local, The Barley, near the river, which has been hired for the post-unveiling celebrations. The open fires crackle, the food, drink and conversation flow, and everyone's in good spirits. Marty's oldest son is joined by a girl; they are the same age Olly and I were when we first met and came to this very pub!

When a group of young actors come in after their matinée performance, Milady and Uncle Edward enjoy holding court. Even Lara and Moya are laughing together. Moya announces that the sale of her cottage is going through and she'll be moving to Cornwall in the new year. Everyone has more drinks. Chrissy and Brad go for a walk along the river, under the supervision of Olly and Dougie, and manage to fall in. That's Olly and Dougie, not the kids. As the afternoon turns into evening, it seems as if practically everyone I have ever known appears. When Heather and Wendy from the support group arrive, I begin to feel suspicious.

I'm about to ask Olly how he knows my cancer friends, when his mate Bob from the Art College proposes a toast and calls for a speech. Olly doesn't say much about the sculpture, but waffles on in an embarrassing but rather endearing way about how drugs are bad and kids shouldn't take them, how you know who your real friends are when you're on a downer and how 'the suits' shouldn't be allowed to quash an individual's creativity (a couple of officials from the council look rather uneasy). Just when I think Olly's speech is safely over, he starts again.

'Now,' he says, 'I know she won't like it, but I also want to say a few words about Gina.' Olly looks at me and grins. 'I really wanted to bring us all together for you. We all know what you've been going through and it's difficult to get together on your birthday because it's Christmas Day, so I thought today would work out well – for a bit of a party. Sorry if I've sprung it on you.'

Olly raises a glass.

'To Gina,' he declares.

Everyone cheers, and more food, a giant cake and an enormous punchbowl are brought out. Leon winks at me; it's clear he's in on this, too. I didn't suspect a thing. The rest of the evening passes in a blur of warmed alcohol, fondant icing and familiar, smiling faces.

I return home with Leon after midnight, leaving the others in the pub. It's been an absolutely exhausting day, but in a good way. Leon goes up to bed while I sit in the front room for a while, the people, talk and laughter of the evening swirling merrily in my mind. Just as I'm about to go upstairs there's a knock on the door.

'Mum,' says Susan, 'I'm glad you're still up. I just wanted to see you, be with you, without everyone else being there.'

'Come in.'

I head for the front room.

'Is it alright if we go up to the top floor?' asks Susan.

'If you want to.'

We climb the two flights of stairs to the attic room.

'It's so different now,' says Susan, looking around, 'but in a way it's still exactly the same. I remember living here, being up high. Do you mind if I sleep here tonight, like I used to when I was tiny? I don't know why, I just want to.'

We pull out and make up the sofa bed, which Susan promptly gets into. I get in beside her. We look out at the clear night, twinkling through the skylights. Susan begins to talk, about her memories of living in the flat, her childhood, and family. She remembers Marty playing guitar and singing at her eighth birthday party. She remembers the song he wrote for her, and the cartoon strips Olly used to draw for her. She remembers the birthday cake Granny made in the shape of a cat, and the scooter she was given, which she promptly fell off and refused to have anything to do with ever again. She asks if I remember the perfume that went missing from my dressing table, the one she wasn't supposed to touch. She says she accidentally dropped it on the floor and the neck broke off and most of the perfume spilt so she hid it in the wardrobe. I tell her I know, I found it that day and chucked it away; the fact the wardrobe reeked of patchouli and sandalwood was a bit of a giveaway.

'Thanks for not telling me off,' says Susan, then she sinks back into the bed and falls asleep, just like that, as an overtired toddler might at the tea table, mid-mouthful.

Leon tiptoes up the stairs.

'Are you coming to bed?'

'I think I'll stay up here with Susan.'

'Is everything alright?'

'I'm not sure. I'll let you know in the morning.'

Leon nods, then returns downstairs.

I lie back on the sofa bed next to my daughter, and join her in a parallel world of dreams and nightmares.

We're woken by the screeching of gulls. It's snowing. We gaze through the skylights at the birds, swooping and calling through the tumbling flakes.

'Can I ask you something?' says Susan.

'Of course.'

'Why was I the last to know about the cancer? Why did you tell everyone before me?'

'Because I'm a coward. Because I hoped it would go away. Because ... we weren't getting on very well, were we? And it's such a burdensome thing, for the person with it and everyone around them.'

'Everything's happened so fast, Mum, in such a rush – from you writing that card and letting me know to now – that I haven't had time to get used to it, to take it in. I feel cheated.'

'Cheated?'

'Cheated by the past, by how we've been. It's fine to quarrel and not be speaking when there's all the time in the world to make up, to build a better relationship. But that's been taken away. I need more time, or I need time to slow down, events to slow down. I want to make everything perfect between us, for us to have good times together, now, in the future, but ...'

'We haven't got endless time?'

Susan shakes her head.

'At least we both want the same thing,' I say. 'I almost feel like I'm living life in snatches, in glimpses, in short scenes, that I'm more alive and things make more sense in my writing than in real life. That's where I resolve it all, where things finally fit, can find their place. But that's no help to you.'

'No,' says Susan, softly. 'It was ... it was good of Dad to organise the party yesterday, to get everyone together. He really has changed. Chrissy loves him, just like she loves you. She's always been such a strong-willed girl, I never realised before what a worrier she is. It's going to be awful for Chrissy when you …' Susan stops herself.

'It doesn't have to be. I have got time to say goodbye.'

'Will you?' Susan asks hurriedly, eyes full of anxiety for her child. 'But what will you say?'

'I'll find a way. We'll both make sure she's alright, together.'

Susan and I embrace, not like wooden statues this time, but as the flesh of each other's flesh and blood of each other's blood that we always were, are and will be.

22

BALLOONING WITH GRANDMA

I'm propped up in bed on five pillows. Being full to the brim with pain relief, I'm numb and sleepy, but I don't want to nod off because Chrissy's just arrived. Leon comes in with the strong coffee I've requested. It'll probably be difficult to get down and a little nauseating, but I want to be more alert. It's cold and bright outdoors, warm and bright indoors.

'Have you finished writing your book yet, Grandma?' asks Chrissy, as Leon takes the laptop from me and puts it on the dressing table, before going back downstairs.

'Very nearly.'

'That's good. Do you know what you want for your birthday yet?'

Chrissy's been repeating this question for weeks. It's the twenty-third of December today and my birthday is on the twenty-fifth; the only thing I have in common with Our Saviour.

'Yes, I do know what I want. I'd like us to write a story together.' I wince as I sip the bittersweet coffee. 'We could begin now, then it'll be ready in time.'

'I'll get some paper,' says Chrissy.

'That's for you for Christmas,' I say, pointing to the large, rectangular, wrapped present on the chest of drawers, which Chrissy has been staring at – not to mention sniffing, prodding and testing the weight of – since it appeared a couple of days ago. 'But I reckon you can have it early.'

'It *is* for me! Can I really open it now?'

I nod.

Chrissy pulls the wrapping from the wooden art case, which opens up like a toolbox and is filled with paints, felt-tips, coloured pencils, pastels, brushes, palettes; everything an arty child could wish for.

'Oh wow oh wow oh wow.'

'You can use it for my birthday story if you like.'

Chrissy fetches some sheets of good-quality paper. I fold them in half, as I usually do, to make one of our books, using the long-armed stapler to fasten the pages together in the middle.

'Grandma Foxling is going to be in this one,' I announce.

'But she *tells* the stories,' says Chrissy. 'She's not been *in* a story before. I'm not really sure what she looks like.'

'Well,' I retort, as petulantly as I can, 'it's what *I want for my birthday*!'

'Oh, okay,' Chrissy readily concedes.

'This is going to be the tale of how Grandma Foxling came to be the narrator of all the other stories,' I say.

Chrissy gathers her face up around her nose.

'How did she?' she asks.

'By learning to fly.'

'Hmm. Go on then.'

'Right, let's begin at the beginning. When Great-Great-Grandma Foxling was a young woman, she fell in love with Great-Great-Grandpa Foxling. Great-Great-Grandma was very grand, and was known as Milady Foxling, and Great-Great-Grandpa was known as Lord. That's the first picture.'

I write the words, then hand over to Chrissy to do the drawings, although we do swap or merge roles sometimes. The great-great-grandparents wear towering wigs, elaborately tailored and decorated clothes and lots of make-up (I blame us watching *The Scarlet Pimpernel* together earlier in the week).

'Marvellous. And they had twin babies, a boy and a girl.'

Chrissy draws a couple of toddlers in equally ostentatious outfits.

'The girl twin grows up to be Great-Grandma Foxling.'

'All these "greats" are confusing me,' says Chrissy. 'What do they mean?'

'Well, one "great" means they're back one generation, two "greats" means they're the people before them. Just like I'm your grandmother, but my mother is your great-grandmother and is in heaven, but your great-great-grandmother is the very old one who lives in Brighton.'

'The one with the purply hair in the wheelie chair?'

'Yes. And Great-Uncle Edward is her son.'

'The other one with the purply hair?'

'Yes, he's my mother's brother.'

'Right.'

'Lord and Milady Foxling have a fine life acting and dancing and dressing up, and so does their son. Oh, let's just call him Great-Uncle Edward Foxling because it's easier. He never marries. But his sister does. Because when she's a young woman – this is Great-Grandma Foxling, remember – she meets a nice young man.'

Chrissy starts drawing my mother.

'Matching hat and gloves and shoes and handbag,' I instruct. Chrissy accommodates.

'What about for Great-Grandpa Foxling?' she asks.

'Hmm. A brown suit. Trousers and jacket that go together.'

'They liked matching things in those days, didn't they?'

'Yes.'

'Do they have a baby?'

'Yes.'

'Is it … you?'

'Yes.'

Chrissy then goes on to draw the baby me in a mix and match of co-ordinating colours from my parents.

'Can you imagine what happens next?' I ask.

Chrissy flicks back through the pages.

'The baby grows up and when she is a young woman she falls in love with … Grandpa!'

'That's right.'

'Have all the "greats" finished now?'

'Yes.'

'Good. I did try, but I didn't really get them.'

'It doesn't matter.'

I instruct Chrissy – in fact I rather take over – on how to draw Grandma and Grandpa Foxling wearing the most horrendous seventies clothes. Grandma's in green, bell-bottomed dungarees and Grandpa's hair is so long it reaches the floor, and birds and butterflies make their homes in it.

'Okay, Chrissy,' I say, when we get back to the book after lunch, 'can you guess what happens to Grandma and Grandpa?'

She smiles.

'They have a daughter, which is my mummy, whose name is Susan.'

'Exactly right.'

'Does it go on and on like that forever?'

'Pretty much.'

'And then she grows up and falls in love with a handsome young man, which is my daddy, whose name is Graham.'

I nod.

'And then … then they have me!'

'Correct.'

Chrissy gently tugs me awake.

'Grandma, look, I've finished. You fell asleep. You're like a baby.'

Chrissy shows me how she's embellished her already colour-ful pictures. As this is a festive time of year, rather a lot of glitter glue and sequins, as well as cotton wool for beards and hair, have found their way onto the pages.

'It's not much of a story,' ponders Chrissy, 'not for a birthday present. It's just a lot of people getting born. There's not even a cake in it.'

'It's not quite finished yet. Tomorrow, Chrissy, we'll finish it then. Christmas Eve. Just in time. For my birthday.'

Christmas Eve morning and it's mild, grey and raining lightly. I will have been alive for forty-nine years tomorrow and I can't recall a single white Christmas, although there *must* have been one at some point.

'You know, Chrissy,' I say, as we settle down to finish the book, 'it's something we don't talk about very much, but it's not because it's bad. Quite a lot of the Foxlings in this book are up in the sky, aren't they?'

'What? Flying?'

'Sort of.'

'Are they having a race?'

'They might be having races. They might be doing anything they like, because they're in Foxling heaven.'

'Oh.'

'Do you want to draw them up there on these last pages? Draw some of them in heaven and some in Foxling Village?'

'Okay.'

Chrissy gets quite carried away with Foxling heaven when she realises the inhabitants can do anything and everything they want there. She then draws the earthly Foxlings at the bottom of the page, looking rather dowdy in comparison.

'Now, the last one left to put in the picture is Grandma Foxling,' I say. 'You'll have to draw her with wings, so she can fly all the way up to heaven.'

'Then Grandma Foxling will look a bit like a ...' Chrissy struggles to find the word.

'An angel?'

'No, a Chagall. We've been doing him at school.'

Well, the education system has certainly improved since my day.

Chrissy's drawing wobbles a bit with Grandma Foxling and she becomes very cross when she can't get the wings right. She goes over and over them until, in a fit of pique, she scribbles over Grandma, turning her into a large, angry blob in the centre of the picture.

'That looks silly now!' cries Chrissy. 'Those stupid wings

wouldn't go right and now Grandma Foxling looks like a lollipop floating in the sky with the stick fallen off. And none of the other Foxlings have wings anyway, so it doesn't even fit. I don't want Grandma to have wings.'

'Yes, silly wings. And I think that looks more like a balloon than a lollipop without a stick. Grandma's just going to have to use that hot-air balloon instead. Draw a basket underneath and put her in it, waving.'

'But you said you wanted wings.'

'A balloon's much better.'

On the back page Chrissy draws a picture of Grandma Foxling in heaven, which is her sitting in a bubble bath, while eating cake and sipping a fizzy drink with an umbrella and bits of fruit in it, with an open book on one side and a laptop on the other. She looks a little disjointed, but not unhappy.

We read through our book together.

'That's a lovely picture on the back. I think that's exactly what Grandma will be doing in heaven.'

'It won't be a surprise tomorrow because you know what your birthday present is,' says Chrissy.

'Maybe you can keep it for me.'

'Keep it? But why? It's yours, I made it for you,' says Chrissy, her voice undulating.

'It's ours, and we made it together. And I get so many presents on Christmas Day because it's my birthday, too. If you keep it for a while, then it'll be a surprise when, when we next see it.'

'I don't understand.'

Chrissy's eyes are so close and wide and clear; I gaze back into her.

'Grandma! We made a terrible mistake. They're not foxes, are they? I've drawn them as people, like us.'

'Well, I don't think it really –'

'But it *does* matter! They're not us. They're the Foxlings. They –'

'Put on the ears and tails, then, the ears and tails.'

Chrissy calms down from the verge of hysteria as she goes through the book adding ears and tails to all the characters.

'Do you want a cuddle, Chrissy?'

'Yes, please.'

She snuggles up with me, hugs tight and cries.

When she's recovered, she brings our slightly crumpled book back out from under the duvet.

'I still don't think it's a very good story,' Chrissy says, as she smooths it out. 'People just grow up and do the same stuff and –'

'Remember, it's all about how Grandma came to be the narrator.'

'But how did she?'

'Well, because she's in heaven, she can look down on every-one else and tell stories about them.'

'But why don't the other people in heaven tell stories?'

'They don't really want to.'

'Oh, of course. They're too busy doing the things that they love. Great-Grandpa is riding his bicycle or reading a newspaper or visiting the moon and Great-Grandma is picking flowers or making bread or playing tennis with Queen Victoria.'

'That's right. And now you know what Grandma will be doing when she goes up to heaven, don't you?'

Chrissy nods.

'You know she'll be smiling and waving to everyone on earth, and that she still loves them all. Especially her granddaughter.'

'And she'll be eating cake?'

'And she'll be eating cake.'

'And she'll be having a nice bubble bath?'

'And she'll be having a nice bubble bath.'

'And she'll be telling stories?'

'And she'll be telling stories. She'll never stop telling stories.'

ACKNOWLEDGEMENTS

A huge thank you to everyone who read various drafts of the book and generously gave their time and perspectives, including: Louisa Burville-Riley, Michael Forrester, Colette Pack, Betty Sbaraini, Eva Sbaraini, Sandra Simmonds and members of two local book groups.

Special thanks to my most meticulous readers: first, Tania Hoser, who literally gave me a line by line assessment; although your constructive criticism sometimes felt like you'd lobbed a javelin into my chest, you were always spot on, and encouraged a slash and burn approach to editing. At the other end of the scale was Craig Dadds: how did we manage to discuss the relative merits of the full stop over the semi-colon for hours on end? How did we ever manage to get through the manuscript at that pace? I don't know, but I'm glad we did, and I'm grateful for your insights and writerly companionship.

Thanks to New Writing South for awarding me an Arts Council England-funded 'free read' from The Literary Consultancy; their comments were both astute and encouraging.

A massive and heartfelt thank you to my agent, Caroline Montgomery, for her sustained belief in Gina, her persistence and patience. If you were ever to be reborn as a canine, Caroline, it would surely be as a tenacious terrier!

Many thanks to everyone at Mercier Press, especially Noel O'Regan and Deirdre Roberts, for transforming the manuscript into a real book, and making the process a rewarding and enjoyable one. And, lastly, a deeply appreciative thank you to Sarah O'Flaherty for the wonderful cover design.

ABOUT THE AUTHOR

Silvia Sbaraini has a background in academia and social science research, and was a freelance editorial script advisor for children's television for a number of years. Her debut novel, *Your Move*, was published in 2017 under the name Silvia Forrester. She has an MA in creative writing and teaches at the Open University. Born in Italy, Silvia was brought up on the south coast of England by her mother and grandmother. She has two daughters, two step-daughters and three granddaughters, so it's not surprising that female relationships, family, love and friendship are frequently the focus of her writing.

Woody Guthrie's

Wardy forty

The Interviews

Phillip Buehler

Woody Guthrie Publications

Published in 2013 by Woody Guthrie Publications, Inc.
125-131 E. Main Street,
Mt. Kisco, NY 10549

LOC Number 2013952390
ISBN 978-0-9897521-1-4

Cover design by Steven Brower
Interior design by Dana Wren, Marywood University

"'Life is tough. You're lucky if you live through it.' Woody Guthrie"
by Nora Guthrie © Nora Guthrie. Photo by Tina Tschirch.
Courtesy of Nora Guthrie.

John Cohen, interview by Phil Buehler,
May 11, 2004 and July 14, 2005,
photo by Phil Buehler.

Ramblin' Jack Elliott, interview by Phil Buehler,
September 20, 2004 and October 16, 2004,
photo by Phil Buehler.

Anneke Van Kirk, interview by Phil Buehler,
March 24, 2006 and April 6, 2006,
photo courtesy Woody Guthrie Archives.

Vincent "Jim" Longhi, interview by Phil Buehler,
September 11, 2006, photo by Phil Buehler.

Harold Leventhal, interview by Phil Buehler,
March 17, 2004, photo by Tina Tschirch.

Sidsel Gleason, interview by Phil Buehler,
April 5, 2004, October 21, 2004, photo by Phil Buehler.

Dr. Vincenzo Cocilovo, interview by Phil Buehler,
May 1, 2006, photo by Phil Buehler.

Marjorie Mazia Guthrie, excerpted interviews:
Joe Klein, 1976 and 1977, courtesy of the Woody Guthrie Archives;
Eddie Elkins, WHRW, SUNY Binghamton, NY, 1978, courtesy of the Woody Guthrie
Archives; Ron Olesko, WFUV, NY, 1977, courtesy of Ron Olesko.
Photo by Jim Marshall. Courtesy of the Woody Guthrie Archives.

Dr. Michael Hayden, interview by Phil Buehler, August 14, 2005 and April 11,
2006, photo courtesy Dr. Michael Hayden.

Jeff Carroll, interview by Phil Buehler, April 20, 2006, photo courtesy Jeff Carroll.

Arlo Guthrie, interview by Phil Buehler,
October 8, 2002, photo by Rainy Hall.

Printed in U.S.A.

TABLE OF CONTENTS

INTRODUCTION

Many stories were told of Woody Guthrie during the period of his life when he was institutionalized at Greystone Park Psychiatric Hospital. Unfortunately, not all of them would fit in the book, "Woody Guthrie's Wardy Forty: Greystone Park State Hospital Revisited." But each was so fascinating that Nora Guthrie and I thought they should be shared in their entireties in this book.–*Phil Buehler*

FOREWORD

Life is tough. You're lucky if you live through it.
−*Woody Guthrie*

I was born in 1950. My father was diagnosed with Huntington's disease in 1951. But years before he had been showing symptoms; erratic behavior, sudden emotional upsets, dizziness, slurred speech, an irregular gait, loss of balance and coordination, facial distortions, and a general sense that something was wrong. For a few years, he entered different hospitals off and on, being treated for everything from alcoholism to schizophrenia. Once the diagnosis for Huntington's was made it was a relief for my mother. He wasn't an alcoholic. He wasn't mentally ill. It was, however, clear that he could not care for himself.

He was hospitalized for the whole of my childhood and I don't have any memories of him without his strange behavior, without Huntington's. Having a sick parent with an unusual illness was all I knew. It was part of my everyday life, and something that I was constantly aware of, and much of the time even ashamed of.

For many of these years he lived at Greystone Hospital in New Jersey. My mother seemed to be able to take some degree of control and acceptance of the situation. I remember her talking to everyone for advice; doctors, friends, lawyers, just about anyone who she could rely on for advice, help, supplies, care, and support. In those years, there were no health organizations, or research groups to go to. She was totally alone and involved in his care while we children were mostly cautious observers dealing with our own silent emotions.

In retrospect, I am constantly stunned that my mother could be so strong. She always seemed to have all the energy necessary to deal with the stresses, the complications, and the responsibilities. I never saw or heard her complain, fall apart, or give up. She confronted it with a sense of unlimited determination and acceptance. She was that kind of person. How strange that when I think of my mother during these years I only remember her smiling.

Most Sundays we would drive out to Greystone Hospital to visit my father. It was a long drive from Howard Beach, Queens to East Orange, New Jersey. On Sundays, when all the other kids were off from school playing in the neighborhood, we would pile into the car for this long journey which was physically and emotionally draining. We drove along the Belt Parkway into Manhattan, then through the Holland Tunnel and onto the New Jersey Turnpike, then some side roads, which took us to the long and dramatic driveway that led up to the hospital grounds. That's when I could feel the fear coming.

The grounds were enormous. We were entering a strange city inhabited by thousands of patients, their families, nurses and doctors. The air seemed thick with that special ingredient that one finds in a place where all is not well. My father lived in Ward 40, more like a barrack, with at least twenty five other patients.

I remember one time walking through the entire ward with beds lined on both sides to get to my father's bed at the very end. The walk seemed to take forever. On all sides were desperate, strange people, either yelling or talking to themselves, unnaturally uninhibited or somber. People with all kinds of things wrong with them. I walked as close to my mother as possible, hiding behind her wide skirt as she greeted patients with a cheery and energetic "hello". I couldn't understand why she wasn't terrified. I was.

Quick to catch on, she decided that we shouldn't take that long walk anymore. We would meet with my father on the grounds outside for a "picnic". It would be more like a nice family outing. There was a magnificent tree with large, sweeping limbs. We kids spent most of our time climbing all around that tree, or perched like monkeys, watching our parents sitting down below on the lawn eating, reading letters, sharing news, and putting their heads together for "parent talk". I was happy to be up in that tree. My father named it the "magicky tree", and we all loved believing it was. It took us so far away from the reality below. How smart of them to create something so special for us. A fantastical setting that could relieve us of so much fear and get us through the afternoon.

At some point, my mother realized that it would be better to bring my father home on Sundays rather than take us to the hospital. We would be able to stay around the house in our normal setting, playing with friends, and able to enjoy our day off.

To do this, she would drive the hour and a half to Greystone, pick him up, bring him home, and drive him back in the evening. All in all, it was a three-hour drive.

At that time, they had not yet built the Verrazano Bridge, which would have cut off about forty-five minutes from the trip. I remember watching them build this bridge, which took quite a few years. Unfortunately, it wasn't completed until 1964 when my father was no longer at Greystone. It's funny, but to this day whenever I see this great, expansive bridge, all I can think of is my mother's dream to get my father faster.

My mother ran a dancing school in Brooklyn where she taught six days a week; the Marjorie Mazia School of Dance. As tired as she might have been, when she brought my father home on Sundays she was upbeat and energetic, even dancing and fooling around to put a smile on his face or make him laugh. She "set the stage" so to speak, and all of us tried as best we could to do our part to put on a happy face or help out.

My father needed so much care. One of the symptoms of Huntington's is the body's constant motion which burns up an unnatural amount of calories. My mother plied my father with high caloric foods: huge chocolate cakes with quarts of milk, multiple hot dogs or fried chicken, and blocks of honeycomb - anything to put back the pounds that he had lost during the week.

She stripped him of his clothes and scrubbed him in the bath, then sprinkled him with talcum powder and chirped "doesn't he smell sweet now!" She would wash and iron his clothes, sew up any tears, and dress him like a mother getting her child ready for a first day of school. Then she would sit with him in the living room as he lay on the couch. She would have to light his cigarettes for him, and hand feed him holding his arms down so he wouldn't knock the food all over. All the while, she played his records on the record player, knowing how important it was for him to remember how much he had created in his life. She was constantly on call until around 5:00, when it was time to head back to Greystone.

Having him at home meant he could have visitors. Many friends came out to visit on these Sunday afternoons and over time these visits turned into informal hootenannies where Pete Seeger, Jack Elliott, Bob Dylan, John Cohen, Sonny Terry and Brownie McGee, and many others came to play music for him. He really seemed to enjoy this. Especially when they played him his own songs.

Meanwhile, us kids were free to romp around and play outdoors, or bring friends in, and generally take part, or not, in the gatherings. My brothers, Arlo and Joady, had both learned to play guitar, mandolin and other string instruments and seemed to connect to the mostly male visitors. I had a harder time. Maybe I felt differently because, as a girl, my model was my mother who was endlessly cleaning, feeding, and hostessing. It seemed there were less options for me.

9

Being uncomfortable and even embarrassed by my father's appearance and physical behavior, I tended to play with my friends outdoors to get away from it all. But the hardest moments for me were when we were out in public, at a restaurant down the street or out visiting. Then I would become painfully aware of the all the stares. My father looked and behaved like a drunk, a bum. I wanted someone to tell them he wasn't a bad man, he wasn't drunk, and he wasn't a bum. He was sick. In contrast, my mother behaved as if everything was completely normal, smiling and chatting away with whomever, which made me feel all the more ashamed of my own discomforts.

Each year, my father's symptoms got worse and worse. With his arms flailing about, I couldn't hug him or even be physically near him. It seemed too dangerous. His slurred speech was impossible to understand, and eventually he lost his ability to speak entirely. There was nothing we could talk about. Finally, he could no longer walk, which meant he could not come home. My mother would continue to go out to Greystone alone to visit. And we grew up into teenagers with other priorities.

But I do remember one particular afternoon. It must have been one of the last times he was home. I was about 15 years old. I wanted to go into Manhattan to see my boyfriend. I remember coming down the stairs from my bedroom feeling very, very guilty. I felt I just had to get out, get away, that there was something else out there for me now. Something better, something fun, something that made me feel so normal. A boyfriend!

For some reason, I stopped and sat down half way down the stairs. I looked at my father lying on the couch. I had to stop running away and do something. I felt I had to ask his forgiveness for my selfishness. I forced myself to look into his eyes for what seemed like a long, long time. I found words inside me that I had to say. I spoke to him, silently. For all the years that I had never really been able to talk to him, I would try.

I sat on the stairs and said, "I'm sorry. I just don't know what to do. I'm sorry that I want to leave, but I just can't stand being here watching you like this, feeling this way. I really want to get out of here."

His eyes seemed to lock with mine. And then they literally began to twinkle.

There, under all the ugliness of Huntington's, under the distracting, wild movements, under the dirty, smelling clothes, under it all, his eyes seemed to become so light and purposeful. His eyes became everything, and everything else disappeared.

He silently spoke back to me. He said, "This is my disease, not yours! Get out of here! Go and have fun! I love you. Do you think I want you to suffer? Go play!"

I look back to that moment as one of the most significant moments of my life, which I thank him every day for. He taught me right then and there what love was, what being a parent was, and even what having an illness was. And then suddenly, everything was okay. I mean everything was okay. Without speaking a word, he told me that the only thing we should ever want is to give our love to each other. Not our suffering. Our love wants us to get out there and enjoy the life that we've been given. He taught me that we'll all have these things called "good and bad times", hard and easy times, work and play times. Times that we'll be needed and times that we won't. Times where others will depend on us, and times where we'll be totally free to do as we please. And that we are here to just take each of these as they come. In that little talk, he owned his own life completely. "This is my disease, not yours". I cried a little, then laughed a little, then hopped on the next train to the city and had a wonderful day.

I hope when you look through Wardy Forty, you'll see this man with his twinkling eyes and mischievous grin, releasing us all to live our own lives completely and wonderfully, taking each day and each situation as it comes. He lived this way consistently. And although Huntington's disease was his own personal trial, he lived with this disease, but he never became Huntington's disease. His understanding of life came through loud and clear.

As I turn these pages, I can finally see a beauty that has taken me over fifty years to recognize. These images are merely ruins, the gross leftovers, the little pieces, chipped and peeling fragments of a life felt and lived so vividly and boldly. I see now how these images are what we all live to transcend. That's what makes this work so profoundly beautiful to me. —*Nora Guthrie*

HOLD ON

My green bush leaf brings Marjorie's words:
Hold on, Woody Boy, hold on!
My red brick wall of building ten:
Hold on, Woody Boy, hold on!
Hold on for the laboring movement!
Hold on for our Union dream!
Hold on for the love that keeps us!
Hold on, Woody Boy, hold on!

The steam from out of my coffee urn:
Hold on, Woody Boy, hold on!
That creaking chair leg asks me plain:
Hold on, Woody Boy, hold on!
Hold on for your highest principles.
Hold on for our Peace to be.
Hold on for the kids that love us.
Hold on, Woody Boy, hold on!

The feather drifting yonder says:
Hold on, Woody Boy, hold on!
In the smile of every face I see:
Hold on, Woody Boy, hold on!
Hold on for the peaceful settlement,
Hold on to our dream of peace.
Hold on to my hand so hot here.
Hold on, Woody Boy, hold on!

My eyes went blind and words I heard:
Hold on, Woody Boy, hold on!
I heard in the swussh of a big bird's wing:
Hold on, Woody Boy, hold on!
Hold on for your workers government.
Hold on to your equal brotherhood.
Hold on to me real good and tight.
Hold on, Woody Boy, hold on!

—*September 2, 1952. Written in Brooklyn State Hospital at the
onset of Huntington's disease.*

Words and Music by Woody Guthrie © Woody Guthrie Publications, Inc.

JOHN *COHEN*

WOODY GUTHRIE—ANOTHER IMAGE

John Cohen's life as a musician, photographer, documentary filmmaker, and artist gave him a unique perspective on New York in the 1950s and 60s. Cohen would see Guthrie at the Gleason's home, or pick Guthrie up at Greystone and take him back and forth to concerts in New York City.

Cohen helped form the folk music group "The New Lost City Ramblers" which helped bring a revival of old-time Southern folk music from the 1920s and 30s. Other members of the group were Mike Seeger—brother of Pete—and Tom Paley, a fellow student at Yale. He took some of the earliest photographs of Dylan when the young folkie first arrived in New York, which were later published in the book *Young Bob Dylan*.

Cohen has long documented folk music via image and sound to create a lasting body of work. He invited me to look through his contact sheets and was extremely generous in offering to let me use whatever photographs I wanted. Some of the photos of Guthrie and Jack Elliott are published for the first time in *Woody Guthrie's Wardy Forty*.

When did you first meet Woody?

He'd appear in person at the Stinson Record Shop on Union Square. This would be 1951 or '52. And he meant so much to me that I would go in just to see him. He was in bad shape. I'm not sure if he was drinking, or what it was, but he would just kind of lay around in the back of the store. And I remember one time I went there, and he was crossing from the center of Union Square, right through the traffic, towards where I was. Maybe he recognized me, I'm not sure. But to see him cross the traffic, like he was going one way and the traffic was going the other way, and he didn't pay any attention to the traffic. It was like, "Get out of my way, get out of my way." It reminded me of Charlie Chaplin trying to deal with life or something, *Modern Times*, and he was just Woody.

You were in the background of that well-known photo taken of Woody in Washington Square Park singing with Ramblin' Jack Elliott – do you remember anything about that time?

It must have been about '53 when Woody appeared at Washington Square Park. He was rambling along with Jack Elliott then, or Jack was following him around, and that's when he'd come back from Florida where he'd burnt his arm and he could hardly play the mandolin. He couldn't play the guitar. But he looked so extraordinary, cause his head was so wild and wooly, and this is before long hair was ever even considered as part of contemporary life.

And then later, I remember Jack and myself went way over on the Lower East Side, and on the fifth floor or sixth floor of a walk-up, there was Woody and he was lying on the floor. Jack was saying, "Woody got his head on upside down" because there was so much hair above and below. It was strange, but that's when I saw just how bad off he was. I just got the feeling that there was no one taking care of him, and he was rambling off with Rambling Jack or Jack was rambling—that he was sort of out there in the world, not connected, not anchored.

Do you have any recollections of your first trip to Greystone?

I can't remember why I went there or what gave me the impetus to go get him, but I know that he needed to get out of there. I had that feeling. I remember the feeling of going to the back entrance, sort of a lobby there. I'd say, "I want to visit with Woody Guthrie." I'd stand there in the lobby and see all of these old men just kind of wandering aimlessly about, sitting here and there. I didn't know what he would look like at that time. And that he emerged from that place is very moving and challenging to me. I just felt that I wanted to bring some enjoyment into that life, and bring him to these concerts or bring him into Washington Square so he could see what was happening. But I don't know what got me off my ass to make that bold move.

Any other recollections about visiting Woody at Greystone?

One time I'd taken Woody from one of the concerts in New York, at Cooper Union, and we were driving him back to Greystone. I remember we were sitting in the front of the Greystone main building, and we'd been talking about this and that. The Ramblers were working on a brochure—I think Woody had seen us play that day, and he liked us playing the old time music and all, so we said,

"Hey, Woody, would you give us some kind of a quote that we could use about us?" And he said, "Oh yeah, New Lost City Ramblers are the best—after me." And we used it. It was really funny, you know. I felt a little guilty about asking him to do it, but he was very folkie and funny.

When did you take those photographs of Woody and Jack Elliott at the Gleasons'?

I think I must have gone to the Gleasons' maybe a total of two or three times with him. And one of those times, I was out there at the same time Jack came back to the States, and he was seeing Woody after all his years in England. I thought there was something special about it. It was simply interesting to have this guy who was carrying on Woody's songs and Woody's character while Woody was sort of being shut down in Greystone.

What was it like to photograph Woody?

I didn't like to see him represented without his life showing. I took a lot of photographs of him, and I would only print the ones where I thought Woody's strength was showing. I didn't ever want to print the ones where he was in trouble, only the ones where I felt that some of his positive life force was visible.

Do you recall any other times at the Gleasons'?

There was a time that I went through his old 78's and go through his writings and make notes of different songs that appealed to me at that moment, just verses and stuff. That's where I first heard some of those other verses to "This Land is Your Land."

You wrote down the verses so you could sing them yourself?

Partly that, and I was also conscious of what they were trying to make it into: "Congress may even make it into a new national anthem." I was really excited to see these contrary verses. They were saying, "It's got to be positive and upbeat," and they didn't really want to accept the skepticism, the other side of things. And I was just reveling in the opposite side. I mean, that's when the Beat Generation was starting, and the question of doubt about the society and all that was really interesting to me. So what did I do in my contrarian way? I took those verses and I put them in *Sing Out!* magazine. It says, "Woody Guthrie, Another Image." I also had the pictures of Woody with his beard and his injured arm from the accident in Florida with the kerosene stove.

So what was the contrarian part of Woody there?

Well, it wasn't contrary. It was just a bigger view, you know, when he talked about "the big wall that stopped me." That wasn't in what was the official verses back in those days. And especially "In the Sunday morning / In the shadow of the steeple / By the relief office / I saw the people / And they stood hungry / And I stood wondering if this land, if this land was made for you and me." "If this land was made for you and me." That whole element of doubt, they left that out, and that's what I thought should be in.

At that time, you were in contact with artists and poets not connected to the folk scene. How did they see Woody?

I was interested in how Woody was being received outside of the official circles. Woody's writing is kind of wild and crazy, and I would show it to these Beat Generation guys, and they were saying, "Wow, this is something—we should publish this," and "Woody is the first white Negro." And I hadn't heard that phrase, but it was a phrase from Norman Mailer around that time. But I liked the fact that Woody's writing was reaching them and reaching me, more than as a folk singer. I thought this was really most important.

In January '59 I was photographing this movie called *Pull My Daisy* that Robert Frank made. And that's when I said to Allan Ginsberg that I was seeing a resemblance between Woody's writing and some of the long phrases in Jack Kerouac's *On the Road*. Allan said that what was interesting to him about Woody Guthrie was that he was in Greystone, and Greystone was where Allan's mother was institutionalized. That was his real big connection. He had a lot of feeling around that. It was not a set of conceptual thoughts, that they were both in the same place, it was a feeling.

One of the ways people today connect with Guthrie today is through Dylan...

It was pretty clear that Bob was very influenced by Woody at the time, not only "Song to Woody," but he was also writing songs like Woody. I did a whole bunch of photographs of Bob in '62. I know that I had certain impressions of him already, and part of it was the Woody Guthrie thing. That picture that we had there in *People's Songs* with Woody with his hand through his mouth—I had Bob pose that way.

And I was thinking at that time, that Dylan was picking up more of Woody from Jack than from Woody. The mannerisms and the style of talking, and when Dylan's first record came out, I thought he was totally lifting Jack Elliott, or he was imitating Jack. But then Bob took off into all this other stuff.

What recollection of Woody do you hold that's not that well known?

When Alan Lomax had this big program at Carnegie Hall. It was called "Folksongs '59," and I'd been photographing it, but I was with Woody, and we were sitting up in a box on the left hand side of the stage at Carnegie Hall. I remember being very moved by the fact that Pete was on stage and he sang—I think he acknowledged that Woody was there—and then he sang that beautiful song "Deportees" that I knew that Woody had only done as a poem.

He had never done music to it, and now someone else had put the music to that song, and Woody was sitting next to me reciting it. That's a private thing that I'll share. At the same time, there's this huge hall with Pete up there singing and getting everybody to sing. They had the big public version of it; I'm hearing the private version of it. It was very touching. I just remembered that. Almost indescribable, although I just tried to describe it.

You were listening inside his head a little bit?

Very close to that, yeah. Closer than you or I are right now.

RAMBLIN' JACK
ELLIOTT

Hey Woody, Your Brother's Here

Ramblin' Jack Elliott was a protégé of Woody Guthrie and a mentor to Bob Dylan. He'd reinvented himself as a cowboy singer, saying, "I was born on a 45,000 acre ranch in the middle of Flatbush." His parents were Jewish doctors, and at fourteen left home and joined the rodeo. His parents eventually found him, and he returned home to finish high school. But he was already inspired by singing rodeo cowboys and their cowboy songs, and began to play the guitar.

Elliott was only 19 years old when he visited Guthrie at a hospital where he was recovering from appendicitis. He then moved in with the Guthries for almost two years. Elliott became Woody's traveling companion for the next five years. A natural mimic, he picked up Guthrie's singing as well as picking style. In 1956, Elliott moved to England, where he recorded six albums and was an influence on the Skiffle movement, which in turn influenced groups like the Beatles and the Rolling Stones. When Elliott returned to the United States in 1961, he met Bob Dylan while visiting Woody at Greystone. Elliott would become both Dylan's mentor and his primary connection to Woody's songs and style.

After initial phone conversations, I finally met Elliott when he played in Bethlehem, Pennsylvania at a Woody Guthrie tribute concert. As we talked alongside the Delaware River, I couldn't help wonder if I was hearing a bit of Woody. A train whistle sounded in the distance, and Jack looked over his shoulder and said, "I hear ya." He must have been anxious to get back on the road.

When did you first meet Woody?

That was 1951. I visited Woody in the hospital about
two times before a buddy of mine invited me to help
him drive his car out to California. So I just jumped in
his car—it was a 1937 Plymouth Concord—and spent 3
months bumming around the West Coast, and eventually
hitchhiked all the way back to New York. Called Woody
up, told him I was back, and he was in good shape, he was
recuperated. In fact, he was playing that night in a party,
a private party in somebody's house in Greenwich Village,
and he said, "Bring your guitar, we'll knock off a couple
of tunes together." And that was the real beginning of the
Woody Guthrie influence on my life.

Was his Huntington's showing then?

It was startin' to show in 1951, you know, before he ever
went to the hospital to get tested, but he didn't know then
it was Huntington's Chorea. Or he didn't want to say
it. He didn't want to believe it. He was too frightened, I
guess. And he was sort of hoping that, preferred to think
that it was just merely alcoholism. Or it was just a looming
fear in the back of his mind in his subconscious. But he
went in the hospital in late 1951, and got tested for a week,
and they said he had Huntington's Chorea. But it wasn't
bad enough to have to be hospitalized. In fact, he was able
to keep free rambling around for the next 3 years.

What would you say his influence was on you?

I was very strongly under the influence of his personality and his style and I imitated him so accurately that it was embarrassing or enraging to a lot of his fans and friends. I put up with a lot of static with them for the first couple of years. When he started being in the hospital and I visited him in the hospital, the other patients they'd say, "Hey Woody your brother's here."

John Cohen thought that perhaps some of your mannerisms, and later Dylan's, were a little bit jerky like Huntington's.

Yeah, it's just Woody had such a powerful personality that you kind of, you started to be like that just from bein' around him, you know? And I just realized when I was imitating Woody, that I was imitating a lot of those strange movements, and the weird way that he spoke was due to Huntington's Chorea, because he didn't know he had the disease. I mean, I'd been with Woody and the family for probably 8 or 9 months by the time Woody found out he had Huntington's Chorea. And it was only a little while after that, that I realized some of those jerky movements and things seemed to be just so unique—and part of his strange personality—were symptoms of that horrible disease.

So looking back, what else comes to mind when you think of Woody before he was hospitalized?

I was never quite so fully aware of just how very, very difficult Woody was until I read that book by Ed Cray. I heard everybody in the world complain about it and I thought well, maybe they just don't appreciate him like I do. But I now understand a lot more about it, because when I first got to know Woody was after all that stuff, after his most creative period had dwindled down and he was just doing a little bit of rewriting some of his old songs. He'd pull out an old song and typewriter, and he'd type up something new, change the words around a little bit. Sometimes he'd show it to me. We played music together for about a year and a half.

When did you make your last trip with Woody?

We made our last trip together in '54. Woody was saving up his beard for a [beard growing] contest in Topanga Canyon. Woody disappeared right after we got to Topanga, he disappeared the very next day. I bedded him down in his tent on the land and never saw him again. He hitchhiked up to Washington State and over to Montana. In '55, I met my first wife June, and we got married in June, and in September we went to Europe. That trip to Topanga was the last one I ever made with Woody, outside of trips to take him back to the hospital from Margie's house.

When you returned from Europe in 1961, you saw Woody again.

The day after I got off the ship from Europe, a big storm

all the way across the Atlantic was blowing hard for the first three days, and I got off that ship and stayed overnight in a hotel in Manhattan, and took a bus the next day out to Greystone Park to see Woody and visited him for about an hour or two. And Bob Dylan was there, a young kid from Minnesota, and we took a bus over to visit the Gleasons, over there in East Orange.

What was that like?

He introduced me to the Gleasons, and I was glad to finally meet them face-to-face and see where they lived. We visited them for an hour or so in their house and then we took a bus back to New York City together, and I took a room in a hotel. Bob moved into that hotel soon after, and he was right down the hall from me, about 3 or 4 doors down the hall from me, on the same floor in the Earl Hotel.

So what was it like the first time you saw Woody after so long? I guess he had really changed.

Yeah, it was marvelous to see how he still was tryin' like hell to stand up straight and walk a straight line—even though he looked like he was drunk or very much fucked up from the disease. Woody was in such a pathetic state, it was very hard to look at him without bustin' out cryin' and it was heartrending just to be in his company. But he always tried to let you know he was still on top of it. He was still in the saddle. He was aware of everything that people were doin' and sayin' and he appreciated it.

What were the trips to the Gleasons like? Who was there?

It was nice to see everybody, the friends and admirers, you know. Peter LaFarge was there, and Bob Dylan, and maybe Dave Van Ronk, and I think Maria Muldaur. There might be anywhere from 3 to 6 people at a time on any one given day. It was usually on a Sunday, and Sid cooked chili and beans and corn bread and all of Woody's favorite country cookin'.

What were your first impressions of Dylan?

Well, I thought he was a cute kid. He had a kind of a round face, peach fuzz, couldn't grow a beard yet. You know, like he was just about 19 years old. He was the same age as I was when I first met Woody. I was 19 and Woody was 39.

I imagine that Dylan meeting Woody at Greystone must have been a powerful moment, with Dylan coming of age and one of his idols—

—Obviously on his way out. It was very sad, and I think [Dylan] was profoundly moved by that, and wrote that great song, "Song to Woody." I've always felt that I too could have—and should have—written a song as a tribute to Woody and my admiration for Woody, which I've never been able to write. I've only written four songs in forty years. I'm not a singer/songwriter. I ain't a songwriter at all. I am a singer somewhat. Oh, I wish I could've written it myself.

Tell me about the drawings you did of Woody while you were at the Gleasons' house. You sang in Woody's style—were you trying to draw in Woody's style?

No, that was my style. It was no work at all for me to sing like him, I'm a natural mimic, but doing it with art is another deal. But I don't care for my drawings at all. Some of them came out good. Some of them are really good. I'm amazed, because I've seen a lot of my old drawings that I don't think anything of at all, I think they're pretty ugly. I'm good on trucks and horses and boats.

Did you see Woody after he left Greystone?

It was years after that. It got to where you couldn't understand a word he said, and he'd been moved out of New Jersey and back over to Brooklyn State Hospital. He was home with Marjorie and all the kids out there in Howard Beach for a Sunday visit, and eating all of his favorite junk food, like a hot dog and soda pop and listening to his records over and over, and people would visit and play him his music. And he liked to listen to that.

When was the last time you saw Woody?

I was in New Mexico in 1967 when Woody died. I hadn't

seen him in about a year. Last time I saw him was around '65. Somewhere around January of '66 or December of '65, we drove out to California in a Land Rover and moved to California. And I didn't get back East again to see Woody, I don't think at all, until he died.

If Woody hadn't gotten Huntington's, how do you think his life would have turned out?

Well, Huntington's is what took his mother away at a very young age, and if you're gonna do "what if," you could say, what if she hadn't had Huntington's? But he had all that other shit happen to him due to his mother being taken away from Huntington's and that was the beginning of a lot of tragedy in his life.

Woody was dogged by tragedy, with his sister who was caught up in a fire, and there were a great number of Americans experiencing a lot of tragedy because there was so much hunger and starvation back in those days in the Dust Bowl and the Depression and rich people losing their money in 1929, and jumping off of buildings and stuff.

If he didn't have the Chorea, I think that he might have, maybe, lived to be 90. He was otherwise very rugged, wiry, and his disposition was straight. I think he would have lived longer, perhaps made even a bigger contribution than he did—but I don't see how anybody could possibly make a bigger contribution in the writing world. It's hard to imagine.

ANNEKE
VAN KIRK

This Haven of Peace

Anneke Vankirk was Woody Guthrie's third wife. She was 20 years old in 1952, and living with her husband of six months near Los Angeles. Anneke's Bohemian spirit fit perfectly with the many actors, musicians and writers living in rural Topanga Canyon. Guthrie's marriage to Marjorie had fallen apart from the strain of his Huntington's Disease, and he'd gone to Topanga Canyon to visit his friend Will Geer. There he wrote "I Ain't Dead," a phrase Guthrie would later use in his letters from Greystone Park.

Anneke met Woody when they both spent time in a potter's studio. A relationship developed, and two months later, they left for New York. Jack Elliott joined them to visit Stetson Kennedy in Beluthahatchee, Florida, only to find him away in Europe. The couple moved into an abandoned bus and shed on the property, where Woody wrote songs and worked on his manuscript for *Seeds of Man*. Anneke described the next three months as "this haven of peace."

That haven abruptly ended when Woody's arm was terribly burnt while pouring kerosene on their cooking pit. He was never able to bend that arm again. They moved to a small fifth-floor walk-up in New York, and were married at the end of 1953. Their daughter Lorina Lynn was born in early 1954. Anneke worked while Woody drank heavily, unable to perform or record. Anneke later wrote, "Sad, sad, sad. No glory here. Not even bound for. Just bound. Bound by illness and the passage of time." Their marriage ended after several violent fights.

Anneke hadn't been heard from in over 25 years. Her whereabouts had become a mystery at the Woody Guthrie

Archives—in fact, she had been living outside New York City. She would only answer my questions by letter because she regretted telling some of her stories to Joe Klein, who repeated them in his book, *Woody Guthrie: A Life*.

Before you met Woody in Topanga Canyon, had you heard of him and his music?

I had never heard of Woody Guthrie prior to meeting him. I knew Leadbelly's music, as my father played "Gray Goose!"—"with a long trail o' goslins!"

What were your first impressions of Woody?

First impression of him, at Bessie Hawes' home, was his alone-ness. When he played, he looked down. He was not, at that time, a conversationalist. Many years later, while I was listening to WBAI, Larry Josephson played an interview with Woody. Hearing Woody's voice, words and thoughts flowing—was stunning! The full impact of just how far along his disease had progressed became real then! However, when I first met him, his stumbly, silent persona was Woody! I loved his hands, found him sexy. His silences attracted me.

What impulse made you changes your life so abruptly after meeting him?

Why do you assume my life changed so abruptly after meeting Woody? I did not lead an orderly life, and leaving David for Woody was par for the course.

Did Woody ever talk about what he was going through?

I didn't give a thought to Huntington's—first, because who knew from it then? Marjorie Mazia, during a later phone conversation, said to me "Annie, don't ever have children!" I didn't think about tomorrow, only the moment. I believe I was incapable of being able to know what Woody thought about Chorea! He did not ever discuss this, or anything. When he did speak, his few words were frozen-mouthed, but surely he had to feel his deterioration.

At that time not much was really known about Huntington's Disease— there was no test, no family support groups. How did you cope?

Coping was not something I was aware of doing early in our relationship. However, after Lorina Lynn, yes, coping was something I did. Especially when Woody started drinking Ballantine Ale and mopping spilled drinks with freshly laundered—by me, after work—diapers! However, even the most difficult lives are easier when one is young.

Jack Elliott spent some time with you and Woody in Beluthahatchee—did you ever talk to him about Woody's condition?

Jack Elliott—whose father, Dr. Abraham Adnopoz, operated on me for removal of a breast cyst—drove the three of us from NYC to Beluthahatchee in a Model A. He stayed for several weeks until Woody asked him to leave. "He sounds more like me than I do." Jack did sound

like Woody. He studied Woody. Jack got on Woody's
nerves as he followed him—his manner ingratiating—and
he just never got the hint that Woody was tired of having
him around. I honestly can't recall what Woody said to
Jack—probably something like, "You better hit the road."

How would you describe Woody's spirit at that time?

I do remember Beluthahatchee—Woody trying to make
adobe bricks, the dogs who strayed in, Foxy and Missy, the
swamp, cottonmouth moccasin snakes, huge turtles sitting
on logs at opposite ends, Spanish moss hanging everywhere.
He worked continuously on *Seeds of Man*, an epic I itched to
alter as it was loaded with Woodyisms—"Wardy Forties."

It all stopped with the fire—

I can't believe he lived through this. The pain must have
been staggering. We went by bus to Jacksonville. The
hospital there refused to take him, as I remember, and
sent us to St. Augustine, which was where we should have
gone first. Woody refused to go to St. Augustine, and
my life became a hitchhike into Jacksonville for ST-37,
a fluid that prevented bandages from sticking to skin. A
naval doctor finally was located who came and took care
of the arm. But he had no physical therapy, no range
of physical motion, nothing. So Woody's life as a guitar
and mandolin picker came to an end. Woody's spirit
remained—what is a good word?—unchanging.

Did you ever visit Woody at Greystone Park?

No, I never visited Woody at Greystone Park. I cut relations to him abruptly.

Was there one event or incident when you made the decision to end your relationship with Woody?

Just that Woody seemed to be steering his life away from me.

Do you remember the last time you wrote or spoke to Woody?

I vaguely recall telling Woody I wanted a divorce—and received a blast of letters from Greystone Park that filled my mailbox for weeks. Then, nothing.

There's a letter in the Guthrie Archives from you to Woody where you wrote that after you get back from Mexico you were going to go to Alaska or Korea, and maybe even Japan. Where did life take you?

I went to Mexico for a divorce. I wanted to go to Japan, but did not. I got married again, had a son, got a job in a long-term care facility, became administrator, and here I am.

Was your choice of a care taking profession in any way related to your experiences with Woody's Huntington's Disease?

My choice of employment, I'm sure, had a lot to do with the "I Wanna Be Loved" Syndrome. In 1986, I went to night school—and kept a day job—to be a Licensed Practical Nurse, and I had a patient for four years with Huntington's Chorea. The terminal end of the disease is horrible.

Is there anything from your experiences with Huntington's that's caused you to rethink about how Woody behaved?

I'm glad I never saw the terminal Woody. The patient I [later] cared for was nothing more than a decaying body, mindless, motionless. He was a psychiatrist, a painter, a strong, creative man.

Have you watched Woody's influence on music today?

Yes, I do hear the Woody influence in much of today's music. But during the time I knew Woody, he took a dim view of highly produced songs. He liked rugged performances. Do you think he'd like Billy Bragg? I think he would have liked Bruce Springsteen.

Why is that?

Springsteen sounds rough and unpolished—qualities high on Guthrie list of likes.

Are there any other recollections you'd like to share?

I wish I could give you more, but think, fifty years ago! Fifty! Who can remember that long ago?

VINCENT "JIM" LONGHI

NOBODY PINNED IT DOWN LIKE WOODY

Jim Longhi, Cisco Houston and Woody Guthrie were shipmates in the Merchant Marine during World War II. They shipped out together as mess men over the next two years on Liberty ships carrying supplies, ammunition and troops across the Atlantic. They were part of the invasions of Italy and Normandy and their ships were torpedoed twice. Longhi's dramatic stories are recounted in his book, *Woody, Cisco and Me.*

After the war, Longhi became an attorney, author and playwright. He fought for the rank-and-file Brooklyn longshoreman, helping fight mob infiltration of the union, and ran for Congress. He was the prototype for Arthur Miller's lawyer Alfieri in *A View from the Bridge* and it has been said he's the inspiration that led to the film *On the Waterfront.*

I met Longhi at his apartment overlooking the East River in Manhattan. He was ninety and some of his memories had faded, but he cried easily telling of Woody and his Huntington's. I feel fortunate to have met him and heard his stories when I did—he died unexpectedly of a fall in November of 2006, less than two months after we spoke.

Tell me about when you first met Woody.

First met Woody the day we shipped out together when Cisco surprised me and said Woody's coming with us. Everybody knew Woody Guthrie, Woody was an icon in the left-wing movement. And so on our first ship, around March '43, that was me and Woody and Cisco in a room, 8 feet wide 8 feet long, double bunks. And that's the first time that I had a real opportunity to talk to him, man-to-man, friend-to-friend. From the moment I met him, which was at the union hall, he was Woody Guthrie; I was awed. And I kept saying things like, "I love what you do," you know, "blah, blah blah," and Woody Guthrie would just brush it off. It was just typical fan and icon. The moment we got on the ship, we became, he became, Woody, not "Woody Guthrie," just Woody.

How'd you wind up in the Merchant Marine?

Cisco and I met when I was drafted and about to go into the Army—that was OK, they probably would've given me a desk job or whatever because I was almost a lawyer—and he says "why don't you come with me in the Merchant Marine?" In front of <my fiancé> Gaby! I was ashamed; I said "OK." I went—my conscience dragged me—not Woody's, coincidentally. Cisco asked me, and that same weekend he said to Woody let's go, or Woody said I'm going with you. And that's how it happened, how Woody, Cisco and me became one. The song, you know [laughing].

When did Woody first mention that he might have Huntington's?

And the first few weeks, after two weeks or so, Boom! Boom! "We're under attack!" I won't describe the attack, but you have submarines that were being attacked by our destroyers with depth charges. And they would "boom" against the side of our ship! But there was a general alarm, we're all on deck with our life jackets or whatever. "Holy shit!" And I was scared. After the general alarm ended we were allowed to go back into our cabins, Cisco was already asleep—nothing bothered that son-of-a-bitch—and Woody was sitting in his bunk just staring. "Woody were you scared?" "Hell no! Only thing I'm scared of is this." Took his unlit cigarette in his mouth, and struck the match, and tried to light the cigarette quickly [demonstrates Woody's shaking hand]. He lit the cigarette, put out the match, blew out the smoke, and he said, "I think I may gotten it from my mother."

What I should do now is take the text from my book, because it's difficult for me now to repeat exactly what Woody said, and you would like to know, without my emotions, because it's not an easy question.

> He lit the cigarette, blew it out. "My mother had the same thing. When her shaking got very bad they put her in a mental hospital. But she wasn't insane. It was something physical, inherited. And I'm beginning to suspect that I have it too." "Jesus," I said. "What did the doctors say?" "They don't know much about it. Maybe only Jesus can help me."

What else did Woody say about Huntington's?

The next thing that comes to mind is that he told me about his mother, in particular how she got worse and worse. And how she had, in a sense, been accused of starting a fire by throwing something, a lamp or something, at her daughter, and her daughter died in the fire. And then, of course, she was hospitalized—that wore very heavy on Woody's mind.

Harold Leventhal told me that nobody was really sure what was wrong with Woody, a lot of them just thought he was a drunk because of his erratic behavior...

Yea, because the disease got worse, he drank more. And more. Yes, he was drunk. Yes he was drunk.

And it masked that he had something wrong?

Yeah, it was the sickness. When Woody came aboard the ship, beside from the ten books that he carried—heavy literature, Darwin, philosophers—he had two bottles of rum. At one time he said that the rum covered his fear. He didn't use those precise words, but the rum, drinking, was medicine for him. Now, from the stories he'd tell me about Cisco and himself wandering, drinking for Woody was very important. And it was always rum. He said, "That's my medicine."

So Woody knew something before he shipped out.

He was aware that things were not right with, call it what you like, anxiety, or whatever, but there must have been some evidence—Woody was a pretty well grounded guy to be worried. Worried enough to drink. So, obviously he was aware, before 1943, when we met, he was aware, I don't know how long before. Must've been two three years before that. He was never an alcoholic, mind you. I never saw Woody drunk. Never gave the slightest sign, he could drink half a bottle of rum, the son of a bitch, and not show anything. But he must've been aware, or he wouldn't repeat that it's good medicine.

After the war, how often did you see Woody?

Immediately after the war, '45, after I got off the ships, I thought I was finished with the sea and every fucking thing that went with it. But somehow or other I got talked into running for Congress on the waterfront, the Brooklyn waterfront. With the mob and the guys, "Oh shit!" So I ran for Congress, it was a very close race—I lost by fifteen hundred to twenty five hundred votes 'cause Woody and Cisco came to help me, and Frank Sinatra too. " Ding a ling ding a ling," back of the truck, you know, a couple of times in the campaign. I was busy trying to organize the longshoreman in the fight against the mob. I ran on the Republican ticket, imagine! Because the only way you get in it, to be in the Democratic ticket, you gotta be a connected guy. Everybody, judges, everybody knows that.

And then Woody went his way. By then, '47, he must've begun to show signs, bad signs, because I would call, and Marjorie would tell me that he wasn't behaving right. I don't remember the exact date, but Woody left Marjorie or Marjorie left Woody. One or the other separated. Woody came to me in my office—by then I was admitted to the bar—he says, "I want a divorce." I said, "What the fuck do you need a divorce for, you're separated, temporarily, I mean you got Marjorie and all that." He says, "I want to marry this girl, I've forgotten her name...Anneke, Anneke. Somehow or other I got a divorce for him, I don't remember the details.

Another thing that comes to mind is, Woody's under arrest, "What for?" Well he had written dirty letters to a girl in Pennsylvania. Cuckoo Woody. Sexually-explicit letters. Somehow or other, the Federal government got them. He was put in prison, on a Federal prison on the West Side, on the river, on the waterfront! Of all places! To make it short, I pushed certain connections that I had.

What connections?

I might as well be more explicit. The mob—which included the officials of the longshoreman's union that we were fighting to overthrow—that whole organization that stole my election. After the election a top mob guy who was in politics—he was not the head of the mob but he was a big force in the Democratic party—he said, "Jimmy, I'm sorry for we had to do that, you know, but business is business." And that was a nice gesture.

And when Woody was in prison, I went to this guy and said, "You owe me. Woody Guthrie is a friend of mine, you don't know who he is, blah, blah, blah." Forty-eight hours later, Woody's released! [slapping thigh] How the fuck it happened, I don't know, but I'm a genius lawyer, I was.

Can I ask who the guy was?

Nah, nah, forget about it. OK I'll tell you. Nah, forget
it. Just for fun's sake, he was called, despite his last name,
Socrates. The most modest, quietest, simple, 75-year-
old man you ever met. Sat on his porch in a rocker in
Rockaway Beach. That's it.

Not long after that Woody entered Brooklyn State Hospital.

As I'm now thinking about it, the hand shaking and the
lighting of the cigarette was repeated when he was in the
hospital—that's the same thing, Woody sitting up in bed,
trying to light a cigarette! I dared not light it for him.
His dignity. He was struggling 'til the goddamn flame
must've touched him and I don't remember whether he
did light the cigarette. I blanked that out, I don't know. I
was just watching this struggle of the two hands getting
together. [Crying] Ah shit, all right, let me get a hold of
myself. [a short pause in the interview]

Did you ever see Woody at Greystone Park Hospital?

No, I didn't want to see Woody. I didn't want to see
Woody.

You didn't want to see him?

No. Under the condition he was in I didn't want to see
Woody. I knew I couldn't help Woody. He'd get no kick
out of seeing me, he'd be shamed if he were cognizant,
he'd be ashamed.

I spoke briefly to Pete Seeger, and he told me didn't want to talk about that time, he just wanted to remember Woody before Huntington's...

That's right, it's like going to my mother's cemetery, I never went after she died, they buried her, I never went to the grave.

When was the last time you saw Woody?

The last time I went to see him to say goodbye. He was far-gone. They say his mind was clear but that his nervous system was destroyed. The last time I went to see him I had to say goodbye. He couldn't speak. The only way he could say yes or no was blinking. He could blink. So I gotta say goodbye to Woody. I say, "Woody, do you love me? Do you love me?" [Smiling and clapping his hands once] He blinked!

So how do you think Woody's life would have turned out if he hadn't gotten the Huntington's gene from his mother?

Ho ho, what a question, mamma mia! Of course he'd have gone on writing his songs, it was like breathing for him. What would've happened to Woody? 1960, the sixties, where Bob Dylan took his place in a sense, you know, young kid, imitating Woody. Not that Woody would have made the revolution of the sixties, but he would've been idolized by the sixties crowd.

The time he went off into Greystone, 1956, was right before the changes in sixties, the civil rights movement...

He was Woody Guthrie, it was Woody Guthrie time! And Woody changed the whole style of entertainment having to do with singing. Nobody today stands up and sings without a guitar. Woody stood up and sang with a guitar. Dylan imitated him. Woody would've been the dean.

Would you have seen Woody being very active politically in all these movements?

Yeah, of course. He would write his songs, he would stand up in Madison Square Garden, he would sing his songs, and that was his activism. But it would cause a wonderful spirit from audiences. Without Huntington's he would've been a very successful artist. When his book *Bound for Glory* came out, the most important critic of the time, the *New York Times* critic, called him a national treasure. You know, a guy in late twenties, maybe 29, 30 years old when he wrote *Bound for Glory*. His artwork, everything, was innovative. Yeah, there were other folksingers before, but nobody pinned it down like Woody.

Any more recollections on Woody and his Huntington's?

No, you wrung me dry. You hear what I'm saying? You wrung me dry.

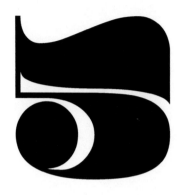

HAROLD
LEVENTHAL

I Wasn't Exactly His Manager

Harold Leventhal's sympathies for leftist causes—combined with his business skills—led him to become one of folk music's most successful promoters. He worked with such celebrated performers as Joan Baez, Harry Belafonte, Johnny Cash, Judy Collins, the Mamas and the Papas, and Neil Young. In 1955, Leventhal organized a reunion concert of the Weavers by persuading each member that the others had already agreed, and that concert helped launch the folk music revival of the late 50s and early 60's. In 1963, Leventhal presented Bob Dylan in his first major concert-hall appearance.

Leventhal became Guthrie's business manager in the early 1950's, after Huntington's had ended career as a performer and recording artist. As Guthrie's disease became more pronounced, Leventhal decided to promote a concert at Pythian Hall as a benefit for the Guthrie children. Woody attended and listened to friends—including Pete Seeger and Lee Hayes—sing his songs. The proceeds from the concert went into a trust fund that was established for the children, which also became the beneficiary of the royalties from Guthrie's songs.

Leventhal later helped establish the Woody Guthrie Foundation and Archives with Marjorie Mazia, and worked closely with her until her death in 1982. He also gave Arlo Guthrie his first job as an office boy, later producing both Arlo's first album and the 1969 film adaptation of *Alice's Restaurant*.

When I interviewed Leventhal in March of 2004, he spoke in almost a whisper, making it difficult to transcribe our conversation. I didn't realize how little time Harold had left, and was saddened to learn of his death in October of 2005.

How did you meet Woody?

Well, I met him through The Weavers. I knew of him, I'd seen him perform at Hootenanny's around 1948, say, 1949, but I didn't know him personally. But because I was manager of the Weavers and he was close to Lee Hayes and Pete Seeger, he would show up at rehearsals and recording sessions, and of course I met him at that time and became friendly.

How did you become his manager?

Well, I want to clear that, I wasn't exactly his manager; I took care of him. At that particular point, he was floundering around between New York and Los Angeles and was beginning to show the signs of the illness—the Huntington's was beginning to show up, which we were not aware of at the time, and we attributed his erratic behavior to a drunk. He may have been, but I think the disease caused a lot of that personal reaction.

Marjorie was concerned about his condition. She got several of us together to create a Guthrie Children's trust fund to look after him. I was part of the group that was given responsibility to take care of him. That was probably about '51. From then on, I kind of was given the responsibility of looking after him professionally, which was a matter of seeing that he was receiving royalties for the songs he wrote that were recorded by the Weavers.

During the exam at Greystone, Woody said he got $10,000 for a song—

Well, that's royalties, probably for "So Long It's Been Good to Know You."

That was the first time that Woody was really making serious money?

I rather think so, yeah [laughing]. Whatever money he earned before was not really writing—it was performing, you know.

Let's talk about the concert that was held to raise money for the family.

It was to raise money to start the Guthrie children's trust fund. We held it at the Pythian Hall because we couldn't hold it in a big place. We weren't sure of people turning out for it. This place, as I recall, maybe would hold about a thousand or more. It was reasonable, and we decided that, I recall, it was Lee Hayes acting as a narrator, Millard Lampell wrote a little script, and we got various performers to do his songs—and, of course, Woody showed up.

I now see what you mean when you said you weren't his manager, that you took care of him.

Yes, right. I began to manage. I submitted his name to go on an ABC-TV show they had at one time called *Hootenanny*, and I was surprised they rejected his name. They'd blacklisted him.

I saw in the archives that there is Woody's FBI files. They were even following him while he was at Brooklyn State.

Oh sure, they kept tabs.

I guess they blacklisted a lot of artists at that time

No other artists, just the Weavers. In the music field, they were the only ones blacklisted.

So what was it about communism and the left wing of the political spectrum that appealed to Woody and you and the Weavers?

Well, probably all for various reasons. I grew up in the South Bronx during the Depression when nobody got jobs. Then people joined left wing movements to get a solution. Lee did it his way, and Pete and the others did theirs. There was a big following, among not only just working class people, but also among intellectuals at that time.

What was Woody's behavior like at that time?

59

My wife and I were running then sort of an old Broadway house where Will Geer would perform. And [Guthrie] would come around with his new wife and baby. He'd come with a guitar, but he couldn't handle that. He was just totally...he couldn't perform. He was visiting Will Geer in the Village and I think he must've created a problem, a disturbance, and I got a call—would I come down and get him out of there, or they'd call the police. And I called another friend that lived in the neighborhood, in the case where I couldn't handle it, and I went down to the Village. Sure enough, Woody created a scene, and I said, "Let's go out without creating any problems," and he left. And then I took him around and bought him some clothes—because he looked pretty bad—and I put him in a taxi and sent him back to Brooklyn State Hospital.

And then he left Brooklyn State, and I believe he showed up at your place before he got to Greystone.

Well, he showed up at my house. I wasn't home then. And he just sat on the floor waiting for me to come there. I don't recall how many hours he was there. And I was surprised to see him, and when I asked why he came. He needed money, and I gave him whatever. He sat for a while in the house, and as typical, his cigarette dropped down the couch and started a fire, which we put out. And he got a burn.

So when he left, did you know where he was going?

I got a phone call in the office from the state troopers in New Jersey. They got the number, Woody told them to call. And they explained that he was picked up for being a vagrant: "Is that so?" I said, "No, he's not a vagrant." And he'd said that he's sick, and I said, "That's true, and that should be taken care of from a medical point of view, rather than arrested." I merely certified what Woody was telling them. The result was that he wasn't arrested, but was committed to a hospital.

How did Woody wind up at Greystone?

I know that he had come off the bus. He wandered around, and came back and the bus was gone.

And he had no money—

He didn't look like he belonged there. They zoned in on that.

What was it like when you went out to visit him at Greystone? Do you remember your first trip out there?

I don't remember if it was the first or the second, but we took a car, drove out there, this huge building looked like from the 1880's, and we were then told it was an insane asylum and Woody was in this place. We went in to see Woody, and he was in less than good condition. But the interesting part of it is he didn't say, "Get me out of here."

We would talk to the attendants or the doctors and try to tell them who he was or what he did. They were skeptical about it. At times he would tell me he wanted a guitar, and the next visit I would bring out a guitar. One visit, he wanted a record player, and I'd bring one out. He couldn't handle the guitar, and even the record machine was a problem for him.

How did Woody feel about Greystone compared to Brooklyn State?

I think he liked it, because he'd go outside on the grass and there was less tension than Brooklyn State.

Did you talk to the doctors out at Greystone?

One time I brought out sheet music with his name on it, records, books, to show the head doctor. He said, "Well, Woody said he was a writer," and I would show him his book, and he didn't even look at it. "He said he wrote songs," and then I showed him the songs on the record and he ignored it all. Because, in the end, he's crazy. And Woody's remark to that was, "It's hard to tell who's the patient here." I did give some gratuities to the people that helped—the nurses, the personnel—and I told them more about his background.

In one of his letters, Woody wrote saying a student nurse played his Bound for Glory album over the hospital's hi-fi system. He signed the letter, "I ain't dead quite yet." What's the story behind that album? It came out right after Woody went into the hospital.

We tried to encourage the record companies to get his material out. Will Geer was the one who supported it. It was Geer's idea. He was in New York working in the theater on Second Avenue, so he was around for some time.

Arlo told me it was important for Marjorie that Woody be part of the folk scene that was emerging in New York.

There were other occasions where I had picked him up, or I had somebody pick him up for me. We had various events with the Weavers. I'd want him to be there, and we'd pick him up for the day, bring him here, and usually Marjorie would take him back.

He couldn't perform?

No, he just sat. It was for the benefit of those of us that were concerned he would be liberated from that place once in a while.

Woody went back to Brooklyn State after Greystone, and then eventually Creedmoor.

We didn't want people going out because Woody could not talk. People came to look at him. Just friends were allowed. To have other visitors that would just be looking at him, it would hurt his feelings. I'd come out, and Bing Crosby recorded one of his songs and I'd play it for him. I played "Alice's Restaurant" for him. He was amused by it.

There were a lot of changes in the country that happened after Woody got sick. If Woody didn't have Huntington's, what do you imagine would have happened?

I would say that he'd be the same way that Pete has been all these years, politically and culturally.

I saw Seeger at the anti-Iraq war protest in 2003.

Yeah. Right. Woody would have been there with him.

SIDSEL
GLEASON

Cowboy Stew

Bob and Sid Gleason lived in a fourth-floor walk-up in the middle-class suburb of East Orange, New Jersey. Their lives changed forever in 1959 as they were listening to Oscar Brand's radio program and Millard Lampell—one of the founding Almanac Singers—telling the story of Woody Guthrie's illness. Listeners were encouraged to write to Guthrie, and that led to the Gleasons bringing Woody to their home almost every weekend. Soon folk musicians from New York City would come out to play with Woody. Visitors included Pete Seeger, Ramblin' Jack Elliott, Peter LaFarge, Cisco Houston, and John Cohen. Sitting at their kitchen table, Bob Dylan wrote down the lyrics to his first serious composition, "Song to Woody," on a piece of yellow lined paper. Bob Gleason—who worked as a New Jersey school teacher—also made a recording of young Dylan that circulates as a bootleg known as *The Gleason Tapes*.

Bob Gleason died in 1993, and Sid moved to California. I finally was able to locate her with the help of Scott Smith, Bob Gleason's son from a prior marriage. He'd been looking for her as well, trying to learn more about the father he hadn't seen since he was a child, and we compared notes. Late one night Scott called to say that he had found Sid.

I would later visit with Sid at her home in Orange County, California. She was 87 at the time, and while our conversations would wander wherever Sid's memory took her, she came back to those experiences which had been the most enduring, especially cowboy stew. She also had a treasure trove of photographs, sketches and other material, some of which are published for the first time in "Woody Guthrie's Wardy Forty." Sadly, Sid passed away in March of 2006 after suffering a stroke.

When did you first meet or hear about Woody?

Oh, I knew him before I went back East [likely 1936]. We were out in Arizona and there's a big river along here, and we were building that [Hoover] dam. I was baking bread and biscuits. I heard this guitar playing and I walked to where the guitar was, and there was Woody. Woody traveled all over the country. He went here and he went there, and he went someplace else and he always took his guitar with him. I went over and started talking to him, and he said, "Well, right now I don't know which way I'm gonna go, but one of these days I'll probably end up at your front door"—and that is exactly what happened a number of years afterwards.

How far of a trip was it from Greystone to where you lived?

Oh not very long. Sometimes I didn't go out there, sometimes Bob went by himself. But, the first time, I went out there because Bob never met him and I had. So we went out there and he comes walking over to me, and the first thing he said, "Where's your guitar?" And I said, "Well, it's at home." And he said, "Okay, I'll come with you if they let me."

So you would just go out and pick him up?

My husband got permission to take him off of the grounds,
which was unbelievable that he got him off there. And
we went up to get him every Sunday, just like clockwork.
I had to make cowboy stew and biscuits for him. I had
a great big cast iron kettle. And he said, "I would crawl
clear out from there for your cowboy stew, I love it." And
every week we'd go out and get him. He'd always say,
"Biscuits this time?" "Yup." "Okay," he'd say.

What was it like when you picked him up?

Sometimes we'd bring him in, and he'd have twenty or thirty
letters tucked inside of his socks. And then, inside of his shirt
and stuck into his pants, he'd have more mail there. He got
all this mail. And the first thing we did was to get him in the
bathtub. And then Oscar Brand always saw to it that he got
a blue shirt and blue jeans instead of you know, dress pants.
The ones the hospital had on him, if he'd put his legs in them,
he'd disappear. He wasn't a big man, he was small.

What was it like at your apartment when Woody came?

The word got around. Next thing you know, sometimes
there'd be twenty or thirty guys or girls who came there.
Then they got started playing. And oh man, I tell you we
were on the third floor of this apartment. Did you ever
hear of washtub bass? Well, there was one of the guys that

played washtub bass, and between that and the guitar, it was a pretty wild affair. The people down on the first floor were just about crazy, 'cause it made such a funny noise downstairs. People came from all over, honey, I'm not kidding. They'd come all the way from Oregon. But it was as I said, pretty wild.

Did Woody ever play guitar when he came out?

He wasn't very good at that time. He was really beginning to get bad.

Things changed when Woody came into your life, didn't they?

I'm telling you, that was the wildest time. All those people would come in there, and I wouldn't have any idea about some of them, and all of a sudden here people would be coming from different places, and it was wild. It was really something. And my husband, he loved music, and he'd sit there and he'd pat his foot to keep time with the music. Oh honey, it was wild, it was wild. Sometimes I wondered, would it ever quit? 'Cause people would come from miles and miles and miles when they found out that he was there. And the parties we had! And that was when I made the cowboy stew, my gosh there was so many of them come. Oscar was the one who gave me the money to get the food because we just couldn't afford it to feed everybody.

Who were some of the people that came to see Woody?

Oh sure. There were a lot of them that came. Cisco Houston.

Jack Elliot was one of the people that came out, wasn't he?

Oh sure. Jack came back from Europe. And then the other one, in fact there's a picture of him up here on the wall—Peter LaFarge. He was on the cowboy end, too.

Tell me about the sketches Jack made.

Oh yes. He would draw Woody sitting on the sofa. And there's one he did of me. And Woody sketched some himself. But Woody's weren't very good, honey. They got so where they weren't good because he was ill.

Do you remember when Dylan first showed up?

Yes, well, he came out and he had probably lived in the gutter for I don't know how long. Oh, honey, you never in your life saw anybody so dirty. He was filthy. You could smell him as he came up the stairs, and I don't have a good smeller. And my husband took one look at him and said, "You get in that tub and stay there until you're clean, or I'll come in with a scrub brush and I guarantee you will be clean!" Well, he was clean by the time he was done.

Did Dylan come out there a lot?

Yeah. He'd come out quite often. And sometimes he'd

spend a week with us.

I understand that Dylan wrote down for you the words to "Song to Woody?"

He was sitting at our kitchen table when he wrote it down. He was always playing Woody's songs, but this was one he wrote. I keep it with pictures my husband took.

Did your husband Bob take a lot of photos when Woody was there?

Oh yes. He took an awful lot of them. He would go to all kinds of places. After he passed away and I moved back West, I didn't know what to do with all the negatives. I talked to someone who said, "They have to be burned, you can't put them in the trash." So they took them out, and we had like a dumpster, and they took them out there to make sure they were all burned up.

Do you have any other memories of Greystone and Woody?

He took care of the people that were there, Woody did. There were just a lot of people there, and sometimes he'd play guitar for them, and sometimes the harmonica, and he'd walk outside, he liked to go out and sit in the sun, and all things like that. They gave him clothes, but by gosh, he'd probably wear about a size shirt that you'd put on an 8 or 9-year old kid.

Nora told me that she has one of his shirts in her attic, and it's so small that it doesn't even fit her son.

Yeah, he wasn't a very big man—but he traveled all over the county.

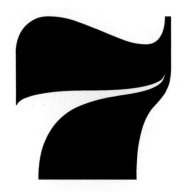

DR. VINCENZO
COCILOVO

A Nice Quiet Smile

I'd been trying for several years to find someone who worked was one of Guthrie's doctors. I had some of his medical records with the last name and first initial of his doctors, but it was still difficult to track down people who had retired fifteen to thirty years ago, and several times I learned that they'd only died in the last few years. I was finally able to connect a Cocilovo that once lived in New Jersey to a telephone number in Connecticut, which then led to a number in Florida. At the end of those calls, I was tempted to ask if he was kidding when Dr. Cocilovo confirmed that he had once worked at Greystone. He was 78.

Dr. Vincenzo Cocilovo graduated from medical school in Palermo, Italy in 1953, and worked at Greystone from 1959 to 1960 while studying for his medical exams. As a psychiatrist and surgeon, Cocilovo worked in both the Admissions Building, where examinations of new patients were conducted, and the Clinic Building, which was for psychiatric patients with physical ailments. Dr. Cocilovo conducted surgery there, as well as Electro-Convulsive Therapy. This was one of the few effective treatments available for certain types of mental illnesses before the development of psychotropic drugs.

The Clinic Building was like a small hospital serving a city of 8,000 patients and employees. Woody Guthrie was transferred there after his diagnosis was changed from paranoid schizophrenic to Huntington's Chorea. After leaving Greystone, Dr. Cocilovo moved to Connecticut, where he helped establish Cedarcrest Regional Hospital. He eventually moved into private practice.

What was your role at Greystone?

I did work in the Clinic Building where I did mostly surgery, and also in the Admissions Building where I worked as a psychiatrist. I had some training in surgery, so they utilized me in both ways. My patients in the Clinic Building were mostly surgical patients. However, I also was also on call and on weekends, or covered the other wards when somebody was on vacation. You have to keep in mind that my recollections are of things that happened fifty years ago. Some recollections are very vivid, but some are cloudy.

Do you remember Woody Guthrie as a patient at Greystone?

Yes, I do. I think he was on the second floor, which was a medical ward or a neurological ward. I liked him as a patient. He always smiled to me whenever I passed by, or when I took care of him. With me, he was always very, very pleasant. He did not interact too much with staff or with patients, because he had difficulties in articulating words. He was in the late stage of Huntington's Chorea. When did he die, by the way?

He died in 1967.

Oh, he was strong. I didn't expect he would last that long. Which is an indication that, all in all, he had pretty good care.

So what else can you say about his condition?

He was walking around but he walked with some difficulties.

While you were there, did he have any visitors?

Yes, the visitor that I recall was one of his ex-wives and her new husband. And I may also recall, but I'm not a hundred percent sure, a young person also coming with them. Perhaps a son, but I can't really remember clearly. It was a young man or woman, maybe fifteen or sixteen. I've a kind of feeling of seeing them with somebody.

That would have been Guthrie's ex-wife, Marjorie. Do you have any memories of her?

Well, she was a pleasant woman, a fairly good-looking woman, and she cared about him. The staff told me that she had put some order in his financial affairs. I never discussed anything with her other than, "How is my husband?" Generally, there was no change except that sometimes he tended to choke.

From what?

From not being able to swallow well. Huntington's Chorea is characterized by choreo-athetoid movements of the arms and muscular groups, slowly affects all muscular groups impairing the ability to walk, to talk, to swallow, and so on. And on some of these occasions we felt we should take some X-rays to make sure that there was no aspiration, no pneumonitis, or anything like that.

When Woody first came to Greystone, they did an examination that diagnosed him as a paranoid schizophrenic. Hospital notes say *that the staff believed him to be delusional after Woody told them that he'd written thousands of songs—and had made $10,000 for writing one song.*

Most likely, somebody didn't know him. The examining psychiatrist may have been a foreigner or something like that, who knew nothing about Woody Guthrie. He would think he was paranoid for saying he had written an awful lot of songs and so on. That was an admission note, and I'm sure the diagnosis must have been changed later on when it became clear that he had Huntington Chorea.

It wasn't for quite a while. He was admitted in June, and they changed his diagnosis in January of the following year.

I can't comment for the note or for the psychologist; most likely he was a resident that admitted him. Did they write a request for a neurological consultation?

No, I didn't see that anywhere.

But when they changed the diagnosis, somebody must have diagnosed him as Huntington's. Do you have the change of the diagnosis?

Yes, it says: "This patient was today presented before the medical staff, the diagnosis changed from schizophrenic reaction, paranoid type to chronic brain syndrome associated with unknown or unspecified cause with psychotic reaction; Huntington's Chorea."

Okay, finally they saw the light.

Were there other patients there with Huntington's at the time?

I remember one where there was a problem with diagnosis because there was nobody in his family that had Huntington's Chorea. Neither of his parents or his grandparents, uncles, aunts or anybody. In view of the fact that Huntington's Chorea is a very hereditary type of disease, people felt that it might not be Huntington's Chorea. However, we then had a conference and the consensus was that a hereditary illness has to start somewhere, and even if this person did not have anybody before him with the illness, he was the first one with the mutation. Clinically he had chorea, and therefore we diagnosed him as Huntington's Chorea. A consultant from Columbia came to see this case, because when we had difficulties we had the Columbia people come in.

What would have been the treatment at that time for someone with Huntington's?

There was no treatment. The only thing that was done at that time was utilizing the side effect of Thorazine. Thorazine tends to give a degree of muscular spasticity that counteracts the choreoid movements of Huntington's. Basically, the patient may have better control of his movement, but the effects are modest. But, of course, it's not a treatment.

His medical notes say he was put on Thorazine – 75 milligrams.

It was a minor dosage.

Then they increased it to 100. And then again.

But still, it's a minor dosage until it begins to show side effects.

What kind of patient was in the clinic building?

Mostly psychiatric patients who were medically ill, or surgically ill. Basically the Clinic Building was a small general hospital taking care of the medical needs of 6,000 patients. It was also a clinic for the staff, so it was a hospital for about 9,000 people.

Was it pretty well known that Guthrie was a patient at the hospital?

Not very well, mostly by the staff in his ward. Others knew that Woody Guthrie was there, but you know, it was not a big deal. He was a patient like any other.

Did you know much about Woody before you met him in the hospital?

Oh, sure. I knew that he had been writing songs, that at the beginning he was a minstrel singing and playing and entertaining the migrant workers in the southwest. And he gradually came to be known.

Any other thoughts you'd like to share about Woody?

Yes, I remember his smile. It was not a big smile. He had a nice quiet smile.

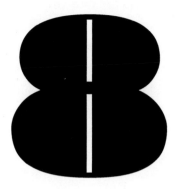

MARJORIE MAZIA
GUTHRIE

Why Is It Hopeless and Helpless?

Marjorie Guthrie was the second wife of Woody Guthrie. She was 24 and a dancer with the avant-garde Martha Graham Dance Company when she first met Woody. She was Graham's assistant and taught Graham's unconventional style. One of her "pupils" was Merce Cunningham, who later formed his own dance company and is considered one of the most innovative and influential figures in modern dance.

Marjorie and Woody were both married when they met but soon moved in together in Marjorie's small Manhattan apartment on 14th Street in Manhattan, where she gave Woody the discipline to finish his autobiography, *Bound for Glory*. Marjorie and Woody had four children: Cathy, who died at the age of four after an electrical fire, Arlo, Nora and Joady. After Woody's behavior became erratic they separated and eventually divorced when Woody met Anneke.

After Woody died Marjorie started the Committee to Combat Huntington's Disease, which later became the Huntington's Disease Foundation of America, a national organization that raises money for research and provide counseling and support for HD families. Researchers supported by the committee would discover the gene for Huntington's as well as develop a test to determine if a person carried the gene. One of the researchers she inspired is Dr. Michael Hayden, Director of the Centre for Molecular Therapeutics at the University of British Columbia, whose interview appears later in this book. In addition to heading a Federal commission on Huntington's formed in 1976, Marjorie traveled internationally to speak to families and medical students about the illness. She died in 1983 at the age of 65 of pancreatic cancer.

I wish I'd been able to meet Marjorie, not only because she was such a large part of Woody's life, but everyone spoke of how special she was. Jorge Arevalo, who was, at the time, head curator at the Woody Guthrie Archives, recognized her absence from drafts of my manuscript and thought that I might be able to include her voice using existing interviews in the Woody Guthrie Archives collection. In addition to the audio-taped interviews conducted in 1976 and 1977 by Joe Klein for his book Woody Guthrie: A Life (1) and Eddie Elkins radio interview for WHRW conducted in 1978 (2), I also located Ron Olesko's college radio interview for WFUV-FM from April, 1977 (3). I've woven together questions and answers from each interview that were relevant to Huntington's Disease and have noted each source with a footnote after each of Marjorie's responses.

—*Phillip Buehler*

What first interested you in Woody Guthrie?

I was on tour with Martha Graham dancing and I didn't know anything about him but my sister said I've got to play a record for you. And she played Woody's first recording of "Tom Joad," which was based on *The Grapes of Wrath*, and the families that traveled with the dust storms and went out to California. And I heard his voice and I was so moved by his voice. And then came the last verse and it said, "Wherever children are hungry and tired. Wherever people ain't free. Wherever folks are fighting for their rights. That's where I want to be ma, that's where I want to be." When I heard those words, I was just—you don't mind if I use an old fashioned word?

Go ahead.

Flabbergasted. I couldn't believe that in those few words, and with the quality of his voice, somebody was saying something that I thought really was me. I wanted to do something. I wanted to identify with people who needed me. I wanted to feel needed.[2]

Three months later a friend of mine had choreographed two of "The Dust Bowl Ballads" and she wanted Woody to appear on the stage with her instead of using a recording. She said "Woody Guthrie's in town and I'm going to see if I can get him to appear with me on the stage." And I said, "Sophie, I am coming!" I pictured what I call a Lincolnesque figure, tall, thin, boots, cowboy hat, sort of western. Don't forget, I'm a city girl. All I saw from coming into the room was a frame of a little fellow with his back to us and he turned around and he had the most marvelous eyes. So we started to talk and I fell in love with him immediately. Later he told me that he felt the same way about me as soon as he looked at me. And that was it–it was as simple as that. [1]

I think one of the reasons Woody liked me was
I reminded him of his mother, whom he lost as a very
young boy. And they didn't understand anything about
what was happening to her with her Huntington's Disease.
Just in thinking back, I would sit at the piano and chord
with him and then he would play and sometimes brush
my long hair, I had very long hair, and he would say that's
what he would do for his mama.

What were those first years like?

Woody didn't want to live right in the heart of New York
because he said he needed open spaces and we went out to
Coney Island. The beautiful ocean in Coney Island and
a lot of beach is not too different from the wheat fields of
Oklahoma. And we lived there and had a wonderful life,
about seven good years. It brings back such wonderful
smiles and memories. And during those years he was
always on the boardwalk, on the beach, pulling the kids
around in wagons up and down the beach, even in the
wintertime when nobody else would even go on the beach.
And it brought a great deal of what he needed, peace and
time to think. [3]

When did you realize that Woody had Huntington's Disease?

Oh, we didn't really know in the beginning what was
wrong, it was only after he had been in the hospital years.

The very first time we went to the hospital, he had had a violent outbreak—and he hadn't been drinking—and he went to our local hospital and they kept him there for three weeks and said he was an alcoholic. And it turned out this is very common because the person has slurred speech or imbalance in their walking, many people think, "Oh, this person's drunk." And Woody was not an alcoholic. And after he was in and out of the hospital several times, a young doctor recognized that he had Huntington's.

Didn't they realize that his mother had the disease?

No, it's interesting, you see, when he wrote that part about his mother in the book [*Bound for Glory*] and here I am typing it away, I said to him one day, "Woody, could you be sick like your mother?" And he said, "Oh no, she has Huntington's." And I said, "Well, could you get Huntington's?" He said, "No, only females inherit it, so I don't have to worry." That's why it completely went out of our minds for years.

Did you have a sense that something else was going on with him?

I really didn't. At first I just used to equate it with Martha [Graham]. Martha did the same thing, she would get angry over something that happened before and blame it on the present. He could be very mean and be angry, and he would say something that hurt my feelings. They were both very much alike in that sense.

Jack Elliott first appeared around that time. How did he manage to move in?

Well, all I know is that he was there for him. And just like I used to like Cisco [Houston] being there, I liked having another person with him that seemed to give me a sense that there was somebody watching Woody. Just like Cisco used to do. He was sleeping in our house almost two years. I was glad he was there. He also helped with the children.[1]

That must have been quite a wrench when he went into the hospital.

Sure, it was terrible. I tell you truly, my children only had Woody for a very short number of years when they were little. You know how kids scribble scrabble on paper? Woody would say, "Tell me what it's about," And then he would write under the scribble scrabble, "the moon is coming down, the rain is going up" or whatever the child said. There was a great respect for the child. When he first went into the hospital the children were 2, 3 and 4 and that short bit, whatever it was, was so great that it broke my heart that they couldn't have more because he was a wonderful father.[1]

How did you deal with that?

Well, it was very hard. We just were told that he was

going to be very sick and that situation was hopeless and helpless. And that everyone advised me to tell the children that their father had died, that they should not see him deteriorate. Everybody, including the doctors. And Woody and I talked it over and I kept saying, "You know, this is crazy." I told Woody we would never eliminate the children from his life, but we were advised that he should go into the hospital and stay there because they thought he was going to be what they call a vegetable at the end of his life. Well, he never was.

I'm sure that the children suffered in ways that I cannot describe because I couldn't speak for them. But we tried to maintain as much as we could of that joyousness that Woody had with kids. I remember a tree in front of one of the hospitals that we called the "Magiky Tree"— the branches go way out and touch the ground so it sort of creates a tent. So I would have the children wait under the "Magiky Tree" while I'd go to get Woody and bring him down and then we'd make a picnic out of it. So I tried to make the visits in the hospital like a fun day.

When we would a restaurant and Woody would drop and slip and slurp all the things because of the involuntary movement, people would stare at us, and I would say, out loud, so there's no question about it, "Oh, Woody's sick today. He sure is." And we'd just make a joke about it. And just, and he would laugh, you know, "Yep." [1]

Dylan used to visit him in the hospital, do you remember anything about those visits?

What's kind of nice is that I remember Bob Dylan and John Cohen. I can't quite remember all of them, but we used to meet in our very dear friends' home in New Jersey, the Gleasons, a lovely couple. And Woody would want to touch the guitar and play it and his hands were uncontrolled and he couldn't play it well from the Huntington's Chorea, so he would just sort of hold it lovingly and strum it very awkwardly, but the other kids would all play the music, so he felt like he was still part of it.[3]

Was Woody aware Arlo was following in his footsteps?

Well, he bought Arlo his first guitar on his sixth birthday. Woody had been in and out of the hospital already. Arlo had always made believe he was playing guitar, you know how kids do when you'd see your father do something. When Woody became ill I wanted the kids to play. I didn't know how to play, I always played the piano, so I went and got a little book—I was determined I was going to take Woody's place after all the music was gone. I taught Arlo a C chord and a G chord and with a few little things like that he got started. And of course, later Arlo always played for Woody at the hospital.[1]

Did he ever hear "Alice's Restaurant?"

Yes he did. "Alice's Restaurant" came out the very year that Woody died. Right before he died I went to the hospital with the brochure announcing Arlo singing at

Carnegie Hall and I just said, "Well look at this, look who's singing in Carnegie Hall, not Woody Guthrie, Arlo Guthrie." The two of us got such a kick out it. Woody never sang in Carnegie Hall. He sang in a union hall where everybody was blowing their noses and talking while he was singing.[2]

I think that Woody was very pleased and very proud and I certainly am, and I think the same of my other children. You know, Joady also plays guitar and is a very good musician and loves music and Nora loves music and is a good dancer. And most important, more than that, they're nice people. Isn't that what's really important? They're nice people that, whatever tragedies we may to face, I think that we can face it with a little more strength than weakness because we're nice people and we have many good friends and friends help. God, you need friends.[1]

What was Woody like in the final days?

And the sad part, really, is that Woody spent all those years in a state hospital because it was presumed that he was going to be a vegetable at the end of his life. He never did become a vegetable. He looked like a vegetable—he couldn't walk, he couldn't talk, his involuntary movement was hard to control—but when I came to visit I could see by the laughter or the look on his face that he enjoyed what I was saying or doing.

Finally, right near the end in 1967, those last couple

of months, I began to call Dr. Wittier over to the bedside and I would say, "Dr. Wittier, Woody is not a vegetable, he knows everything I'm saying." I made three cards, a "yes," a "no," and a "question mark" and I spread them out on the bed and I said "Woody, let's show Dr. Wittier that you know everything I'm talking about." And I asked him questions to which I knew the answer. And he would make a face at me as if to say, "You know I was born in Okemah," and I said, "Yes, I know I know, but I want Dr. Wittier to see that you know and that your memory is still functioning." And Woody kept showing me that although his memory wasn't perfect, he was still a whole person. But he looked awful. And imagine what it as like, having a functioning brain and living with 44 men who were mentally incompetent.[2]

How did you get started with the Committee to Combat Huntington's Disease?

When Woody became ill I was told that the case was hopeless and helpless. Assuming that was so, I just said, well, I've got live with hopeless and helpless. And if my children have the disease, I'm going to have to live with that too.

But after a long period, in and out of that hospital, I said to myself, "Why is it hopeless and helpless?" And with my kids now being old enough to be able to take care of themselves, I went to Dr. Whittier, who was in charge of Creedmoor Institute, where Woody was at that time, and said I want to help. And he introduced me to some other scientists and they said, "You might be able to help if you could just find families. We believe that this disorder is all over the world, it is hidden, families don't even know they have it, and those that do are so ashamed they don't tell anybody because there's a stigma attached." With that kind of help, I began to look for families with this disease and then founded the Committee to Combat Huntington's Disease. We found the disorder was much more prevalent than anybody believed possible.[2]

Now you're also working with the Woody Guthrie Foundation...

Well, I must tell you how that came about. When I started the Committee, there was a group of very beautiful young people who were writing letters to Woody. Now they were not interested in Huntington's, they're the people who are really keeping Woody's work alive, but maybe they'd like to do something to help me and on that basis I started the Woody Guthrie Foundation.

The Foundation has three purposes. The first is to help me with my work in Huntington's. Another is to try to do the kind of things that Woody would have done if he were alive. We just gave a grant to a young woman who's been following the migratory workers around. You know, they're still there. And she's preparing a beautiful photographic essay on child labor and what it's like out in the fields today. And the third goal of the Woody Guthrie Foundation is to get all the material that he left us, all the things I call "The Archives" into some kind of condition so that young people can come to the archives, can read what he wrote, what he stood for, and then go out and write their own things.[2]

If Woody was around today, what do you think he'd be writing songs about?

Everything. You know, he read the paper every single morning. And wrote the headlines into a little notebook of the songs he was going to write about. And I think whatever he'd saw today, that's what he'd write about.[2]

Marjorie Mazia Guthrie, excerpted interviews:
(1) Joe Klein, 1976 and 1977, courtesy of the Woody Guthrie Archives.
(2) Eddie Elkins, WHRW SUNY Binghamton, NY, 1978, courtesy of the Woody Guthrie Archives.
3) Ron Olesko, WFUV, NY, 1977, courtesy of Ron Olesko.

DR. MICHAEL
HAYDEN

THESE ARE EXCITING TIMES

Dr. Michael Hayden is a world leader in research involving Huntington's Disease, and is currently the Director and Senior Scientist of the Center for Molecular Medicine and Therapeutics at the University of British Columbia in Vancouver. He's established one of the world's first clinics for the diagnosis and predictive testing of Huntington's Disease.

Dr. Hayden first began to study Huntington's Disease as a young doctor in South Africa. During his studies, he traveled to the U.S. in 1977 to see Marjorie Guthrie when she headed the Committee to Combat Huntington's Disease. She helped him immigrate to the United States and they remained close friends until her death.

While there have been amazing advances in the treatment of mental illnesses, there is still no cure for Huntington's Disease.

What were your first impressions of Marjorie Guthrie?

I traveled in the United States in 1977 to see Marjorie at the Committee to Combat Huntington's Disease. I was a young South African physician-scientist, doing my PhD on Huntington's Disease in South Africa. From the moment I met her, there was kind of chemistry. She became like—I wouldn't say a mother, that's a bit strong—but I would certainly say Marjorie was incredibly warm and loving to me. She brought out Woody's books and records; I still have them. She gave me all of Woody's songs that he wrote for children, and she said to me, "I want you to sing these songs to your children." She was incredibly inspirational, and we saw a fair amount of each other.

Did you speak to Marjorie about Woody?

The first thing we did was to speak about Woody. I asked her what it was like to live with this illness. She spoke about how Woody was ill, but how there was also so much spirit in Woody.

What was it like to be with Woody when he had Huntington's?

Marjorie was very protective of Woody, and Marjorie didn't really want anybody to know how bad it was. She was always underestimating the burden. But it was really tough. Woody was unpredictable, and sometimes it was hard to differentiate between Woody and his illness—because the illness itself led to these movements, but also to a change of personality. Marjorie also spoke of going to the hospital as frequently as she did, and the exhaustion associated with it, and the frustration with the medical system. She spoke of the difficulty getting the care that she wanted for Woody and that he needed, and the lack of knowledge and the impact of the lack of knowledge.

The doctors at Greystone diagnosed Woody as paranoid schizophrenic when he first arrived there.

She took me to a concert where Arlo was playing, and we spent time together, and Marjorie spoke about how he was initially misdiagnosed, that there was so much ignorance that was present. Many of the experiences I had in South Africa were echoed in her experience with Woody twenty years earlier.

Woody's answers to the entrance exam questions has him claiming to have written all these songs, and to have gotten $10,000 for a song—but since the Greystone staff had never heard of him, they thought he was delusional and put him on Thorazine.

Thorazine is basically an anti-psychotic, which really blunts you as a person and diminishes symptoms—but removes some of who you are. Marjorie was so aware and so sensitive to all of that.

What else was did Marjorie tell you about that time?

She spoke about the importance of a working health care system. That's why for her, when she founded the Committee to Combat Huntington's, the issue about public education and information was very important. This had been sort of the dreaded illness—the inherited madness—that went from family member to family member. People kept this totally in the closet. Marjorie wanted to bring this out, to allow people to realize that this is an illness just like any other, for which they hold no blame.

So this was the first place these families could connect with others.
Marjorie was able to empathize with so many people, and
served as inspiration for the formation for lay groups in
general, for patient-led organizations. There were very few
in the mid-1970s, and I think what Marjorie did has been
replicated for many diseases. It's different to what was
established in other organizations that were focused just
on research.

*Did Marjorie talk about the chance that her children might have
Huntington's?*

She was really worried whether something could be done
to make sure that her children don't have to suffer in a
way that Woody suffered. Marjorie knew that each of her
children had a one in two chance of getting this and she
was deadly worried about it.

*I spoke to Arlo about the test to see if someone carries the
Huntington's gene.*

We were part of doing these first predictive tests, and
we've been following persons who participated since they
were first done in 1986. It was the first predictive test for
any genetic, DNA based disease, for an adult onset illness.

*I understand that most of the people at risk—like Arlo—don't
choose to take the test.*

That's correct. If you look at the number of people that have taken the test, in Canada it's between 18% and 25%. But what's interesting is that when they did studies before the test was available, 75% of people said they would like to take the test, but they weren't asked when they would take it. So the question is in the fullness of time, how many people will take the test? Who knows? From Arlo's perspective, the reason that most people aren't taking the test is because there is no therapy to alter the course of the illness. If there was, I think there would be a dramatic uptake for predictive testing.

Why would someone want to take the test now, knowing there's no cure for Huntington's?

Our view is not that it's good or bad to take the test. Rather, it's a very private decision that each individual needs to make. We need to explore with them, the pros and cons of taking the test. And I can understand why people choose to, and I can understand why people don't choose to. But for many people, living at risk is extremely difficult because of the uncertainty. And people often live their lives as if they are or are not going to get this disease. Some people say, "I'm 50% at risk, but I know I'll never get it." Other people say, "I know I'm going to get it."

So some people might be better off knowing the answer?

Yes. For some people, the information itself is powerful.

For many people, knowing is itself a catalyst for all kinds of things. The uncertainty is paralyzing for some. And knowing that they are going to get the illness, at some point, allows them to plan, and take all kinds of actions. We've been following people now for close to twenty years. It's mostly been good, but not all. It's complicated and complex.

How do different people react to the tests?

We've had some unusual responses in predictive testing, where some people have lived their lives as though they are going to get it. So they've had a vasectomy, they've never been involved in long-term relationships, they've been involved in death defying sports activities from bungee jumping to hang gliding, they've incurred high debts. Because they thought they were going to get this disease, they borrowed a lot of money and took insurance to cover that because they think they're going to die soon of HD. We gave results to such a person, and we told him he wasn't going to get Huntington's Disease, that he will never get it, and he collapsed. The way he described it: "I'm just normal, I'm just like everyone else now, I'm boring."

Human behavior is so complex. The responses have been varied. We've had many people who are pre-symptomatic today who are living very full and fulfilled lives, and there are some people who were told they were not going to get Huntington's who are not doing that well.

The complexity of people's reactions is pretty wide, it seems. It must be an emotional roller coaster.

Today in the clinic, there were five patients. One was a young girl, age twenty, who had come in for pre-test counseling. The four other people I saw today all had learnt that they had inherited the mutation. And that's tough.

I can't imagine how hard that must be.

It never gets easier to tell that to somebody. What does get easier now, for the first time, is that there's hope. For the first time, we can say Huntington's Disease has been cured in a mouse. That's very recent data. Now we just need to translate that information to humans. And that gives people a lot of hope for the future.

How would you compare treatment of Huntington's in Woody's time, to his mother's time, and to today? There have been so many changes, yet it seems like much has stayed the same.

When you compare what he went through and what his mother went through, there was not a lot of change. Paranoid schizophrenia was a very common misdiagnosis—as were others including Parkinson's Disease, Alzheimer's, all kinds of psychiatric illness and people were just locked away. I would say since Woody's time, the big changes that have occurred are with the incredible revolution in molecular biology, and the work associated with what Marjorie did—which was to make sure that people knew about this illness, and understood that patients with HD weren't drunk and weren't wicked, but were ill, and were suffering.

What do you think Woody's life would have been like if he hadn't gotten Huntington's, or a cure had been available back then?

I think it's very important that we don't glorify HD; it's a terrible, terrible illness. I think that HD eroded his talents. There's no question that Huntington's Disease made him much less than he could have been. He's a legend and was an incredible human being, and such an important person in American history, but Huntington's made him less. It eroded every aspect of who he was until it killed him. So what would Woody have been like without Huntington's? He would have been greater. He would have gone on longer. And we would have had much more from him. He was tragically cut down too early by this terrible illness.

How is your lab approaching Huntington's?

The setup that we have here is very much inspired by Marjorie's philosophy, from caring to searching for a cure. Our research focuses on DNA testing for HD, understanding cell death, and then new approaches to and doing various clinical trials. The goal is to be able to predict and then prevent HD, to help turn Huntington's Disease into a something like a serum cholesterol test, where you'd know that this would be a gene that you carried, and then there would be something to do to prevent the progression or the onset of the illness.

So where do things now stand in the search for a cure?

What's remarkable in Huntington's Disease is that there's a small set of cells in one nucleus in one part of the brain that's particularly susceptible to the neurotoxic effects of the mutant gene. This can be recapitulated very accurately in the mice. We've learned about what happens first, which cells are involved, and we've learned about what different processes are perturbed early in the illness. Then we've been able to model those pathways to see what happens to the illness, and we now have been able to ameliorate Huntington's Disease in the mouse. There are certain drugs already out there that offer some hope that they may perturb the pathways that have been shown to be involved in Huntington's.

Would a cure for Huntington's be applicable to other diseases or genetic mutations?

I think it's likely. If you're able to stop the process of death in the medium spiny neurons—which are the most important neurons where Huntington's Disease has its manifestation—I suspect that we'll be able to have an impact on cell death in other diseases like Alzheimer's Disease.

It sounds like great progress has been made.

These are exciting times and my goal, personally, is to stop working on Huntington's Disease. I'd like to close my HD lab because we have a cure, or something that truly ameliorates this illness, and the major problems have been overcome. I'm hoping we can bring this to an end so I can work on other things that also inspire me—write some poetry, write some books about Marjorie.

Marjorie must have been very special.

I remember going to the Congress on Huntington's Disease in Japan, and Marjorie invited myself and Carleton Gajdusek—who was at the meeting and won the Nobel Prize for medicine for his work on scrapie and Kuru—to get up very early and climb Mount Fuji. It was a long walk, and at the top, Marjorie decided she wanted to dance. Of course, Marjorie was a dancer with Martha Graham, and as the sun was rising, Marjorie danced. I still remember Marjorie dancing at the top of Mount Fuji. She was a very inspirational person, very caring, very loving with incredible energy, great humor, great charm, and a very special spirit.

10

JEFF CARROLL

THIS IS YOUR LAST CHANCE NOT TO KNOW, RIGHT?

Jeff Carroll was 24 when he learned his mother in Seattle had Huntington's Disease. It was 1999 and he was serving in the Army in Kosovo, in one of the first peacekeeping units deployed by NATO to allow the return of Albanian refugees after the withdrawal of Serbian troops. When his tour of duty was over, Jeff returned to his wife Megan and then enrolled in the University of British Columbia on the G.I. Bill.

Jeff went through predictive testing in Dr. Michael Hayden's clinic at the Center for Molecular Medicine and Therapeutics—and was found to carry the Huntington's gene. He now works in Dr. Hayden's lab while studying for his PhD., helping to search for a cure to Huntington's Disease.

When did you first hear about Huntington's?

At some level growing up, my brothers and my sisters knew that my grandmother had something. Looking back, I don't really have a clear image in my mind, I only have the vaguest memories of her talking or walking or anything. Probably somewhere along the line, someone had told me Huntington's Disease, but it didn't click or make any impact on me as to what that meant in terms of heredity.

So when did you really become more aware of what Huntington's was?

The only reason we started talking about Huntington's Disease at all was when we all found out mom was sick. That's when everything obviously became kind of un-ignorable. Grandma was just kind of unmentioned.

How did you decide you wanted to get tested?

I always knew I wanted to be tested. If I were to tell you that you're at risk for a genetic disease, you would have some gut reaction as to if you'd want to know whether you had it or not. And I think that gut reaction would probably be true. In my experience, my siblings kind of knew what they were going to do, and not all of them have carried it out yet, but everybody's sort of on the path to either be tested or not. You either have the kind of personality where you have to know, or you have the kind of personality where you can't know.

For you, was it only a question of when you would find out?

Yes. It was after my second year of university that I actually went through the predictive testing, which is essentially a series of four appointments. Once I was out of the Army and established in school, it was time to get tested. So I called the predictive testing center at UBC. It's during the third appointment when you actually get your results. In fact it's really structured and intense. There's a lot of counseling, and there's a neurological exam, quite a lot more.

It sounds more like intense therapy.

It is, if your genetic councilors are good, and your neurologists are good, and the program is good. This is your last chance to not know, right? And if you get an answer you don't like, you can't change it. You can't go back, ever. So it is intense. They strongly encourage you to talk about things that you may not want to talk about, like "What about kids?" and "What happens to my employment if I get sick?" Essentially, they bring up these issues that you're trying to avoid.

What was it like when you were told your results?

The day you get your results—intellectually, there's nothing else scheduled for that day. You get to the clinic, you walk in, you see the neurologist, and he gives you a number. And this number essentially dictates, with great certainty, your future. Like this is going to kill you, or it's not. So we came in, and they just sat us right down and said, "Do you still want this number?" I said that I did, and then he said, "Well, we've tested your DNA extracted from your blood, and we found that you have 42 repeats, which means that—given time—you will develop symptoms of Huntington's Disease."

It's all very medical, and very explicit and very formal, so there's no confusion. I told the neurologist that I wanted to help, that I wanted to be involved. I had mentioned it to him and the genetic councilor throughout the process, and he said okay. So after that, my wife and I went and had a ridiculously expensive meal and a whole bunch of wine—which was the plan, whatever the outcome had been. Then, right away, I got in touch with Michael [Hayden].

You're now a PhD student working in Dr. Hayden's lab.

I'm a year and a half into my PhD program. I go to work everyday, and all I do is work on therapeutics for Huntington's Disease—like applying many of the basic fundamental scientific discoveries that were done in our lab, and others, and trying to applying those at the therapeutic level to see if we can make a difference.

It must be pretty unusual for someone with the Huntington's gene to be working in a lab searching for a cure.

I always thought I was going to be the great motivation, you know, the in-your-face reminder of why we're here, and what you have to do and why you should be working hard, and it just didn't turn out that way. What really happened was that people didn't need to be pushed any harder than they already were. They'd push themselves. So it's just an incredible inspiration for me to be around these people that don't really have a good reason—in quotes—for working 70 hours a week. But they do, and they do it because they love the science, and because they're attached to the patients they've now come to know.

How much did you know about Woody Guthrie before you started researching Huntington's?

I didn't know a lot. My parents kind of grew up with the music of that era, so it was around, and obviously I knew about it. But I really got a more personal connection when Nora Guthrie came and visited the lab. By then, I guess I'd heard the Billy Bragg CD's and was a little bit more aware of Woody's music, but I didn't really know anything about him or his history. I guess I knew more about Marjorie than Woody, because of her work with Huntington's.

So what was the personal connection you made with Woody?

Nora came and talked to us about her dad, about HD and everything, and she had family videos of her father. At first he's sitting with Arlo strumming guitar, playing around, and he doesn't look affected. And then by the end, he's just this ravaged person, and the sort of focal point of this is his guitar. In the beginning he's so at home with the guitar. Do you know Ani DiFranco, the folk singer? When she plays guitar, the guitar is like an extension of her, and that's exactly what he looked like. His guitar looked like a part of him, and then by the end of the videos he looked like he barely knows how to hold it. And that, for me, was just—what a devastating disease. To take something you love, in what should be the prime of your life, and just slowly destroy it while your family's watching. That was a really intense reminder of how fucking terrible Huntington's Disease is, and what it does to people.

So the connection you made wasn't to his music?

Just seeing him losing something he loved, you know what I mean? It kind of struck me as a symbol for the disease in general. It does that not just to your hobbies or your work or you pastimes, but it does it to your family relationship—to everything in your life. Everything you love is going to be stripped away in front of you, and enough of you is going to be there watching it that you're going to know what's happening.

It's like people kind of have these "what if" discussions all the time: Would you rather die instantly or whatever, and everybody always says I'd rather just go quickly, like that's the sort of standard answer to that question. Nobody says that they want to watch all their skills and abilities and loves and thoughts and everything else slowly die while they're still watching. Seeing that aspect of Woody's life on the video really brought that home.

So is working in the lab really about changing all of that for you?

Personally, I guess I'm a bit of a fatalist. Given my genetic status, this is the most useful thing I could do with my time. All of us only have a limited time. In the cosmic scheme of things, it's not much, and I'm trying to do something good with the time I have. It's the big joke, that we all know we're mortal, right? Well some of us know it more than others. It's a real motivation to try and do something.

When I last spoke to Dr. Hayden, you and your wife were in somewhat of a dilemma about having about children. If a cure for Huntington's is coming, you could have kids—and even if one of them carried the Huntington's gene, a cure could be available in the future.

That's been really an interesting story over the last year. Knowing that I had this gene mutation allowed my wife and me to undergo a process last November called Preimplantation Genetic Diagnosis. "PGD" we call it. And PGD is a process that I didn't even think was a possibility last August, which was when Michael first mentioned me to you. It became available in British Columbia as we were going through this process of thinking about kids.

So Megan and I did a pretty traditional in vitro fertilization cycle. On the third day of the culture of the embryos in a dish, an embryologist separated one of the eight cells from each of the embryos—which doesn't hurt the embryos if you do it right—and Fedexed each of the cells to Detroit. Then they tested each of these single cells for the presence or absence of the Huntington's mutation. By doing this, we could implant only the two embryos which were unaffected by HD. Now my wife is five months pregnant with twins, neither one of which will have HD or any risk of HD.

Congratulations--that's really amazing.

Thanks. I'm terrified. Not of the HD thing, the twin thing. So these are the first babies in British Columbia that were born or will be born through this process. And that's really a big testament to the power of this information.

So if you hadn't gone through the testing, you might not have had children—or put off the decision to have children for years?

Yeah, absolutely. It's hard for me to say what I would have done if I hadn't tested, but it definitely wouldn't have been this.

11

ARLO GUTHRIE

THE MAGIKY TREE

Arlo Guthrie was born in 1947, and is the eldest son of Woody Guthrie and Marjorie Mazia Guthrie. He was nine years old when his father entered Greystone, and 13 when his father was transferred to Brooklyn State. His father would pass away when Arlo was 19 years old. Arlo grew up surrounded by musicians like Pete Seeger, Lee Hays, Leadbelly, Cisco Houston, and Ramblin' Jack Elliott. He learned to play the harmonica from Bob Dylan.

His career took off in 1967 with the release of "Alice's Restaurant," an 18 minute and 20 second satirical protest of the Vietnam War draft. He went on to star in the 1969 Hollywood film based on the song. He later performed "Coming into Los Angeles" at the 1969 Woodstock Festival, and had another hit single with Steve Goodman's "City of New Orleans."

In 1991, Arlo purchased the church featured in the film "Alice's Restaurant," and converted it into the Guthrie Center—an interfaith meeting place for people of all religions. Arlo continues to tour 10 months of the year, with his annual Thanksgiving concert at Carnegie Hall somewhat of a homecoming.

What comes to mind when you think of Greystone and that period of your life?

It's amazing. What I really remember is the journey there and home. It took about an hour or so, maybe more. And I was just thinking about this the other day—ever have those feelings like, I've been on this road a zillion times, more than I could count? And I remember coming back, coming into the Lincoln Tunnel into New York, coming down that big sort of ramp with all the cars and buses. So what I really remember as a kid was the journey. How you're just sitting there dreaming, looking out the window as a kid, and those images stay with you. Then of course I remember pulling up to Greystone on this big avenue, like a promenade almost. As a kid, I thought it was an entire city, of course—which it really was, so I wasn't that far off.

And then we would go outside and my mom and dad would basically just talk and go over all the news and info, and the kids—we would just play. Me and my brother and my sister were just jumping around and playing. Eventually, we were actually playing music together.

And of course there were these two trees that are still there—I went to see them just a few years ago—that we used to call the "magiky trees." It was like a weeping cherry, or some odd kind of tree that you couldn't really see through in the months when there were leaves on it. We would just climb in those things and stay there for hours. Then we would get in the car and we would all go home. That was our trip.

How did it feel to visit your dad out there?

To us, it was just a normal thing. My dad was in the hospital, and we would go see him. I understood that he was sick, and it was clearly visible. Over the years, of course, as I got older, I knew more and more about it, and was actually responsible for him to some extent. As I said, when I went back recently, it wasn't any different. You know how sometimes you go back to a place and it seems smaller? Greystone didn't seem any smaller. It seemed exactly the same.

When did you find out what your dad was suffering from?

Well, I didn't all of a sudden realize that he had Huntington's Disease. Over the years my mom sort of gradually introduced whatever she knew. Actually, in the beginning, no one knew anything. Even my dad thought that he was suffering from alcoholism, or God knows what. He was convinced he couldn't have the same disease his mom had, because he had some misconceptions about how it was transmitted. And so, little by little, at the insistence of my mom, even the doctors had to learn stuff. She was very wonderful that way. She had some concerns about her kids, obviously, and she really spent a good decade or two discovering what was going on. So there wasn't one moment when I suddenly was told something. It was gradually over years—first we realized our dad was sick, then he had some sort of disorder, and blah blah blah, and, little by little, we sort of knew what was going on.

How did that period have an impact on your life?

I don't know. Obviously everything had impact. How do

you say what influences your life? Certainly not consciously, it didn't. I also realized that at some point I was at risk for the same thing, and so were my brother and sister. So there are obvious implications in what are you going to do with your own families, and other things. Personally, seeing as how there wasn't anything you could do about it, at some point it was a little late to have these concerns.

They've developed a test for Huntington's. Did you ever consider that?

I had absolutely no interest in taking a test. If there was some result that the test could give you that would alter something, that would be different. But the information alone doesn't do anything. If I had taken the test before I got married and had kids, I would have had to decide if I wanted to get married and have kids. By the time the test came along, my kids were grown up already. So that wasn't going to be a factor.

So you know at some point or other the medical profession, the modern age, presents us with all kinds of hoops to jump through. One of those hoops is these sort of tests that determine your predisposition to one thing or another. And when there's nothing you can do about the result it seems like an odd thing to want to take the test. I mean, if they came up tests for your likelihood to get hit by cars, would we rush to take that test too? Or your likelihood to keep a job for a long time? Or your likelihood to have a successful marriage? There are all kinds of tests that you could take. For me, the question I have to answer is, when do you stop testing and start living?

Why did you go back to Greystone?

I went to see if those trees were still there—I wanted to get some pieces of them. Or at least find out what they were. And of course we had to drive around in our big tour bus looking for that. And we came up through some back road or something. We didn't come in sort of the main way. And we're driving around and around looking at all these buildings, and I'm saying, "You know I don't think it's that one. Not that one. Not that one." It was driving me nuts, and of course, I'm with a bus full of people who are saying, "Come on, man, it's not here, you're wasting time, we've got to get to the gig." "No, it's got to be here somewhere. It's got to be here somewhere." And all of a sudden—bam!—there it was. "Stop the bus! There're the trees!" It was like the whole world came into focus after not making any sense. And I went out and they weren't any different than I had remembered. They were exactly as I had remembered them.

I actually went into the office—I didn't plan to—but I just went in there. And I walked upstairs and I said, "I'm Arlo Guthrie, and I wonder if you have some information on my dad here?" And they said, "Actually, we do, and we saved it because it was Woody Guthrie's information. Everybody else's was just thrown away because we don't keep records after twenty years." And I went and collected all of my dad's stuff, and they gave it to me right then and there.

So your connection to Greystone now is those two trees?

Yeah. That was that. I have no connection to really any of the buildings. No, I was not impressed by any of that, although I was later on. I remember the era when that place was thriving. I don't know if it was thriving in a good way or not, but it was filled with people. It was like a city. At some point, I realized that the idea was that people did not generally want to support their sick relatives or neighbors for too long, especially those dealing with mental illnesses.

    At one point, I guess, these places were built so that they wouldn't be a burden on society. You could throw away your odd child, put him in one of these towns, almost like sending people to Australia from England years ago. Penal colonies. And so it's no wonder why they ended up in this sort of notoriously bad scene. They were set up from the very beginning to be away from the world, and not be a part of it. Greystone is a real monument to that. It still is. Any halfway competent cult could do very well there.

What do you imagine Woody's life was like out there?

I think it was probably miserable. He was ever the optimist, but that had to be very tough. I mean it was fairly desperate there. There are some funny stories that he tells early on of when they brought him in. They didn't really know what he had. I remember my mom was called by a German psychologist who said, "Mrs. Guthrie, your

husband is really ill and we're glad they brought him in."
She says, "Oh, tell me what's going on?" He said, "Well,
first of all, he's got delusions of grandeur. He thinks he's a
well-known singer and has written books and people were
singing his songs." She said, "What do you mean?" He
said, "He thinks he's well known." She said, "He is well
known!" They said "Oh."

And then, within a short time he's in this ward—
they didn't know where to put him—where he's with
other people who they consider, like him, to be mentally
deranged. And so that's whom he's talking to, who he's
hanging out with everyday. No one knows who he is. But
then one day another patient comes over and says, "I
know who you are. You're Woody Guthrie, the famous
singer." He says, "Yes, I am." The guy says, "I loved your
book, *Bound for Glory.*" "You read my book?" "No, I ate
your book." I mean, moments like that are probably the
few highlights of his time there, you know.

How important do you think those visits were to your dad?

In our family, my mom and dad had an obvious love for
each other that extended beyond their marriage, extended
before their marriage—through it—and beyond it. A love
and appreciation for each other as artists and human
beings and as parents. And I think she tried to make the
most of that under very difficult circumstances—not to
everyone's complete satisfaction, ever. But she did the
best she could and I think she thought it was important to

maintain some kind of family relationship.

Even though she was married to other people at the time, and even though my dad had been remarried at one point briefly. They had one of those timeless movie-type of loves, you know. And it's very obvious in all of their writing and all of their actions. They would sit together, and they would talk, and they would share their lives as best they could.

At some point or other, we'd take my dad out of there. We took him from Greystone over to people's homes in the area. And we would play music and we would goof off and we would try to integrate him in the world that was celebrating the very things that he thought was important. I mean, his work was booming as he entered Greystone. And I think my mom really wanted him to understand and participate in it to some extent, as much as he could. And that's what we did. That was our life.

THANK YOU

FOR MAKING "WOODY GUTHRIE'S WARDY FORTY" BOOK POSSIBLE

Denise Antonazzi
David Bradburn Aragon
Bob & Cynthia Atkinson
Joanne M. Austin
Jack Beard
Don Beck
Michael D. Bifulco
Henry James Briscoe
Timothy J. Brown
Judith Bryan
Alicia Mallory Byrd
Sara Campbell
Scott & Anna Canoni
Bill Cermak
Marie C. Chrobak
Dr. Jon Coren
Jeremy Craig, SP-USA
Phil Dourado & Sandy Sulaiman family
Keith Edwards
Melanie Dee Elbert-Buck
Claudia Ellerman
Bob Estes
Johan Falk
Jerome E. Fischer
Vincent Fitzsimmons
Nancy E. Fleischer
John Rutledge Foster, Jr.
Yoshiki Furusawa
Roxanne Matos Gerardo
Scott Giddings
Ed Glaser

Godfrey
Fran Gormley
Francie Grace
Tim Green
Gordon Guge
Kent Gustavson
Anais & Kieran Hammock
Janet Heettner
David Herzig
Ron Higgins
Ron Hochsprung
Paul B. Holloway
Brian Scott Hudson
Harry Hutson & Mikey DoddsMary S. Igoe
Alf Ingum
Barry James
Jennifer G. Jesse
Sheila Kaminsky
Will Kaufman
Kevin & Punam Keller
Kyle Kiefer
Michael Kleff
Robert Kopsell
Ralf Lothar Korbmacher
Mary Twichell Kushner
Richard Lemargie
Harris Levy
Ann & Mark Lyncn
Bill MacAllister
Dave Marsh & Barbara Carr
Angela McBride

Eileen McCarthy
Alan Michell
Frederick D. Miller
William "Wild Bill" Miller
Elizabeth Mitchell & Family
Andrew Moss's Mom Kate
Michael Mullen
John E. Mulroony
Eric Prescott Murphy
Antonio Leandro Nascimento
Wendy & David Newton
Elizabeth C. Nichols
Kenneth Mikio Ogawa
Barry Ollman
Jane & Stephen Peart
Vaune Peck
Deeper Roots Radio
Susan B. Redge, MD
Barbara S. Reich
Michael Resnick
Wayne D. Rooks
Jason E. Roselius
Steve Rosenthal
Norman A Ross/Broadside Magazine
Cole Quest Rotante
Jay Rury & Shelley Caldwell
Sue RyanDonald J. Santoski
Allison Scagliotti
Sue Schier
Troy Joseph Schoenfelder
Chuck & Pat Schulze

Allan Seward
Debra Roeder Shaw
Jessie Shaw
Richard & Dana Sherwood
Doug "Scout" Shevlin
John Shreve Shreve
Steven Siegel
Paul H. Siegmund
Ian MacKenzie Smith
Baden and Arlene Soong
Danny B. Stein
Patrick Stewart
Mark Strait
Carney Strange
Aura Sullivan
Jennifer Tarlin
Garland Thomen
Emilie Van Trieste
Robbie Wasserman & Marjorie Kalter
Dubs Waun
Wieske/Glenday, HD Family
Charles & Jessi Young
Anonymous-7 donors
+ 311 additional Kickstarter donors

With special contributions from:

The Woody & Marjorie Guthrie Family

The Anita B. & Howard S. Richmond
Foundation